Snugglepot
and
Cuddlepie
at sea

Retold by Anna Fienberg
Illustrated by Vicky Kitanov

Angus&Robertson
An imprint of HarperCollins*Publishers*

Angus&Robertson
An imprint of HarperCollins*Publishers*, Australia

First published in 1997
by HarperCollins*Publishers* Pty Limited
ACN 009 913 517
A member of the HarperCollins*Publishers* (Australia) Pty Limited Group

HarperCollins*Publishers*
25 Ryde Road, Pymble, Sydney, NSW 2073, Australia
31 View Road, Glenfield, Auckland 10, New Zealand
77–85 Fulham Palace Road, London W6 8JB, United Kingdom
Hazelton Lanes, 55 Avenue Road, Suite 2900, Toronto, Ontario M5R 3L2
and 1995 Markham Road, Scarborough, Ontario M1B 5M8, Canada
10 East 53rd Street, New York NY 10032, USA

National Library of Australia Cataloguing-in-Publication data:

Fienberg, Anna.
The world of May Gibbs.
ISBN 0 207 19076 3 (2).
I. Gibbs, May, 1877-1969. Complete adventures of Snugglepot and Cuddlepie. II. Kitanov, Vicky.
III. Title. IV. Title: Complete adventures of Snugglepot and Cuddlepie.
A823.2

Printed in Hong Kong
9 8 7 6 5 4 3 2 1   97 98 99

The World of May Gibbs

Here are the adventures of Snugglepot and Cuddlepie. They were Gumnut babies, almost brothers. This is how it came about.

When Cuddlepie was just a few hours old, a great wind arose and lifted him out of his mother's arms. The wind carried him far away, over tree-tops and hills, until it dropped him in a spider web. Luckily, a kind Nut saw him fall, and gently carried poor Cuddlepie home.

Now this was the home of Snugglepot, and the kind Nut brought them up side by side as brothers, happy and strong.

Snugglepot and Cuddlepie were Gumnuts who lived in the big, busy bush. One day they left their cosy home in a gum tree, and set off to see the world. On the way they met kind Mr Lizard, and he invited them to ride on his back.

Mr Lizard became the Nuts' greatest friend, and told them many things about the world. But the most important thing he said was this: 'Look out for the bad Banksia men. They are a rough and nasty lot, with scrubby beards and evil gleaming eyes. They have hearts as black as a hole in the ground.'

Snugglepot and Cuddlepie shivered when they heard this, and promised to be careful.

Well, one hot morning, Snugglepot woke up and stretched. 'I would like to go to the sea,' he told Cuddlepie. 'We have travelled far, but we've never seen what lies *under* the water. I've heard there are giants. I would love to see one.'

'Me too,' said Cuddlepie, 'but only in the distance.'

The two Gumnuts looked at the sleeping Mr Lizard. He was resting so peacefully, they decided not to wake him.

Because it was such a hot day, crowds of other Nuts and Blossoms were lined up along the waterfront. A big ship called *The Snag* was lying in the harbour, and when the Captain came ashore he asked Snugglepot and Cuddlepie to go sailing with him.

Snugglepot nudged Cuddlepie with delight, and they hurried on board. The leafy sails filled with a sudden breeze, and away went *The Snag*, dancing over the waves like a big green butterfly.

Snugglepot and Cuddlepie leaned on the rails and looked happily out to sea.

'Isn't it gummy!' said a voice nearby. The Nuts turned to see a pretty smiling Blossom with a ragged skirt.

'Yes!' cried Cuddlepie. 'It's juicy!'

'It's tree top!' chuckled Snugglepot. 'What's your name?'

'Ragged Blossom,' she said. 'At least, that is what I call myself.'

'Didn't your mummy give you your name?'

Ragged Blossom sighed. 'I don't have a mummy, or a daddy. I am an orphan. I've never had anyone to look after me.'

Cuddlepie felt tears coming into his eyes. 'Well *we* can look after you,' he said, putting his arm around her. 'We can be your new family, can't we, Snugglepot?'

'Scrub and rub me!' cried Snugglepot. 'Of course we can!'

The three friends spent the afternoon telling each other their life stories. But suddenly a big wave lifted up the ship and plonked it down with a thump. The friends went sliding along the deck, flop, bump, and fell down into the deep dark hold.

'Where are we?' asked Cuddlepie.

'In the bottom of the boat, I think,' said Snugglepot.

'Ssh,' whispered Ragged Blossom. 'I can hear voices.'

They all kept very still and listened; and some way off, in the darkness, they heard the Captain's voice.

'Now listen,' he was saying. 'As soon as the moon is gone and the dark night comes, over they go, all three of 'em.'

'Ay, aye! Sir,' growled a voice. 'Squeeze and breeze 'em!'

'Stone and bone 'em!'

'Drop and drown 'em!'

The Nuts held their breath. They knew now who the Captain was, and they knew he was going to have them thrown into the sea.

'He's a Banksia man,' whispered Ragged Blossom. 'But why does he want to hurt *us*?'

'The Banksia man has a heart as black as a hole in the ground,' said Snugglepot. 'He is the friend of Mrs Snake and she is our enemy because we once saved Mr Lizard from her clutches.'

'Oh dear Mr Lizard,' moaned Cuddlepie, 'I wish he
were here now. He'd tell us what to do.'

'Well,' said Snugglepot, giving Cuddlepie a comforting
pat, 'it's bright moonlight tonight, so they won't attack.
We'll just have to escape.'

While the moon was still high, the Nuts and Ragged Blossom crept out of the hold. Tiptoeing along the deck, they could hear rumbling snores from all around the ship. Snugglepot found the ladder and hauled it over the side. At the bottom of the ladder was a little lifeboat.

Snugglepot helped Ragged Blossom down the ladder and Cuddlepie crawled after them. But just as they were rowing quietly away, they heard a snarling voice.

'Lash and smash 'em! They're getting away!'

Snugglepot looked up to see the Captain leaning over the rails. He threw his cap into the sea with such force that it knocked Cuddlepie sideways, and he fell out. The boat turned over and out fell Ragged Blossom and Snugglepot, like two little peas shooting from a pod. The last thing the three friends heard above water was the wicked black laughter of the Banksia man.

Down fell the Nuts, down went Ragged Blossom,
until they reached the sandy bottom.

'I can't stand up!' said Ragged Blossom, and she
turned upside down again.

'Hold on to me,' said Snugglepot. 'That's right,' and
they all clung to a sea bush, and began to giggle.

'Look at all the bubbles you're making when you laugh!' said Cuddlepie. 'Do you feel wet?'

'I'm wet all over,' said Ragged Blossom, 'but I don't feel wet.'

'Neither do I,' said Snugglepot. Then they laughed and laughed till they forgot to hold on to the sea bush and over they went, upside down again.

After a while they managed to swim upright, and to catch their breath. They discovered that they could breathe under the water as well as on top of the water, and that was a splendid discovery to make.

'This is gummy!' grinned Ragged Blossom.

A crowd of Fish Folk came swimming round them – such strange people – all pressing close to look at them.

'What's going on here?' asked a loud, fierce voice.

'Oh no, it's John Dory,' murmured the crowd, and they all stood back, for John Dory was a very important Fish Folk.

'Who are these round pink people?' he shouted. 'Where do they come from?'

Everyone was afraid to speak as he strode along and picked up the two Nuts in one fin, and the Blossom in the other. He stood glaring around at the crowd.

'Do they belong to anyone?' he roared. 'If not, I'll bite their heads off!'

Everyone was too nervous to say anything. But little Ann Chovy came forward and said, 'Oh please don't hurt them. Give them to me, I like them.'

John Dory was so surprised at anyone speaking to him so boldly that he fell in love with Ann Chovy then and there. 'If you will promise to marry me,' he said, 'I'll give them to you.'

Now Ann did not love John Dory, but to save the lives of the poor Nuts and the Blossom, she said, 'Yes, I will marry you.'

When he heard her answer, savage John Dory became quite gentle and gave them to her to keep, saying, 'They are yours; if anyone hurts them, he shall dry.' For in Fish Land 'dry' means the same as 'die'.

So Snugglepot and Cuddlepie and Ragged Blossom went to live with Ann Chovy. That night they saw John Dory swim quietly up to Ann and say, 'To earn your love, I will never be fierce again, or greedy or cruel. I'll try to be kind to you, Ann, and to all the creatures in the sea. I swear by the fins of Neptune.'

Ann looked up at him. She put her arms around his neck, and smiled.

The Gumnuts and their friend Blossom were very happy in Ann's house. She made them new caps of green seaweed trimmed with pearls, and gave them a pet fish, called Frilly. He was a lovely little fish – pure black and white, and so clever. He followed them everywhere, and they soon grew to love him.

Ann Chovy's house stood in the middle of a pretty garden, with flowers and trees of every colour growing in it.

At night the Nuts and Ragged Blossom went to bed
in funny little shells jutting out from the wall, and
every morning they woke to the sound of the fishes
bubbling in the garden. For breakfast they ate sea
grapes, and for tea they had tiny prawns.

They went to see the sea horses in their stables, and
watched the little coloured fishes swim about
overhead. 'Just like the birds do in the Bush,' said
Ragged Blossom.

'Oh sting and wing me, let's go down the road and
see what we can find,' said Snugglepot, who was always
wanting to discover something new.

They mounted their horses, and called to Frilly to
follow them. They were off. Soon Ann Chovy's house
with its garden and stables was just a speck in the
distance.

Cuddlepie began to feel nervous. 'Maybe it's time to
go back and see what's for lunch,' he said.

Just then a strange darkness began to thicken the
water. Cuddlepie felt as if it were choking him. He
looked about wildly, but he could no longer see
Snugglepot and Ragged Blossom. It was as if they were
swallowed up by the darkness. He felt a soft fin on his
cheek. It was Frilly.

'Don't worry, we'll find them,' he said. Frilly guided Cuddlepie's horse down, down into the murky blackness. They went down until they reached the bottom. The water cleared a little, and they could just see a monstrous Giant Squid sitting glaring at them from the door of his cavern.

Frilly started with horror. There, in the dark of the cavern, were the pale faces of Snugglepot and Ragged Blossom.

'What do you want?' growled the Giant, waving his long arms about. Frilly was so afraid, he couldn't move or speak.

The Giant stretched out a great arm towards him, but, just as he was about to catch hold of Frilly, a huge creature dashed past. With his great jaws wide open, the creature struck the Giant a terrible blow.

Quick as lightning Frilly darted into the cavern.

He seized Ragged Blossom by the dress, putting his
head under Snugglepot and lifting him onto his back.
Then he swam, quicksticks, out of the cavern. The two
giants were struggling and groaning, and the water
bubbled and foamed about them.

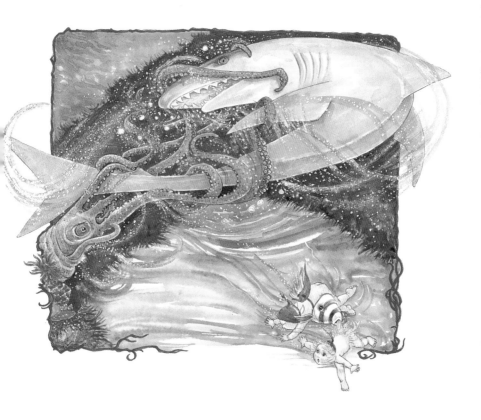

'Follow us!' he called to Cuddlepie, who was weeping near a seabush.

Quickly they went, further and further away from the terrible Giants. At last they reached a wall of coral. Poor Frilly sank upon the coral as if he were dead. The Nuts and Ragged Blossom bent over him in distress.

'Oh Frilly, dear Frilly!' said Blossom, 'how brave you were! Poor Frilly, we were so heavy, and you saved us.'

Soon Frilly stopped panting, and began to feel better. They all lay for a while upon the rainbow-coloured coral, and watched the sea cucumbers creep by.

'Well,' said Snugglepot at last, 'now we have seen a giant under the water. *Two* giants, in fact.'

'Yes,' shivered Cuddlepie. 'And up close, too.'

'And I don't want to see any more,' said Frilly. So they mounted their horses and began the homeward journey.

As they were climbing into their shell-beds that evening, Cuddlepie sighed.

'What's up?' said Snugglepot.

'I was just thinking about Mr Lizard. I wonder if he's ever seen a sea giant. I'd love to tell him about it. I miss him - and the Bush.'

'Well, scrag and rag me, I do too, but there are just a few more things I'd like to see in the underwater world first. What about you, Blossom?'

'Hmm,' agreed Ragged Blossom thoughtfully. 'I have heard of a Princess who lives in the sea. It would be gummy to see her.'

'We'd just better not turn into Fish Folk, that's all,' Cuddlepie warned as he inspected his toes. 'If we're here too long we might grow tails!'

And so, making funny fish faces at each other, they giggled and chatted and planned their next adventure, under the sea.

Subkingdom EMBRYOPHYTA ●

Mosses and Liverworts

Phylum BRYOPHYTA

Class Hepaticae—*liverworts*
Class Anthocerotae—*hornworts*
Class Musci—*mosses*

Vascular Plants

Phylum TRACHEOPHYTA

Subphylum Psilopsida
Subphylum Lycopsida—*"club mosses"*
Subphylum Sphenopsida—*horsetails*
Subphylum Pteropsida
Class Filicineae—*ferns*

(Cone-bearing Plants)

Class Gymnospermae
Subclass Cycadophytae
—*seed ferns and cycads*
Subclass Coniferophytae
—*ginkgo and conifers*

(Flowering Plants)

Class Angiospermae
Subclass Dicotyledoneae
Subclass Monocotyledoneae

The Story of the Plant Kingdom

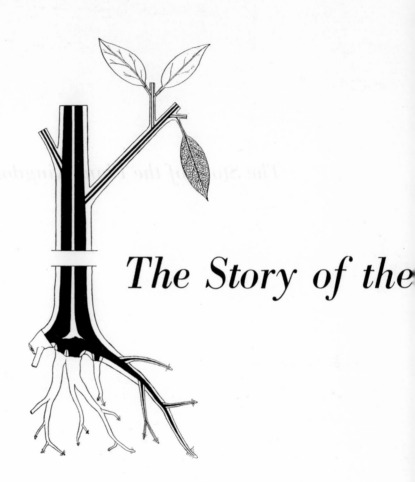

The Story of the Plant Kingdom

The Story of the

Plant Kingdom

Original Edition by MERLE C. COULTER
University of Chicago

Revised by HOWARD J. DITTMER
University of New Mexico

THE UNIVERSITY OF CHICAGO PRESS

Library of Congress Catalog Number: 59-10424

THE UNIVERSITY OF CHICAGO PRESS, CHICAGO 37
Cambridge University Press, London, N.W. 1, England
The University of Toronto Press, Toronto 5, Canada

Preface

The original version of *The Story of the Plant Kingdom* was written in 1935 by Professor Merle C. Coulter to serve as a textbook in botany under the new Chicago College Plan, which aimed to provide a "respectable minimum of general education." Dr. Coulter's text took its place in that division of the plan called "Introduction to the Biological Sciences."

Although prepared in the interest of a specific university's curriculum, the book soon found wide acceptance by other institutions and by non-academic persons in search of botanical information presented in readable form.

After more than twenty years it was apparent that the book needed revision and reorganization to bring it up to date. Dr. Coulter did not wish to undertake the revision himself, so an invitation was extended to me through the University of Chicago Press. An outline of the proposed reorganization was submitted to Dr. Coulter and the University of Chicago Press. The suggestions made were accepted, and the writer was given a free hand to revise the text as seemed appropriate in the light of present-day trends in botany.

Before any of the manuscript could be sent to Dr. Coulter for his advice and criticisms, he became seriously ill and passed away. His untimely death was a great loss to his many friends and colleagues and the botanical field, to which he contributed so much.

In the revision an attempt has been made to preserve the character and maintain the novel form of presentation so beautifully handled by Dr. Coulter. While the style is much the same, the organization of the chapters is completely different. Only the first and last chapters remain in their original position. A few new chapters have been added, and most of the others have had considerable revision.

The most radical change is that involving classification. The first edition used the terminology and in general the Engler-Prantl system. This revision uses the system devised in part by Dr. Oswald Tippo. This system places the major groups in phyla rather than divisions or subdivisions. Although still largely an artificial system, it is more logical from a phylogenetic viewpoint, and in addition it is an easier system for the student to learn.

Along with the change in classification, the lines of descent have also been modified. In the first edition, the main line of descent was from the Chlorophyta through the Hepaticae and Anthocerotae to the Filicinae. The latter were considered as precursors of the heterosporous pteridophytes, and these in turn gave rise to the seed plants. In the present system, the Hepaticae are presumed to have descended from the Chlorophyta but not to have given rise to the higher pteridophyte groups. Instead, the lower pteridophytes, the Psilophytales, were derived from the green algae, either before or contemporary with the Hepaticae. From these early pteridophytes there arose the club mosses, horsetails, and, somewhat later, the ferns. The higher seed plants are considered to have arisen from a very primitive group of seed ferns. In this system greater emphasis is given to the development of vascular tissue and its organization and less to heterospory.

In this book we begin with the higher plant, after a single introductory chapter, to permit the student to become familiar with the organs and tissues and physiological activities. The phyla of the plant kingdom are then presented in successive chapters, using the ontogenetic and phylogenetic approach as each new group gives us a more advanced stage in the evolutionary scheme.

This is, of course, an elementary textbook. Although a number of terms have been added to this edition, a definite effort has been made to keep the technical terminology to a minimum. There are subjects which could have been added, but limiting the size of this book to a one-semester course meant that we could not include everything that might be considered desirable in a thorough treatise of botany. Biological principles are included throughout, and it is hoped that the reader will be stimulated to study more advanced work in this field.

In his Preface to the original edition, Dr. Coulter expressed his indebtedness to Dr. Paul Voth for his preparation of the illustrations and to Dr. John Beal, Dr. Ralph Buchsbaum, Dr. George D. Fuller, Dr. Victor Johnson, Dr. George K. Link, Dr. Charles A. Shull, and Dr. Paul Voth for their very helpful criticism of portions of the manuscript. Our gratitude continues in this revision, and, in addition, I am indebted to Jeanne R. Janish and Serafin Ramon, who prepared the new diagrams and drawings; to Fern L. Sweeney, who typed most of the manuscript; to Dr. Eugene W. Rypka for his critical reading of the manuscript; and especially to Dr. Paul Voth, who read this revision and again made many helpful suggestions.

HOWARD J. DITTMER

Contents

I. *The Origin of Life and the Primitive Plant*

Covering the earth is a green mantle of life called vegetation. From this luxuriant growth of plants we obtain, either directly or indirectly, all the food we eat, the clothes we wear, the homes we build, and even the oxygen we breathe. Because of their economic importance, as well as biological significance, the study of plants (botany) has become increasingly important. Possibly botanical science arose from the basic human needs for food, shelter, and clothing, but botany has now become a highly technical science with thousands of scientists seeking in every phase of research new ways to increase our production, obtain new products, and develop new varieties to make our world a better one in which to live. The science of botany is now more important than ever, for we face a rising tide of world population which we are told will double in the next fifty years from its present estimated number of 2,600,000,000.

Botanists have described about 350,000 different species of living plants, which live in a variety of habitats. Common experience tells us that within this vast assemblage there is tremendous variation in structural and functional characteristics. It appears to be a chaotic array of living forms until one finds some system which connects and relates all members of the plant kingdom in an orderly and understandable way. To date, man has discovered only one fundamental concept which is successful in accomplishing this result, and that is the concept of organic evolution. There is so much evidence to justify belief in this concept that biologists are convinced of its validity. Organic evolution derives all modern plants from very primitive ancestral types through a process of gradual modification.

How these early ancestors were first brought into existence is another question, a question to which no one has as yet found a very satisfactory answer. Of course, biologists usually do their own speculating on this problem and come to favor certain hypotheses. The most plausible guess seems to be that the first living organisms upon the earth were derived from non-living materials already present; but just how this occurred remains a mystery, for man has not himself been able to produce life from non-living materials or to discover anything of the sort occurring spontaneously in nature today. This does not preclude the fact that man may someday be able to do so, for in very recent years the study of viruses has been giving us a better picture of just what life is and how it may have originated.

Like the sun, the atmosphere, water, and the soil, so animals and plants are also composed of atoms and molecules. The largest of these molecules are proteinaceous, and, when these protein molecules are combined in the correct proportion, we may have a simple form of life. Virologists tell us that the virus may be no more than this; yet to some it seems to have all the properties we associate with "being alive."

You have often heard the statement that if we were reduced to our mineral molecular content our bodies would be worth about ninety-eight cents. What makes us worth so much more? The answer is life. But what is life? Where does it come from? Where does it go? Of what is it composed? If you were asked to define life, what would you say? Obviously the answer is not an easy one. It is a component of neither the air nor the sea, nor is it made up of elements contained in the earth's crust; but it is something found in the body of every living plant and animal. Life is an intangible. It is physiological activity which is always associated with protoplasm, the substance which separates the organic world from the inorganic. We associate life with the processes of growth, metabolism, reproduction, and response to stimuli. All living things have these properties.

Life is present in the egg and sperm as two separate entities; then with fertilization it becomes a single life in the new individual. But what makes life so different? Is the life of a tree really different from the life of a cat or a human? We seem to think so. Yet each is really produced in the same way; it is only the body structure that is different. Functionally, in order to keep life in the body, each organism requires the same things—oxygen, water, minerals, food, and an active metabolic unit to use these substances. Eventually life is lost by each organism. In old age the metabolic processes decline until oxygen, water, and food can no longer be used; then life is ended. If serious injury or disease disrupts the metabolic processes, life departs.

We have not answered the question, "What is life?"

No one knows. It is a fascinating subject, and any biologist, whether botanist or zoologist, is interested in such a discussion. Our purpose is merely to point out that, basically, life in plants is no different from that in animals. There is a difference in how it behaves and in its activity, but life arises in plants under the same circumstances as in animals and ends for the same reasons and in the same way.

Biologists generally agree that life began with one or a very few simple types of organisms over a thousand million years ago. By a process of reproduction these early organisms perpetuated and multiplied their kind. For the most part the offspring resembled their parents, but occasionally one of them differed. This original difference may have been very slight, but, because it was perpetuated, it provided a starting point for greater changes. Some generations later, one of the descendants of the new type changed further, the second change being added to the first. Thus, by an accumulation of small changes over a great many generations, there emerged at last a type of organism that differed to a significant degree from its original ancestor. Meanwhile, other lines of descent from the same ancestor may well have perpetuated themselves without modification. At the end of this period, therefore, individuals of the two types, old and new, existed side by side. The common ancestor had left two types of descendants. Evolutionary divergence had occurred.

In our attempt to visualize the very primitive plants, we might hope to get our most reliable clues from the fossil record. Actually this avenue of investigation has yielded very little information. The earliest plants apparently left little or nothing in the way of fossil remains; their tiny, delicate bodies did not lend themselves to fossilization, as did many of the higher plants. A fossil may be in the original form, with a replacement of the plant tissue by mineral deposition, cell by cell, or it may be an impression left in soft clay which gradually hardened and resisted all forces of disintegration. Small unicellular organisms have left no complete fossils and but few impressions. However, another type of fossil, the trace, has been associated with these small delicate plants. In the earliest sedimentary rocks there are many deposits of carbon which suggest that living organisms were once present, but these traces do not tell us what they were like. Only in rare instances do these rocks reveal outlines of what may have been the bodies of simple algae.

With the fossil line of inquiry blocked, we draw what conclusions we can from a survey of the forms that are now living. We must look to the form and structure of these organisms to supply ourselves with the information we want. From a study of human history and from our study of the later chapters of the fossil record, which are comparatively clear, we get the impression that things complex have usually been derived from things simple, rather than the reverse. By extending this idea, we are certain that the earliest plants were the simplest plants. We can do no better, therefore, than to give our attention to the simplest forms that are living today, on the assumption that these have descended with relatively little modification from the earliest ancestral types.

About the nearest approach to utter simplicity that we can find in living organisms appears in a small and decidedly inconspicuous group of plants known as the **blue-green algae.** From this group we have selected about the simplest of all, a unicellular form belonging to the genus *Gloeocapsa.* The body of a single *Gloeocapsa* plant is far too small to be seen by the naked eye; we must examine it under the high power of the microscope to get any adequate idea of its structure. When we look at it in this way, we see a tiny, nearly spherical body, consisting of a wall inclosing a mass of granular material. Actually this material, which looks granular, is of a jelly-like consistency and is nothing more or less than **protoplasm,** the essential living substance, the truly living part of the body of every plant and animal. But the protoplasm that we see in the body of *Gloeocapsa* should be thought of not merely as a certain amount of the living substance but as being organized into a definite unit which we call the **cell.**

The surrounding wall, which is merely a lifeless product of the protoplasm itself, has its function in maintaining the shape and providing protection for the living substance within. The type of wall that we see is a feature that serves fairly well to distinguish plants from animals. The organized protoplasm of plant cells (but not of animal cells) is inclosed by cell walls composed exclusively, or in the main, of **cellulose.**

Probably no concepts have been more significant and fruitful in the development of biology than those that are included in the so-called "cell principle." Robert Hook in 1665 observed the units of structure in cork, and, since these tiny structures reminded him so much of the cells in a penitentiary, he gave them that name. Later, in 1838, Schleiden observed that plants were composed entirely of cells, and the following year Schwann made the same pronouncement for animals. The expression "cell principle" includes two component concepts: (1) that the bodies of all plants and animals are composed of cells, and (2) that new cells are derived only by the division of pre-existing cells.

The higher plants and animals, such as ourselves, have multicellular bodies, with sometimes as many as several billion cells structurally and functionally co-ordinated in the body of a single individual. Cells of higher plants vary between 1/250 and 1/2,500 inch in diameter, while some of the very smallest cells of bacteria may be only 1/25,000 inch in diameter. It has been estimated that a single mature leaf of an apple tree contains 50,000,000 cells. If we multiply this figure by 6,000—the approximate number of leaves on an average-size apple tree—we can arrive at a figure for the total number of cells in the leaves, but this does not include the cells in the fruits, stems, and roots. Many of the simpler plants and animals, however, have bodies that are unicellular. *Gloeocapsa* falls into this category, for the entire individual consists of only one cell. This, then, is one reason for regarding *Gloeocapsa* as perhaps our simplest plant; but this reason alone would not suffice, for there are actually many thousands of plants and animals which are one-celled bodies.

Gloeocapsa is bluish-green in color; this is the effect of two soluble pigments, a blue pigment called **phycocyanin** and a green one, **chlorophyll,** which suffuse the protoplasm. The blue pigment is a comparative rarity in the plant kingdom, appearing in the blue-green algae and but rarely in the red algae. Its function is not well understood, but it may facilitate the manufacture of food in these algae under the limited light conditions in which they usually live. Chlorophyll, however, is as famous as any substance in the biological world.

Present in all green plants, it has the remarkable power of enabling the plant to manufacture food out of materials which themselves possess no food value. Chlorophyll bears a remarkable similarity to hemoglobin, in the blood of animals. A plant that is **chlorotic,** that is, losing its green color and becoming yellowish, may have its color rapidly restored by supplying it with iron. Similarily, when a human becomes anemic because his hemoglobin percentage is low, the administration of iron often stimulates the production of hemoglobin and restores color to the blood.

Green plants are independent organisms, for they are capable of maintaining themselves in the absence of other forms of life. Here we see a second reason for regarding *Gloeocapsa* as primitive; the earliest organisms must have been independent. They could not have parasitized something which did not exist. Once again, however, the criterion is not decisive, since this same independence is characteristic of most of the members of the plant kingdom.

In nature, *Gloeocapsa* lives at the bottom of shallow pools of fresh water. Some of this water diffuses through the cell wall into the protoplasm, along with a certain amount of carbon dioxide, which is dissolved in the water. Out of these two simple raw materials, the energy supplied by sunlight, and by virtue of its possession of the green chlorophyll, the protoplasm manufactures food for itself.

Living protoplasm is a going concern, always in a dynamic state. It is constantly in motion, carrying the granules and cellular inclusions to various portions of the cell. As we shall see later and as can be demonstrated in the laboratory, the chloroplasts in the cells of higher plants are circulated within the cell by the streaming protoplasm so as to place each plastid for a time in the most favorable light position. Like a running motor, the cell demands a continuous supply of fuel. Otherwise it will stop running, and death will occur. For fuel the living organism can make use of only a limited class of substances—substances which not only contain energy but contain it in a form that can be released and put to work by the organism. This is the category of substances that we refer to as **food.** *Gloeocapsa* manufactures its own food and consumes the larger part of it as fuel to keep its protoplasm alive.

Some food is stored up against a future need. If this were not the case, the plant would probably die under those conditions (notably lack of sunlight) which prohibited food manufacture. Among the higher plants, special storage depots are usually present. Most plants store their excess foods in the form of carbohydrates; animals store mostly fats. *Gloeocapsa*, however, can do no better than to store a certain amount of food rather diffusely through its protoplasm, since it has no specialized tissues.

A portion of the manufactured food is devoted to growth. Displaying the power which more strikingly than any other distinguishes the living from the non-living, *Gloeocapsa* converts part of the food into additional protoplasm. Protoplasm, of course, is a very complex substance made up of carbohydrates, fats, proteins, minerals, and other compounds. Its production involves not merely transformation of the food but also the addition of certain other chemical elements that are available in the surrounding medium. The resulting growth appears as an increase in the size of the *Gloeocapsa* cell, with a gradual stretching of its rather elastic wall and the production of new wall substance by the protoplasm. Growth must also include repair. In many-celled organisms some cells of the body are frequently lost, either by accident or in the course of the ordinary life processes. Repair may be thought of as involving the same fundamental transformations of food as occur in connection with growth. Growth, however, brings an increase in the size of the body, which is not the case in repair. In a single-celled organism such as *Gloeocapsa* the phenomenon of repair should doubtless be admitted as a hypothetical proposition, but it would be difficult to demonstrate in such a simple plant.

In the main features of food manufacture and food use, *Gloeocapsa* does no more or less than any green plant. Its uniqueness lies in the fact that it accomplishes all this with a cell that is exceptionally simple. The protoplasm of *Gloeocapsa* is homogeneous; all parts of the protoplasm appear to be the same, and apparently all parts engage in the various life activities. It is this simple, undifferentiated protoplasm that provides our third reason, and our best reason, for regarding *Gloeocapsa* as one of our simplest plants.

The fourth reason appears in connection with its reproduction. Under favorable conditions *Gloeocapsa* continues to grow rather steadily. When the cell has reached a certain size, it simply pinches in two in the middle to form two small "daughter cells." These daughters round out into separate spheroid cells, each with its own elastic wall, and the two remain together, along with the rest of the plant's cells, within the common outer plant wall.

This is the simplest conceivable type of cell division, and we speak of it as **reproduction by fission.** Two individuals now exist where before there was but one. Reproduction could be no simpler than this so that there we have reason No. 4 for regarding *Gloeocapsa* as representing the extreme of simplicity.

The two new individuals proceed to carry out their lives quite independently of each other. Later they reproduce according to the same simple program—probably not much later, for in such simple forms the "life cycle" (i.e., the sequence of events that attends from a given stage in one generation to the corresponding stage in the next) is very brief. Under highly favorable environmental conditions, one generation in some of the blue-green algae may be consummated in less than one hour's time. Perhaps we should cite this feature, too, as a criterion of primitiveness for *Gloeocapsa.* Certainly it is a prevalent condition in simple organisms, while the more complex bodies of higher forms must pass through quite a succession of stages before they become mature and capable of reproducing.

In the higher plants special reproductive organs are differentiated from the vegetative body, but in a blue-green alga, with its single-celled body, no such differentiation is possible. Here reproduction is accomplished by simple division of the vegetative body itself. We refer to the main body of any plant—the part that carries on the ordinary life processes, or "vegetative" processes—as the "vegetative body." The term is as applicable to a one-celled plant as it is to the higher forms. Thus we say that reproduction of *Gloeocapsa* is by **vegetative multiplication,** as reproduction by fission is called in plants.

In this connection the point should be made that *Gloeocapsa* is primitive not simply because it reproduces by vegetative multiplication but because this is the only mode of reproduction it possesses. Actually, many of the higher plants, while introducing new and more specialized methods of reproduction, retain as well the power of vegetative multiplication, so that at times they produce new individuals through separation from the parent body of groups of cells which appear to be ordinary vegetative cells.

One of the characteristics of blue-green algae as a group is the production of **mucilaginous sheaths.** *Gloeocapsa* is no exception, for apparently the outer part of its cell wall becomes changed (through some action of the surrounding water or by an accumulation of metabolic waste products) into a transparent covering. Commonly, two daughter cells will remain side by side, stuck in the matrix which is provided by the old mucilaginous sheath of the "parent," and often the old sheath persists to hold four "granddaughters" together. The two or four cells so associated are, however, mutually independent, so that we refer to such a formation as a "colony" rather than as a many-celled individual. If any agency breaks up the colony, the individuals

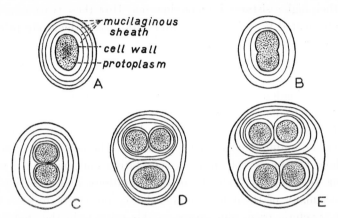

Fig. 1.—The blue-green alga, *Coccochloris*, which is somewhat larger but closely resembles *Gloeocapsa*, discussed in the text. *A*, single one-celled individual; *B*, cell division in process; *C–E*, colonies.

will apparently live when separated quite as successfully as they had lived side by side (Fig. 1).

Although most blue-greens share with *Gloeocapsa* the several features of simplicity that we have described, the form of colony produced by others is somewhat more complex. Very often thousands of individual cells are stuck together in a transparent mucilaginous matrix which represents the combined output of all of them. In nature, therefore, the blue-greens are most commonly encountered in the form of slimy masses (spheroid or amorphous) growing in shallow fresh water or upon damp rocks. Some, however, grow in salt water and some on damp soil and the moist bark of trees. One of the members of this group is responsible for the characteristic color of the Red Sea—showing that "blue-green" algae may sometimes contain a conspicuous red pigment, *phycoerythrin*, as well. They grow successfully in hot springs at a temperature far beyond that which most other plants could endure. Around the hot springs and geysers of Yellowstone National Park there are so-called sinter deposits, and in connection with these there is a plentiful growth of blue-green algae. These forms are able to resist not only great heat but also extreme cold. They can also tolerate great dryness and strongly alkaline water. Altogether, the resistance of this group exceeds that of all other plant groups, save only the bacteria. The relation between their universality of distribution and their high resistance is an obvious one. How these two characteristics are related to the simplicity and antiquity of the group provides an interesting field of speculation.

The closest relatives of blue-green algae are apparently the bacteria, with resemblances which impel most biologists to place the latter in the plant kingdom. Aside from this, it is difficult to place the bacteria, for the group displays a mixture of plantlike and animal-like characteristics. Like the blue-green algae, the bacteria have single-celled bodies and undifferentiated protoplasm; like the blue-greens, they reproduce by simple cell division (vegetative multiplication), multiplying very rapidly under favorable conditions; and, like the blue-greens, many of them have extraordinary powers of resistance. In truth, bacteria excel blue-greens in this respect; in the spore stage some are able to survive in boiling water for several hours.

The big difference lies in the fact that most bacteria lack chlorophyll and cannot manufacture their own food. Hence they are usually "dependent," directly or indirectly, upon other living organisms. The combination of dependency, ubiquity, high resistance, rapid multiplication, and microscopic (or even ultra-microscopic) size makes this group the great disease-producer among man and other organisms. For this and other reasons bacteria are of tremendous economic importance, and in recognition of this importance most universities now maintain distinct departments of bacteriology. We shall return to bacteria in chapter x, in a context that will bring out more clearly the significant roles that they play in the organic world.

II. *The Modern Plant Body*

We have seen in chapter i how plants of great simplicity grow, reproduce, and carry on the other life activities. Let us now take a look at one of the higher plants before we return to the primitive forms and the evolutionary development of the entire plant kingdom.

The typical higher plant is an organism made up of roots, stems, leaves, flowers, and ultimately fruits and seeds. The activities of a plant are largely divided between the organs which make up that plant. Each is so constituted that it is able to carry on certain functions better than other organs. Therefore, it would seem desirable to look at each of the major parts separately from the standpoints of structure and function and to observe their gross morphology.

LEAF

The typical leaf of a higher plant is composed of a broad **blade** with a slender stalk, the **petiole,** by which it is attached to the stem. At the base of the petiole, in the axil which forms the union of the leaf with the stem, is a bud called the **axillary bud.** Coursing through the petiole and expanding into the blade are the **veins** which carry water, minerals, and food materials. Veins are exposed on the lower surface of the leaf more prominently than on the upper surface. It is also apparent that leaves are green. This color is due to chlorophyll, which is contained in minute cytoplasmic bodies called **chloroplasts** and is a substance of importance in the life of every green plant.

STEM

No part of the plant varies so greatly in its structure as the stem, as we shall soon see when considering a plant's response to its environment. In some plants the stem is almost nonexistent; in others it makes up over 90 per cent of the bulk. For example, the stem of a carrot, in its first year of growth, is nothing more than a growing point imbedded in the basal portion of the fleshy root, while a sunflower in one year of growth may produce a stem over fifteen feet tall. Some major functions of stems are evident: (1) they give rise to leaves; (2) they form the conducting channels between the leaves and roots for the *translocation* of all solutes in the plant; and (3) where present, they usually serve as support.

ROOT

The roots of most plants are in the ground, but there are many plants, particularly in the tropics, which grow with their roots freely exposed in the air. The two chief functions of roots are anchorage for the plant and the absorption of water and minerals, which are conducted (through the vascular system) to those parts of the plant where needed (Fig. 2). Roots usually are very slender, many-branched structures, although a few form extremely large storage organs, aiding greatly in the total economy of the plant.

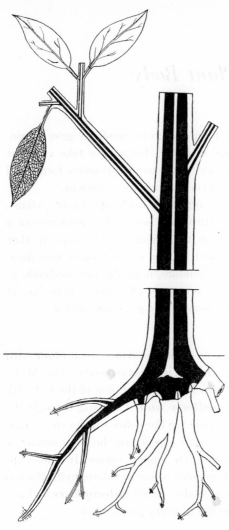

Fig. 2.—Idealized diagram of the modern plant body, to show how the vascular system (darkened) traverses roots, main stem, stem branches, and leaves.

FLOWER

Roots, stems, and leaves make up the *vegetative* portion of the plant and in some cases may reproduce the plant by vegetative multiplication. The flower, however, is the organ of *sexual reproduction.* In some cases the flower is perfect, i.e., containing both male and female organs; in others it is imperfect—that is, the flowers contain either male or female parts but not both. The male organ is the *stamen,* which produces the *anther.* In the anther, or pollen sac, are produced the *pollen grains* which contain the sperm necessary for the fertilization of the egg in the female organ. The latter is the *pistil,* whose primary structure is the *ovary.* After fertilization of the egg, the ovary ripens into the fruit; the fertilized egg inside develops into the embryo and with its associated parts becomes the *seed.* As in the vegetative parts, there is considerable variation in the flower, not only in the number of different parts but in their form and structure as well.

RESPONSE TO THE ENVIRONMENT

Thus we see that the body of the flowering plant may be cast in any of a great many patterns, for flowering plants live in an extremely wide range of environmental conditions and show corresponding adaptations. Most of these higher plants can be easily recognized as conforming to one of three general forms: "trees," in which the stem is large and erect; "shrubs," in which the stems are smaller and more numerous and the general habit of growth is bushy; and "herbs," in which the stem is tender, with woody tissue much reduced. Some stems, however, sprawl horizontally over the soil surface, and some remain buried beneath the surface, sending into the air nothing but the leaves (and flowers). Other stems assume a climbing or vinelike habit, while some even perch upon other plants and maintain no soil connections of their own. A tropical forest presents a dense, tangled array of all these types and is a striking illustration of how plants may occupy every last little niche that will somehow provide them with the materials and energy which they require.

Many of the higher plants can withstand the rigorous climate of very high altitudes and latitudes, though of course there are many more which can live successfully under tropical conditions. It is the availability of water that limits the distribution of plants more than any other single factor. The barrenness of the desert is usually attributed to this factor alone, as is evidenced by the rich plant growth that is usually possible when irrigation is introduced. Some flowering plants maintain themselves successfully in near-desert conditions. These are characterized by certain rather obvious adaptive features: highly developed water-retaining layers; small, thick leaves, or none at all; very long roots to reach the water table; and large water reservoirs within the tissues to store water. At the other extreme are the few flowering plants that live in a water medium. These plants reveal the same body structures, but their tissues lack the cutinized cell walls so necessary for terrestrial plants, and, since water and various types of floats buoy the leaves to the surface for easy exposure to light, mechanical tissue is not necessary for support. With all this variation in form, however, the flowering plants exhibit only one fundamental body plan. There is always the organization into roots, stems, and leaves, along with a conducting system for the translocation of water, food, and minerals.

III. *The Leaf*

The leaf is the primary organ in the process of food production. The average leaf on a tree growing in temperate climates is only about 1/150 of an inch thick. Yet within this structure are a number of tissues, all functioning as a co-ordinated unit in the life activities of the plant.

ANATOMY OF THE LEAF

The outermost layer is the *epidermis* (Fig. 3), which is made up of many interlocking cells with cutinized outer surfaces. Generally the *cuticle* is thicker on the upper epidermis than on the lower. The thickness of the cuticle regulates to a certain degree the amount of water lost from the epidermal cells as well as the rate of diffusion of gases between the atmosphere and the cells. The epidermis is perforated by numerous lens-shaped "breathing pores" called *stomates* (Fig. 4). Each pore is circumscribed by a pair of sausage-shaped *guard cells.* The inner walls of the guard cells are much thickened, while the outer ones are quite thin, a factor which is very important in the opening and closing of the stomate. Changes in the shape of guard cells in response to variations in external conditions will increase or decrease the size of the breathing pore. This feature is of adaptive value in closing the portals of escape for water vapor when the dryness of the surrounding air endangers the welfare of the plant. Of course, the degree of efficiency shown in this adaptive adjustment of the size of the breathing pores varies considerably among different species of plants. When the stomates are open, they are the chief path through which the gases of the atmosphere—including oxygen, carbon dioxide, and water vapor—move freely.

In most terrestrial plants the stomates are more numerous on the lower surface than on the upper surface of the leaf, while in floating leaves, like those of the water lily, stomates are restricted to the upper surface. In vertical leaves (e.g., grasses) the stomates are about equally divided on both surfaces.

Between the two epidermal layers is the *mesophyll,* or middle leaf. Except for the veins, the bulk of this tissue is made up of cells which contain chloroplasts. Those which lie just below the upper epidermis, as in the case of a typical horizontal leaf, occur in a

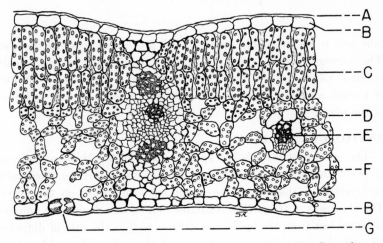

Fig. 3.—Cross-section of typical angiosperm leaf. *A,* cuticle; *B,* epidermis; *C,* palisade parenchyma; *D,* spongy parenchyma; *E,* vein; *F,* intercellular space; *G,* stomate.

relatively compact palisade arrangement. These cells are thin-walled *parenchyma* cells and, because of their resemblance to a palisade or row of stakes, are called *palisade parenchyma.* Cells below the palisade are more isodiametric in shape, arranged in a somewhat irregular spongy pattern, with numerous large intercellular spaces between them, which is the reason they are termed *spongy parenchyma.* This loose arrangement, and the lesser spaces between the palisade cells, permits a free circulation of gases throughout the leaf. Each stomate opens into an irregular air chamber which, in turn, communicates with this system of intercellular spaces in the mesophyll.

Both palisade and spongy mesophyll cells contain chloroplasts imbedded in the cytoplasm which surrounds the large central vacuole in each cell. The chloroplasts are about two to four times more numerous in palisade cells than in the spongy cells, and in many plants the number of palisade cells greatly exceeds that of the spongy parenchyma.

In his study of a twenty-one-year-old catalpa tree, Turrell had the opportunity to provide us with some unusual figures. He counted 26,040 leaves on this tree. He then classified them according to size and measured them for external surface area. He found that these leaves had an externally exposed surface of about 390 square meters and that within the epidermis there were about 1,850,000,000 stomates. He then made microscopic sections of leaf samples and by complicated formula calculated the internal surface exposed by the mesophyll cells to be about 5,100 square meters. Most of this internally exposed surface area was in the palisade layer.

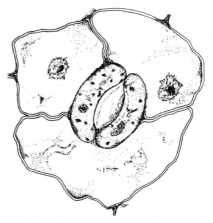

Fig. 4.—Surface view of a stomate, showing two sausage-shaped guard cells, central pore, and three adjacent epidermal cells.

In an investigation of an elm tree it was estimated that there were about 400,000 chloroplasts to each square millimeter of leaf surface. Since a mature elm tree may have over 100,000 leaves, it has been calculated that the total exposed area of the chloroplasts may amount to as much as 140 square miles. Compare this to our own red blood corpuscle area, which is estimated to have a total surface area of about one acre.

The significance for such investigations becomes apparent when we realize that all substances entering or leaving a plant go through these surfaces. The vast intercellular spaces provide a reservoir for the carbon dioxide and oxygen which diffuse through the cell surfaces in the processes of photosynthesis and respiration. It is these surfaces which also lose water in transpiration.

The arrangement of the veins (*vascular bundles*) gives a very characteristic appearance to the leaves and is spoken of as *venation* (Fig. 5). Some leaves, such as those of an elm tree, have a prominent midvein with major veins coming off it laterally the entire length of the leaf. This is called *pinnate venation*. *Palmate venation* refers to leaves having five or more major veins arising at the base

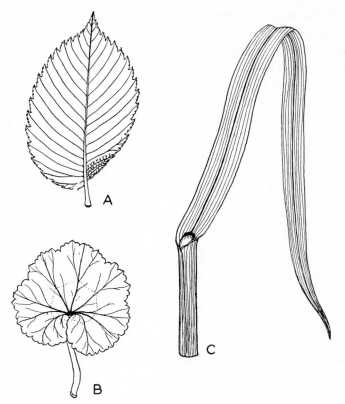

FIG. 5.—Leaf venation. *A*, elm, pinnately veined; *B*, geranium, palmately veined; *C*, corn, parallel veined.

of the blade and then radiating upward and outward. Catalpa and mulberry leaves are examples of this type. Both pinnate and palmate venation are also classified as *net venation*. Leaves such as those of iris and grasses have a number of veins about an equal distance apart from the base to the apex of the blade. These are *parallel-veined* leaves.

All leaves, regardless of the type of venation, have numerous tiny veins branching freely into the mesophyll spaces. Very few cells in a leaf are more than two or three cells away from a vein. Water and mineral salts are continuously delivered to the mesophyll cells by the water-conducting cells in each vein. Food is ultimately picked up by a separate group of food-conducting cells in the vein and transported to storage areas in the stem and root and to other cells where it is used in growth and repair.

PHYSIOLOGICAL ACTIVITIES IN THE LEAF

Matter and Energy. The theoretical viewpoint that characterizes modern natural science takes much of its flavor from two fundamental principles which have been revealed by the investigations of the physical scientist. The principle of "the conservation of matter" tells us that, though matter may pass from one form into another, it is never destroyed or created anew. The principle of "the conservation of energy" tells us that, though energy may pass from one form into another, it is never destroyed or created anew. It is in the light of these principles that the physical scientist explains the origin, the nature, and the characteristic action of the non-living objects which make up our world, both those which were produced by nature alone and those which were artificially assembled by man.

For a long time it was felt that these two laws were inapplicable to living organisms. Even today the doubt persists, and a perennial controversy goes on between the "mechanists" and the "vitalists." According to the mechanistic view of life, the living organism is a "machine," and one may hope to explain all the activities of the living organism in terms of the (known or knowable) laws of physics and chemistry. According to the vitalistic view, the living organism is something distinctly more than a machine, and there are at least some of the very important activities of the organism that can never be explained in mechanistic terms; for some of the phenomena of life transcend, and are therefore not subject to, the (known or knowable) laws of physics and chemistry.

With very few exceptions the men who are making contributions to biology are mechanists. The reason for this is not difficult to see. Scientists, as a rule, have been sufficiently intelligent to avoid tasks that are clearly hopeless. If a young biologist takes the vitalistic view, he concludes that the more deep-seated and important phenomena of life are beyond the reach of human analysis and so refrains from throwing himself into an investigation that he thinks is hopeless from the start. But if he is a mechanist, he has the faith that his research efforts will some day be rewarded, that by finding out a great deal about the living organism he may come to find out the causes of its activities in essentially the same way that he can understand the workings of a man-made machine. The substantial contributions to biology have been based upon the products of research. It follows, therefore, that the leading biologists of today are mechanists.

By no means everything about the living organism has been interpreted successfully in mechanistic terms. What remains to be interpreted is undoubtedly greater in amount than what has been interpreted already. Even so, a great deal of progress has been made in the last century and a half; already a great many of those activities of the organism which were once thought to be vitalistic and inscrutable have received clear-cut mechanistic interpretations. The progress made has been not merely theoretical but highly practical. We are in debt to the mechanists for a great deal of what goes to make up modern civilization—e.g., modern medicine, public hygiene, agricultural methods. Conceivably mechanism may turn out to be relatively superficial, in final analysis; but there can be no doubt that it has been highly useful, and the end of this usefulness is not yet in sight.

When one attempts to assign the original authorship of any such far-reaching concept as the mechanistic concept of life to any single individual, he usually finds himself confronted by a difficult and doubtless a profitless task. Regardless of formal authorship, the investigations of Lavoisier in 1790 (shortly before he was guillotined) probably carried as much weight as anything else in convincing the biological public of the essential validity of the mechanistic concept. Already scientists had seen the validity of the concept of the conservation of energy as applied to the inorganic world. It remained for Lavoisier to demonstrate that it applied equally well to the organic world.

By burning fuel, a machine converts the energy in that fuel into the energy of work and the energy of heat. In this process the full totality of energy appears on both sides of the equation. All the energy that was in the fuel is transformed into work or heat. No energy is dissipated into mere nothingness, nor is there any energy left over (provided that the burning has been complete).

Lavoisier showed that the same applied to the living organism. He demonstrated that the energy released by actually burning a given quantity of food was exactly equal to the amount of energy that the living organism itself could secure from this food, and that the utilization of the food by the organism was in essence combustion, just like the burning of fuel in a steam engine. Since that time biologists have come increasingly to think of the living organism as a machine, a machine which always requires fuel because it is always running.

Accordingly, plants and animals take their place along with non-living things in the grand cycle of energy. For its work and for life itself the organism is always dependent upon some source of pre-existing energy, since energy is never created anew upon this planet. And the energy that goes into the organism is never destroyed, since every bit of it is transformed into work that is done by the organism, into heat that is dissipated from the organism, and into a chemically stored form of energy that exists in the body of the organism, not only while it is alive but after it is dead.

Plants and animals are also part of the cycle of matter. Every bit of the matter that is in the organism has been derived from pre-existing matter in a non-living form. And all the matter that has been in the organism returns once again to a non-living form.

With respect to energy and with respect to such matter as plays no other role than that of fuel, the living organism is like a man-made machine. With respect to that matter which becomes a part of the body, it is quite different, for man has never yet been able to make a machine that could grow or repair itself.

These considerations serve to point out certain questions that must be answered if we are to understand the plant or the animal. From what source and in what form does the organism get its energy? From what source and in what form does it get its matter? How does it use the energy to accomplish work and to stay alive? How does it use the matter to accomplish repair, growth, and reproduction? We shall attempt to provide partial answers for these questions. No one has as yet been able to answer them fully.

All the energy and most of the materials which supply the bodies of living organisms in general can be traced back to the process of food manufacture in green plants. So far as is known, the fundamental process is the same in all organisms that contain chlorophyll, from the blue-green algae to the flowering plants. A single description will serve, therefore, and it would be well to work out that description in terms of the flowering plants, which constitute practically the entire food source for modern man and his domesticated animals.

Photosynthesis. Food manufacture by the green plant is known technically as photosynthesis, meaning "synthesis with the assistance of light." The materials necessary to carry out this process are carbon dioxide, water, light, and chlorophyll.

Carbon dioxide comes from the atmosphere, where it is present to the extent of about 0.03 per cent by volume, or 3 parts in 10,000 parts of air. Small as this quantity may seem, we find that field corn removes the carbon dioxide from 3.1 tons of air per acre in its growth period of about 120 days. When photosynthesis occurs, the carbon dioxide passes through the stomates and through the intercellular spaces of the mesophyll, where it comes in contact with the moist cell walls. Here it diffuses in dissolved form through the cell walls into the protoplasm, becoming available for the action of chlorophyll in the chloroplasts. Carbon dioxide enters the leaf because it is in higher concentration in the atmosphere than within the leaf. On the other hand, oxygen, which is released in the photosynthetic process, becomes more concentrated within the leaf and therefore diffuses outward through the stomates into the atmosphere.

Water in terrestrial plants comes mostly from the soil; it moves into the roots, into the conducting elements, up the stem, and out into the leaves, where it finally reaches the chlorophyll-bearing cells. The amount of water actually used in photosynthesis is small compared to the total amount necessary to maintain life in the plant. Most of the water which falls on the land is lost in runoff, evaporation from the soil, replenishing the subsurface water table, and transpiration from the plant. Nevertheless, it takes about 386 pounds of water to produce 1 pound of plant material in corn.

Chlorophyll is absolutely essential to the photosynthetic process; yet its precise role is not completely understood. Chlorophyll, in all but the most primitive plants, is located in the tiny disk-shaped chloroplasts. It is made up of two greenish pigments: **chlorophyll a,** which is blue-green in color, and **chlorophyll b,** which is yellow-green. In addition, the chloroplasts also contain **carotin** and **xanthophyll.** The former pigment is yellow-orange in color, and xanthophyll is a light yellow or lemon shade. Plastids which are dark green usually have very little of the carotinoid pigments present, and those areas in leaves which are light green and yellow usually have more of the carotinoid pigments than the chlorophylls. Chlorophyll has the ability to absorb energy from the sun, which apparently causes it to act as an enzyme to bring about the chemical reaction of converting carbon dioxide and water into sugar.

The source of energy utilized in photosynthesis is light, generally sunlight; in the absence of light the process cannot be accomplished. The visible colors in the spectrum are red, orange, yellow, green, blue, indigo, and violet. Not all these colors are absorbed by the pigmented parts of the leaf to the same degree in either quantity or quality. Furthermore, the structure and color of the leaf will alter the amount and kind of light absorbed. It is estimated that for most terrestrial plants less than 2 per cent of the absorbed energy is converted into chemical energy, although in shade plants it may run over 10 per cent. Of the different colors, the reds and blues are the most important for photosynthesis, while the yellows and greens are mostly reflected. However, simple plants living many feet beneath the surface of the ocean use more of the yellow, green, and blue pigments, probably because the other wave lengths of light cannot penetrate much beyond fifty feet of depth in the ocean.

Now that we have considered the different substances involved in photosynthesis, let us consider the actual process itself. The combination of carbon dioxide and water to form food actually involves quite a series of rapid chemical transformations. For our purpose, however, the process may be summarized by the following comparatively simple chemical equation:

$$6 \ CO_2 \ + \ 6 \ H_2O \xrightarrow[\text{light energy}]{\text{chlorophyll}} C_6H_{12}O_6 \ + \ 6 \ O_2.$$

(carbon dioxide)　　(water)　　　　　　　　(glucose)　　(oxygen)

Even without a knowledge of chemistry, the student can comprehend the significant features of this equation. As in all chemical equations, this one designates merely the proportions in which the various atoms and molecules react, not the absolute quantities. Reading from left to right, the first term designates six molecules of carbon dioxide, each one of which consists of one atom of carbon in combination with two atoms of oxygen. The second term similarly refers to six molecules of water, each of which contains two atoms of hydrogen in union with one of oxygen. The third term refers not to matter but to energy, the energy that is provided by sunlight. The horizontal arrow means that those things on the left are being transformed to those on the right. The formula $C_6H_{12}O_6$ stands for glucose, one of the simple sugars.

Among foods in general, the biologist recognizes three great categories: carbohydrates, fats, and proteins. Carbohydrates are composed of only three chemical elements, carbon, hydrogen, and oxygen, with the hydrogen and oxygen being usually in the same 2:1 proportion as in water. Carbohydrates contain many subcategories, of which one of the most common is that of the sugars. Of the many known sugars, glucose is the one that plays the most prominent role in the economy of plant and animal bodies, since it is in this form that most carbohydrates are assimilated.

The equation above tells us that one molecule of glucose is produced and that this molecule consists of a combination of six atoms of carbon with twelve of hydrogen and six of oxygen. The final term of the equation designates six molecules of oxygen gas. In the form of the free gas, such as that which occurs in our atmosphere, each oxygen molecule consists of a union of two atoms of oxygen. To summarize: photosynthesis involves a combination of six molecules of carbon dioxide with six of water and, with the energy of sunlight, yields one molecule of glucose as a main product and six molecules of oxygen as a by-product. (The six molecules of oxygen will diffuse out into the atmosphere unless they are used in the process of *respiration,* which will be described shortly.)

In our simple equation, energy is designated on the left but not on the right. This does not mean, however, that it has been lost. Instead, it is incorporated, in the form of chemical energy, into the molecule of glucose. Glucose may be thought of as the primary food, that from which all other foods are built. All foods contain energy, that same energy which was incorporated into the glucose in the process of photosynthesis. Since all living things depend directly or indirectly upon photosynthesis by green plants, it follows that every increment of growth, however tiny, and every active movement, however slight, and every second of maintenance of life itself throughout the countless billions of plants and animals on the earth are made possible only by the energy of sunlight.

The glucose molecules that result from photosynthesis—and enormously large numbers of such molecules are produced during every second of illumination in every working chloroplast—exist in a state of solution in the water which suffuses the chloroplast and the surrounding cytoplasm. Some of the glucose is shortly put to use in the economy of the cell in which it was manufactured. More of it, however, diffuses out through the wall and through a few adjoining cells until it reaches the food-conducting tubes that are a part of the nearest vein. Within these tubes it may travel a shorter or longer distance, traversing leaf, stem, and even root, for these tubes deliver glucose to the tissues at all levels of the body.

Respiration. Whether glucose remains in the cell where it was produced or is moved to some other cell of the body, it will be put to one of several uses. A great part of it is used as fuel to supply the protoplasm with the energy needed to support its various activities. This release of energy is not a violent "burning," such as we see in the firebox of a steam engine, but it is the same general phenomenon. Both are "combustions" or "oxidations," i.e., chemical changes in which oxygen is combined with the fuel in a manner to release its contained energy. In the burning with which we are familiar, the oxidation is very rapid, much energy is released in a short time, and high temperatures are generated. The type of oxidation that occurs in a living organism is at a much lower rate; energy is released slowly, steadily, in graded steps; and at no time is a high temperature generated. All cells of all living organisms, plant and animal, carry on this oxidation during every minute that they continue to live. In the vast bulk of cases the chemical reaction involved is the same in detail; in a few organisms and in a few tissues the reaction is the same in principle but different in detail. The process referred to is called *respiration,* and we will confine our attention to the more common form of respiration at this time.

The common form of respiration involves the following chemical reactions, which amounts to an item-for-item reversal of that of photo-synthesis:

$$C_6H_{12}O_6 + 6O_2 \rightarrow energy + 6CO_2 + 6H_2O.$$

Free oxygen combines with glucose in such manner as to release the energy that is contained within this fuel and in so doing breaks down the glucose into carbon dioxide and water. Respiration of this sort is a thoroughgoing, complete form of oxidation which gets out of the fuel all the energy that is to be had. In other words, carbon dioxide and water, the material products of respiration, retain no energy that is available for living organisms. Accordingly, these two substances may be thought of as the "ultimate wastes" of living organisms. It is apparent, therefore, that photosynthesis and respira-tion are compensatory processes; together they provide for a cycle of matter and energy, through which the same atoms of matter (but not the same energy) may pass repeatedly.

Food Usage and Storage. Glucose is of value to the plant not only in the energy it yields but also in providing most of the material that is incorporated into the structure of the living body. For struc-tural purposes glucose is transformed either into more complex carbo-hydrates or into still other substances. In the typical plant a large part of the body consists of lifeless cell walls. Cellulose, the character-istic cell-wall substance, is a complex carbohydrate. The cellulose molecule is a very large one and is produced by the union of a great many glucose molecules which have been condensed by the loss of water. The essential material that composes wood (i.e., the walls of the wood vessels) is a modified cellulose. The chemical formula is expressed:

$$(C_6H_{12}O_6)_n \rightarrow (C_6H_{10}O_5)_n + (H_2O)_n.$$

Fats also play some part in the structure of the plant body and a larger part in the structure of most animal bodies. Fats are apparently an essential part of most protoplasmic membranes. Like carbohy-drates, fats are composed of only the three elements, carbon, hy-drogen, and oxygen, but in a different proportion and arrangement. In the plant body fats are produced by transformations of carbo-hydrates and hence are also derivatives of the original glucose.

With fats and carbohydrates alone, however, there could be no protoplasm. Though protoplasm is full of mysteries as yet unsolved by the biologist, he is at least assured that the most conspicuous components of protoplasm are the proteins. Protein molecules are exceedingly large and complex. In addition to carbon, hydrogen, and oxygen, they always contain nitrogen, usually sulfur, and often phosphorus as well. Hence it is impossible for the plant to construct its proteins by a mere transformation of carbohydrates. Even though the other elements constitute only a small part of the protein molecule, that small part is quite essential. For "protein synthesis," therefore, the plant must be provided with nitrogen, sulfur, and phosphorus. These elements occur in the form of various salts in the soil. Going into solution in the soil water, the salts diffuse into the roots, are carried upward through the conducting tubes of the wood, and diffuse out again to the various living cells of the body. Though photosynthesis can go on only in the green parts of the plant and only during the daytime, it appears that protein synthesis can be conducted by any living plant cell at any time. The cells combine glucose with nitrogen, sulfur, and phosphorus to build up the complex protein molecules, and most of these are at once transformed into new protoplasm.

The fact that animals are dependent on the photosynthesis of green plants is probably as generally emphasized as is any principle of biology. However, the fact that animals are also dependent upon the protein synthesis of plants is often overlooked. The animal body has the power to transform carbohydrates into fats and the reverse, but from neither of these can it build entirely its own proteins. For that purpose it is quite dependent upon plant proteins. In digestion the animal breaks down the large molecules of plant proteins into smaller components (amino acids) and later reassembles these components in new combinations to build proteins of the type that are characteristic of the body of that particular animal.

In the body of the green plant, then, the glucose may be used as a source of energy and structural material in respiration or in growth. It may also be disposed of in a third way. Nature has endowed plants with an unconscious thriftiness, the tendency to store up some food against a future need. This is obviously of adaptive value, for it serves to tide the plant over a period of hard conditions when photosynthesis would be difficult or impossible.

Not only is glucose the most serviceable form of fuel for plant and animal respiration; it is also the most efficient form in which food can be transported from one part of the body to another. Not only is it highly soluble in water, the medium of food transport, but it readily diffuses through cell membranes and cytoplasm, because its molecule is smaller than that of most other foods. When it comes to food storage, however, glucose is inferior. More energy can be stored in a small space if the glucose is transformed into some more compact form of food.

To a very limited extent the green plant stores food in the form of protein. This occurs to a variable degree in seeds, notably those of beans and peas, but is usually of very slight importance in the economy of the plant body. Nor does the animal body store much food in the form of protein.

In one respect fats are the best of storage forms; gram for gram, fat carries more energy than do carbohydrates and proteins. Even so, plants make little use of fats for storage purposes, save in the case of some seeds, such as the castor bean, which is the source of the justly famous castor oil. In general, animals go in rather extensively for fat storage. Not only is fat a reserve food supply for animals, but in the "warm-blooded" animals its distribution near the body surface provides a blanket against the loss of heat.

The favorite storage form in plants is starch, a complex carbohydrate that may be stored very compactly. The chemical formula which describes this condensation reaction is the same as that given above for the formation of cellulose, e.g.,

$$(C_6H_{12}O_6)_n \rightarrow (C_6H_{10}O_5)_n + (H_2O)_n;$$

yet starch and cellulose do differ in other respects. In animals, too, the primary food reserve is a form of starch that is very similar to plant starch.

In the unicellular plant, starch storage must occur somewhere within the confines of the very cell that has conducted the photosynthesis. Commonly one or more spheroid accumulations of starch occur imbedded right in the chloroplast. The same thing occurs to a more limited extent in the flowering plant, but here the many-celled body makes possible the development of special storage tissues. Hence we find that, though some food stores are distributed rather diffusely through most cells of the body, there is usually some one region in which the bulk of stored food is concentrated.

Considerable storage of food occurs in the central or pith region of some upright stems. The cane sugar of commerce is derived from this portion of the sugar-cane plant, and the corresponding tissues of various palms are used extensively as a food source by the natives of tropical regions. In such cultivated plants as kohlrabi, cauliflower, and broccoli there is a moderate amount of food storage in those

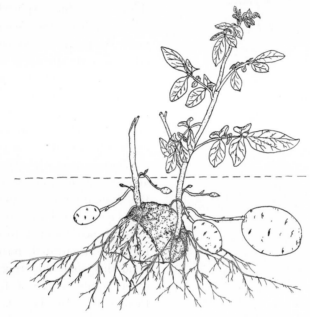

Fig. 6.—Diagram to show how potato plants arise (by "vegetative multiplication") from a bit of tuber and how these plants, in their turn, produce a new generation of tubers on underground branches from the main stem.

aerial stem parts that we eat. Many flowering plants, notably the ordinary grasses, store food in horizontal underground stems. By this device part of the product of the photosynthesis of one crop of leaves is saved to support the rapid development of a new crop of leaves. The Irish potato of cultivation is a prodigy of starch storage. Though the things that we call the "potatoes" are underground parts of the potato plant, they are not roots but specialized underground branches from the stem that are known technically as "tubers" (Fig. 6).

Quite a number of roots are conspicuously enlarged, e.g., fleshy. In these cases, in addition to carrying on their ordinary functions, the roots devote a large part of their tissues to the storage of food. Common illustrations of this phenomenon appear in beets, carrots, turnips, parsnips, and sweet potatoes (Fig. 7).

There is usually not much concentration of stored food in the leaf. It is not primarily for their fuel value that man eats such things as lettuce, spinach, and celery. Where the leaves are more fleshy, as in cabbage and artichokes, the fuel value is somewhat higher. Still higher in stored food are the modified leaves of bulbs, such as the onion, which man eats, and the tulip and hyacinth, which he does not eat.

Whatever may be the nature and extent of food storage in the vegetative parts, the plant may be depended upon to endow its seeds with stored food in a highly concentrated form. Beyond this, some flowering plants divert quite a bit of food to their fruits. In these last two cases, of course, the food storage is of value not in tiding the individual plant itself over a period of hard conditions but rather in giving the young a good start in life and in getting them widely distributed.

The tendency of many plants to concentrate their food stores has played a large part in molding the anatomy, physiology, habits, and general culture of

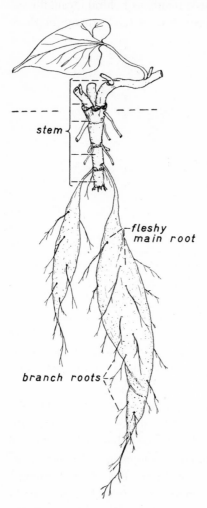

Fig. 7.—Lower portion of a young sweet potato plant with its fascicled root system of fleshy main roots.

man. Grazing animals have a chewing and digesting apparatus that is structurally and functionally adjusted to handling large quantities of plant material which provide much cellulose but little starch and sugar. Man could not survive on such a diet. Instead he exploits the special storage depots of plants that he finds in their seeds, fruits, and other parts and, to make matters easier for himself, breeds new varieties of plants in which the food storage is more plentiful, more accessible, and in a more palatable form.

We have seen, then, that the disposal of glucose in the living plant falls into the three channels of respiration, growth and repair, and food storage. But what becomes of all this material and energy when the plant dies?

Some passes into the bodies of offspring, through the instrumentality of the seeds and the gametes themselves. For most seed plants this would represent only a small fraction of the total material.

If the plant merely dies and falls to the ground, we note that it does not persist indefinitely but disintegrates and decomposes, adding its substance to the soil. This decomposition is not spontaneous; it is caused by the bacteria of decomposition, whose activities will be more fully outlined in a later chapter. By returning to the soil (and to the air) the matter that has been locked into the bodies of plants and animals, these bacteria play an important role in maintaining the cycle of matter in the organic world.

Under natural conditions, however, by no means all the green plants meet their fate in this comparatively peaceful manner. The majority are directly exploited by dependent organisms of larger size than the bacteria. To some extent the fungi, and to a greater extent the animals, incorporate the substance of the green plants into their own bodies. The selfsame carbon atoms will often, in fact, exist successively in the tissues of a herbivorous animal and those of a long series of carnivorous animals, until at last the final carnivorous form dies without being devoured. But the bacteria of decomposition almost always take their toll in the end, for it is they that at last break up the animal bodies and put their materials into circulation again.

There have, however, been situations in which the bacteria of decomposition have been balked. During the times of the "coal measures" there was an accumulation of the dead bodies of many large plants in swamp waters which inhibited bacterial action. Time and the pressure of sediments which accumulated above gradually transformed this organic material into the relatively pure form of carbon which constitutes our coal of today. Hence the energy which man releases by burning coal in modern times can be traced to the sunlight of several hundred million years ago, when it was locked up by the photosynthetic activity of those ancient plants. Most of our high-grade coal is the transformed bodies of more primitive vascular plants, having formed long before the flowering plants had been evolved.

Plants with Modified Habits. From the foregoing descriptions, the student may have the impression that all vascular plants are endowed with a machinery for photosynthesis which makes them quite independent of other organisms. Actually, this proposition must be qualified by exceptions of two types.

1. So far as is known, the higher green plants are indirectly dependent for their nitrogen supply upon the activities of certain groups of bacteria. The process involves the nitrogen cycle, which will be discussed in the chapter on bacteria.

2. A very few of the flowering plants have adopted unusual nutritive relationships that are characterized by a partial or complete dependence upon other organisms. One of these plants is the well-known mistletoe, which might be called a partial parasite (Fig. 8). Although this plant contains chlorophyll and can carry on its own photosynthesis, it does depend upon a host plant for its water and minerals. Mistletoe develops modified roots which penetrate its host's tissues and absorb fluids from the vascular cylinder of its host, sometimes leading to the death of the host.

Some other seed plants may be complete parasites. Broomrape is a frequent inhabitant of sand dunes (Fig. 9). It attaches its basal portions to the roots of one or more inhabitants of the dunes and derives not only food and mineral salts but anchorage as well from its host. Another example is dodder. It grows as a slender vine over and into the tissues of its host, absorbing the necessary food for its survival.

Weird nutritive relationships are seen in the insectivorous plants, whose capacities for devouring animals have often been exaggerated in popular fiction. The common sundew plant is a little form only a few inches in diameter, with tiny spoon-shaped leaves (Fig. 10). It captures insects on the "flypaper principle" through exudation of a sticky substance from glandular hairs on the leaf. After an insect gets stuck on the glandular hairs, the leaf gradually closes over the insect and digestion begins. Venus's-flytrap has a hinged, trap-shaped leaf which actually snaps shut upon the unfortunate fly that touches the sensitive "trigger-like" hairs on the leaf surface (Fig. 11).

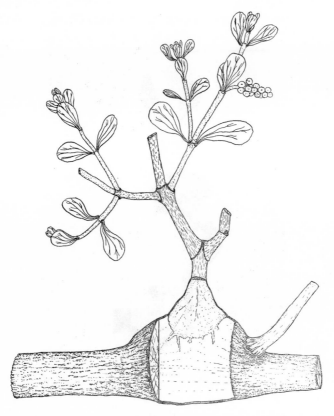

Fig. 8.—A mistletoe plant bedded in a branch of its host, shown in partial section to reveal the intimate nature of the connection.

Another type includes several species of pitcher plants which are fairly common in California and the Gulf states, and are found to a more limited extent in the Great Lakes region (Figs. 12*A*, 12*B*). The leaves are modified into elongated reservoirs. Insects, falling into these reservoirs, encounter structural features in the form of downward-pointing spines that make it next to impossible for them to extricate themselves. In all cases enzymes are secreted which digest parts of the bodies of the captured insects and thus provide a certain amount of nitrogenous food that is absorbed by the plant. But in all cases capturing insects is only a sideline with these plants. They use the small amount of food they get from insects, but they

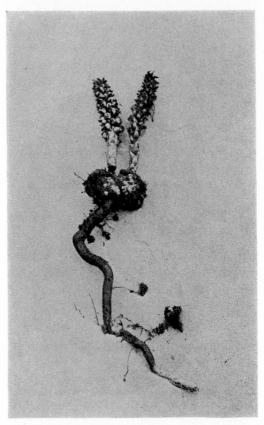

Fig. 9.—The broomrape attached to the root of its host (which has been dissected out of the ground and thrown on a background of sand).

are green and the bulk of their nutritive needs is supplied by photosynthesis.

Transpiration. One of the most serious problems confronting a plant is loss of water. Obviously this is not a problem for aquatic plants, but to terrestrial forms control of water loss becomes a necessity for survival.

External conditions greatly modify the rate of transpiration in a plant. Water loss varies according to soil conditions, season of the year, time of day, rate of air movement, temperature, and percentage of humidity. Farmers and conservationists have long been aware of these conditions, and consequently they try to give as much protection

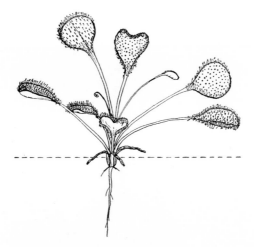

Fig. 10.—The sundew

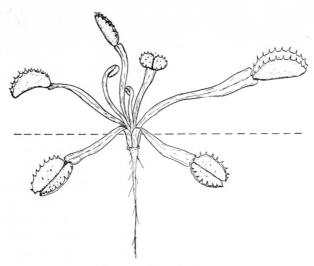

Fig. 11.—Venus's-flytrap

to plants as possible. Orchards on the leeward side of a hill, away from the prevailing winds, will produce more fruit than on the windward side. Shelter belts of trees on the windward side of a field will increase the yield of wheat and other grains by as much as five bushels per acre. Similarly, we find that most truck crops, fruits, and vegetables yield better in quality and quantity when the rate of transpiration is reduced.

FIG. 12A.—Habit view of pitcher plants. (Photograph by Walter M. Buswell)

Most plants are adapted by successful growth structures to retard the loss of water in one or more ways. One of the best things that a plant could do would be to close its stomates when exposed to drying conditions. Although this would decrease the rate of transpiration considerably, it would not stop it entirely since much moisture is also lost directly through the epidermal cells. However, a plant cannot close its stomates for any length of time because that would also cut down the intake of carbon dioxide needed for photosynthesis and the intake of oxygen needed in respiration. Therefore a plant cannot really control its loss of water to any great extent but must simply

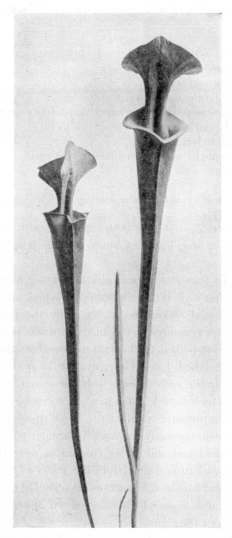

Fig. 12*B*.—Another type of pitcher plant, showing leaf modifications

take advantage of its morphological structures, handed down to it by its ancestors.

Following are listed some of the adaptations occurring in different plants which are credited with reducing the loss of water to some degree.

1. Leaves reduced in size, even to the extent of spines
2. Heavily cutinized epidermal layers
3. Reduced numbers of stomates
4. Stomates only on the lower surface of the leaf
5. Stomates in sunken pitlike areas rather than freely exposed
6. Multiple epidermal layers
7. Multiple palisade layers
8. Compact mesophylls with reduced intercellular space
9. Hirsute covering
10. Glandular hairs
11. Ability of the leaf to curl, thereby cutting down its surface area

Not all the points listed have been experimentally proved effective in retarding water loss, but they show possible adaptations toward that end.

Guttation. In addition to transpiration, water may be lost from the plant in another way. When the humidity is high and transpiration is low, the continued absorption of water by the roots may build up such high water pressures as to cause rupture of some of the cells in the leaf tip. Soft-bodied fruits such as tomatoes may split when this condition is reached. Leaves have multicellular structures known as **hydathodes** at the ends of some veins or near the margin of the blade, through which liquid water may be forced in droplets when the internal water pressure is sufficient. These droplets often appear as "dew" on grass in the early morning in summer when atmospheric conditions are ideal and soil water content is near the saturation point. Water of guttation differs from the water of transpiration in one big way. Water lost in transpiration is pure H_2O, while that lost in guttation contains sugar which is forced out along with the water as it comes up from the roots.

Economic Importance. Leaves are for the most part responsible for all products produced by the plant, since it is here that most of the food is manufactured. Nevertheless, most of the products we obtain from plants come from parts other than leaves. Some coarse fibers, like sisal and Manila hemp, come from long-leaved plants. Some drugs, such as atropine from the belladonna plant and nicotine from tobacco, come from leaves. A good many vetegables are eaten at least in part for their leaves—e.g., celery, chard, cabbage, water cress, lettuce, and others. Some leaves are the sources of tannins and dyes; others are important from an aesthetic view. In general, many leaves are of considerable economic importance, but compared to roots, stems, flowers, fruits, and seeds, their total value is less.

IV. *The Stem*

FUNCTIONS

The stem is often the most conspicuous feature of a plant. In woody species it forms the greatest bulk of the body, and in the majority of plants it is the main axis to which all other organs are attached. The functions of a stem, however, are secondary to those of leaves and roots.

Possibly its most important function is to give rise to leaves, but in addition the stem supports leaves by placing them in a favorable position for photosynthesis. The stems also serve as a connecting channel between roots and leaves through which water and mineral nutrients are carried from the roots to the leaves. Food materials produced in the leaves are also carried downward in the stem to the lower portions of the plant, where the food may be used and stored. In addition to leaves, the stem also supports flowers and fruits and aids in the dissemination of seeds. Some stems are modified for the storage of foods; others are capable of vegetative propagation; and, of course, many are green and carry on photosynthesis much of their lives.

APICAL GROWTH

The stem has at its terminus a very small region of actively dividing cells which is referred to as the *apical meristem.* These cells are all about equal in size and when viewed under the microscope are in various stages of cell division. Each divides to form two cells which mature, usually within a period of several hours. They in turn divide to form four cells which again mature and divide. Thus we have growth continually taking place at the apex of each stem. Growth is usually most active in the spring, but throughout the year some cell division is always occurring. Just back of the meristem is a zone in which the cells are increasing in size, particularly in length. This is called the region of **elongation.** Just back of the region of elongation it is evident that the cells, which up to now have all looked alike, are beginning to differentiate into their respective tissues. It is called the region of **differentiation** or, when all the tissues are formed, the region of **maturation.** All of this takes place in the upper few millimeters of the stem tip. Surrounding the tip we find a number of tiny leaflike structures which form a protective covering for the soft growing point. The leaflike structures are **bud scales,** which inclose not only the tip but the leaf primordia as well. *The whole structure* is a *bud.*

In spring when a **terminal bud** becomes active, it begins to grow out and away from the bud scales. As the bud scales fall off, they leave small ridged scars around the stem (Fig. 13). These are the **bud scale scars** and denote the beginning of a new year's growth. The age of a twig can be determined by the number of bud scale scars left at each year's growth. As the new growth continues, leaves are formed and **axillary buds** are produced within the axil of each leaf (Fig. 14). Wherever a leaf develops from a stem, we refer to that area on the stem as a **node.** The distance between two nodes is an **internode.**

In autumn when the leaves drop from the tree, they leave a scar where they were attached, and this is called the **leaf scar.** Within the leaf scar are a number of minute scars left by the breaking of the vascular system at this point, and they are therefore termed **vascular bundle scars.** During the growing season the axillary buds have been gradually increasing in size. Now that the leaves have fallen, the buds are no longer in an axil, so they are called **lateral buds** as opposed to the terminal buds.

Lateral buds may be of several types. They may produce a branch with several leaves and consequently be called **branch buds,** or they may produce flowers and therefore be *flower buds.* Occasionally in a few trees, but more commonly in shrubs, both leaves and flowers are produced by the same bud, which is then called a **mixed bud.**

Although all higher plants produce buds of one or more types, these structures are very diagnostic in the identification of plants.

Each plant has a bud characteristic of that species: some are resinous, others dry; some are red, brown, black, etc.; some are large and smooth, others small and hirsute. The buds also are arranged in a definite pattern on the stem. Some plants have two buds at a node *opposite* each other. Others have one bud at a node *alternately* arranged. In a few trees, and many shrubs, the buds come off three or more at a node in a *whorled* arrangement. Herbaceous stems have a similar arrangement, but the buds on woody plants are much more conspicuous since they persist throughout the year; herbaceous stems die down to the ground each year.

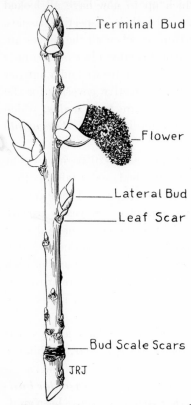

Terminal Bud

Flower

Lateral Bud

Leaf Scar

Bud Scale Scars

JRJ

FIG. 13.—A western cottonwood twig in early spring, showing conspicuous terminal bud, two lateral buds which may become side branches bearing leaves, and a lateral bud that has developed into a flower. Bud-scale scars at the bottom indicate location of terminal bud of the previous year.

INTERNAL ANATOMY

If we cut a horizontal slice through a young stem and examine it under the microscope, we are at once impressed with the concentric, target-like arrangement of the tissues (Fig. 15). At the outside is the *epidermis*, a single compact layer of cells endowed with heavy waterproofed walls to cut down the loss of water from evaporation. Within the epidermis are stomates which have the same function as those in the leaf epidermis. Farther in is the *cortex*, a zone consisting of several layers of relatively unspecialized cells in which a certain amount of food storage occurs. In the young stem some of the outer cells of the cortex contain chloroplasts which are active in the manufacture of food. Next within comes a zone which includes the *phloem,* together with certain other specialized tissues. Within the phloem is the **wood** (**xylem**), but between the two lies a single layer of cells known as the **cambium**. It is the cambium, as we shall see, that is largely responsible for the stem's increase in diameter. Within the wood, at the very center, is a core of loosely arranged, unspecialized cells known as the **pith**. In the young stem all of the aforemen-

FIG. 14.—A western cottonwood twig in summer, showing new growth with leaves and new axillary or lateral buds which have arisen in the axils of the leaf petioles.

tioned tissues have been derived from the region of cell division at the stem tip.

These tissues which have arisen from the apical meristem are termed **primary tissues.** They now consist of a central pith; xylem, arranged in a broken cylinder; cambium, a ring of brick-shaped cells; phloem, the thin-walled, food-conducting elements; cortex, usually used for the storage of food materials; and the outer

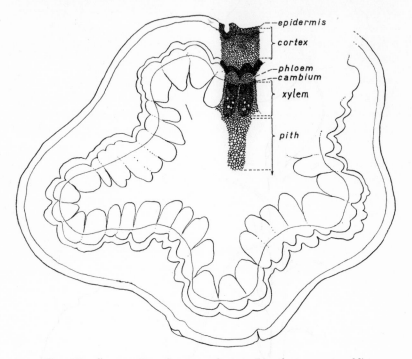

FIG. 15.—Cross-section of young oak stem (less than one year old)

ring, the epidermis. Since no other tissues are produced in stems, it would not be possible for them to increase in diameter any more except for a slight increase with the enlargement of the cells. Nature has provided for this new growth by having cambium as an embryonic tissue. The bulk of tissue that one finds in the cross-section of an old stem has been derived secondarily from the cambium layer. If one were able somehow to dissolve away all other tissues, the cambium of the entire stem would be seen to have the configuration of a very thin-walled stovepipe. Actually the cambium is in close contact with a zone of xylem on the inside and a zone of phloem on the outside. Throughout the life of the plant the cambium cells retain the capacity to divide and form daughter cells.

When a cambium cell divides, one of the resulting daughter cells carries on the characteristic cambium capacity, while the other gradually becomes differentiated and adds itself to one of the adjoining tissues. At a given division it may be that the outer of the two daughter cells continues to be cambium, while the inner of the two gradually becomes specialized into a wood cell and adds itself to the mass of wood cells that is lying just inside. A little later the cell which is now the cambium divides, and in this case the inner of the two daughter cells may continue to be cambium, while the outer of the two adds itself to the adjoining phloem. In this way the cambium, "working alternately with both hands," continues to increase the amount of wood and phloem as the stem grows older. Actually at times there may be several new wood cells formed in succession before a phloem cell is formed. The net result is that in the course of a growing season the total number of new wood cells added is markedly greater than the total number of new phloem cells. In this action all the cells of the cambium cylinder keep pace with one another (under ordinary circumstances), so that the stem as a whole, though steadily increasing in diameter, maintains its cylindrical form.

Inevitably the addition of new wood within forces outward not only the cambium itself but all tissues which lie outside the cambium, while the addition of new phloem is a second effect which forces outward the old phloem, the cortex, and the epidermis. A time is soon reached when the epidermis, stretched beyond the limit of its elasticity, is ruptured. The resulting exposure of moist cells to the drying influence of the atmosphere might work a great deal of harm to the plant were it not that the exposed cells of the cortex meet the situation with an adaptive response. A single layer of cells near the outer edge of the cortex now becomes the **cork cambium.** "Working with both hands," as did the main cambium, it proceeds to lay down several layers of "cork" on the outside and adds new cortex cells on the inside. Cork is a tissue which consists of tabular layers of cells, each endowed with thick walls that are impregnated with a waterproofing material called **suberin.** As a protection against loss of water, it is probably even more effective than the original epidermis.

The first cork layers may themselves be ruptured by the increasing diameter of the stem, in which case newer and younger zones of cork will form beneath them. The roughness of the bark of many trees is the result of this repeated rupturing of the surface and the formation of new cork within.

In examining a cross-section of an old stem, therefore, one would look in vain for the epidermis. In its place there is a zone of cork, the thickness and the roughness of which will vary with the species examined. Just beneath this there may remain some unspecialized cortex, then the phloem, and last the single cambium layer, which has continued until death at its work of providing new phloem and xylem. Though wood may constitute only a relatively small area in the young stem, the cross-section of the old stem presents a very different picture (Fig. 16). Now by far the greater bulk of the cross-section area consists of wood, beside which the pith at the center and the tissues outside the cambium are of little significance. The reason the wood area is far larger than the phloem is that the cambium actually produces more wood than phloem. In addition, the older wood cells, with their thick, resistant walls, persist almost indefinitely, while many of the older phloem cells are crushed in connection with the expansion of the stem.

When one examines the cut surface of a stump or felled tree, his eye is usually caught by the concentric **annual rings.** Identification of these rings is quite possible with the naked eye, but an interpretation of them requires microscopic examination together with some understanding of the action of the cambium. During the many years in the life of the tree the cambium continues to live and to work, but the quality and quantity of new wood that results depend upon the external conditions that obtain at the time. During spring and early summer, when conditions (notably water supply) are at their best for the growth of the plant, the new wood cells develop into conducting tubes of large caliber. During late summer and early fall, when conditions are "on the wane," the cambium continues to lay down new wood, but this develops into cells of much smaller caliber. During winter the cambium ceases to produce new wood and, the next spring, starts all over again with its annual program. The result is that the large-calibered cells of **spring wood** are laid down right next to the small calibered cells of the **summer wood**

of the preceding year (Fig. 17). This can be seen in detail under the
microscope, and the contrast between the two types of wood is so
great as to produce a line which can usually be detected quite clearly
even with the naked eye. Each line or ring therefore represents one
year in the growth of the tree, so that the age of the tree can be

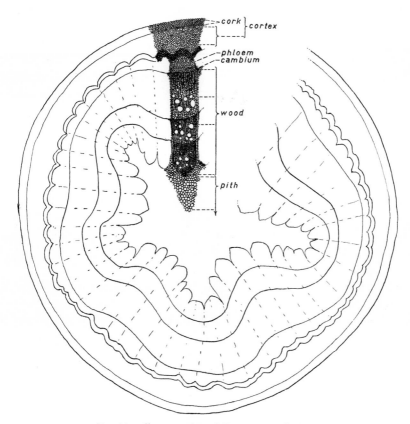

FIG 16.—Cross-section of three-year oak stem

determined by counting the annual rings. In rare cases, when a period
of decisive drought occurs in the middle of the growing season,
what are apparently two rings will be produced in a single year.
The expert is able to distinguish these extra or "false rings" from
the true annual ring.

The study of tree rings is known as **dendrology,** and the study of
tree rings in relation to history is **dendrochronology.** An examina-

tion of the cross-section of an old tree will tell us something of the variation in climate through the past few centuries in the locality in which that tree was grown. If the growing season is a good one, the resulting annual ring will be wide, while a poor growing season yields a narrow annual ring. Since good and bad seasons have occurred more or less at random through the past, each ten-year period has left its own distinctive record in the two rings. Thus, if the period from A.D. 1090 to A.D. 1100 is recorded by a peculiar sequence of large

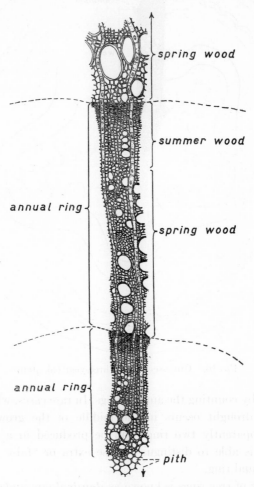

FIG. 17.—Enlargement of a bit of the cross-section of an oak stem, showing the first and second annual rings and a portion of the third.

and small rings in the wood of one tree, all other trees of that locality will be found to yield that same distinctive sequence for that time period. The same sequences will appear in timber that was felled long ago and incorporated into ancient buildings. Archeologists of the Southwest have been dating Indian ruins in that area for many years, using this technique.

We have not made a distinction between different woods, but this seems to be a good place to do so. **Hardwood** trees, for the most part, are those which have broad leaves that usually fall off seasonally.

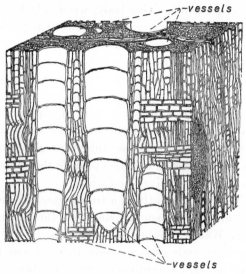

FIG. 18.—Three-dimensional enlargement of a piece of wood, showing the large vessels (tracheal tubes) imbedded in a tissue of smaller wood cells.

Such woods are characterized by xylem cells which are termed **tracheal tubes** (Fig. 18). This type of cell has no end walls but forms a continuous tube up and down the stem with the union of many cells "welded" together end to end. This type of wood is **porous.** The wood of most broad-leaved trees grown in temperate zones is made up of the larger spring wood cells alternating with the smaller summer wood cells. This type of wood is **ring-porous.** In many tropical trees and some temperate ones also, the gradation in size of xylem cells is not so abrupt. Frequently, large cells are also found in the summer wood along with those in the spring wood. This type of wood is *diffuse porous*. *Softwoods* come from trees with scalelike or needle-like leaves. Usually the leaves persist for more than one year, and consequently we call these plants evergreen, although not all of them are. Wood in these plants consists of *tracheids*. These cells are generally narrower and shorter than tracheal tubes, and they have end walls. Water is conducted up these cells from one to the other through *pits* which are abundant not only in the end walls but in the side walls as well, where they are used for lateral conduction. Softwood trees which have tracheids but lack tracheal tubes are therefore *non-porous*.

Like all other parts of a living body, wood, which is 100 per cent xylem, is a product of living cells. When wood is produced, certain cells are considerably enlarged and their walls impregnated with a substance known as *lignin*. This substance makes for rigidity and a certain amount of elasticity, which gives the plant mechanical support it would not have from thin-walled cells. When xylem cells are fully developed, they die, and their protoplasm disintegrates. It is in this dead condition that the wood cell serves the plant, for its skeleton walls provide a hollow tube through which water and soil salts can be transported and also provide the support necessary to hold tons of branches, leaves, and fruits.

To serve the plant efficiently as a transporter of water, this wood must run not merely through the stem but through the roots and leaves as well. Water absorbed near the tips of the roots passes into the lowermost ends of the woody tubes. From that point it moves upward through a continuous series of these natural pipes, through the length of the root, through the main stem itself, and through all the branches. Just as the main "cable-like" mass of wood cells in the stem "breaks up" into smaller bundles that lead out into the branches, so also the bundles within the branches yield still smaller bundles that run out into the leaves. This process of subdivision continues within the leaf itself, and there one can usually follow it by superficial inspection, for the bundles of woody conducting tissue are represented by the visible veins of the leaf.

One can see how the main vein breaks up into progressively smaller elements which run through all parts of the leaf and thus provide for an efficient delivery of water to every living cell. To get any adequate picture of the whole plant as a working unit, therefore, one must think not merely of wood as a tissue but also of its organization into the elaborate and much ramified vascular system.

The vascular system, however, includes a second component that is as necessary as the wood. Wood provides merely for the conduction of water and soil salts from the roots to the other parts of the plant. Provision must also be made for conduction of the food that is manufactured in the leaves to the many other parts of the plant that are unable to manufacture food for themselves.

The transportation of food is carried on in phloem. Like the wood cells, these phloem cells are elongated and pipelike, but they do not have the thick walls found in wood. Phloem tissue is made up of two major types of cells, **sieve tubes** and **companion cells** (Fig. 19). The sieve tubes are the elongated cells used in conduction, while adjoining them, often several to an individual sieve-tube cell, are the companion cells. The companion cells have a large amount of protoplasm and a very conspicuous nucleus in each cell. They are said to direct the metabolic activities of the sieve tubes. The latter have no nuclei when mature but do have protoplasm. The end walls

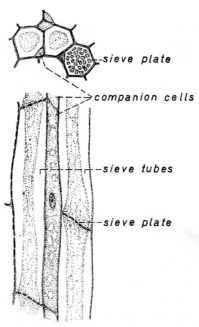

Fig. 19.—Cross-section (*above*) and longitudinal section (*below*) of a bit of phloem. The sieve tubes conduct the food, passing it along from cell to cell through the sieve plates. The function of the companion cells is closely associated with the metabolism of the sieve tube.

of the sieve tubes are not completely dissolved away, as in the tracheal tubes, but, sievelike, contain a number of small apertures through which the food passes. Even though these sieve tubes contain protoplasm, they do provide channels which are adequate for the transport of food. The upward movement of water and soil salts through the wood is much more rapid than the downward movement of food through the phloem.

Like xylem, the phloem is organized into a connected system which extends throughout the entire plant. The arrangement of the system is easily described, for it corresponds exactly with that of the wood. Wherever in root, stem, or leaf there is a bundle of wood cells, right beside it is a (usually smaller) bundle of phloem cells. Structurally, in fact, the two components are united so compactly that botanists commonly speak of a "vascular bundle" as a structural unit that contains both wood and phloem components and often cambium too. Correspondingly, when the botanist says "vascular system," he is referring to the entire conducting system of the plant, with its parallel elements of wood and phloem.

The great antiquity of some trees has been shown by counting the annual rings. Many of the giant sequoias were over three thousand years old when cut down; some of those now standing and still living are thought to be even older. Very likely the oldest living things in the world today are the bristle-cone pine found at the timber line in the mountains of eastern California. They are estimated to be over four thousand years old.

Some of the idea of the prodigious growth which has occurred in the sequoias can be seen from their size. The General Sherman tree is now about 272 feet tall. It probably would be much taller, but lightning destroyed its crown several hundred years ago. It has a basal diameter of 36 feet, but the bark, which includes the phloem, accounts for less that 4 feet of this diameter. The lowest limb, which is 7 feet in diameter, is 120 feet above the ground. The volume of the tree is 600,000 board feet of lumber, or in other words, enough lumber to build 35 five-room homes. This gives us some idea of the power of growth, and nearly all of that growth is in the xylem, which came from the division of that single row of brick-shaped cells, the cambium.

The entire discussion of stems thus far has been based upon that type of stem in which the vascular elements have been arranged in one great vascular cylinder, with wood, often in many layers, surrounding a central pith and with cambium and phloem in zones immediately outside the xylem. Vascular cylinders of this type characterize all "woody plants" and most broad-leaved herbs as well. The groups concerned are the gymnosperms ("cone bearers") and the dicotyledonous plants of the angiosperms.

A second group of angiosperms, the monocotyledons, has a stem structure quite different from the above. The stem of the monocotyledon characteristically has no vascular cylinder and no cambium. A few large xylem vessels together with a few phloem cells are organized into separate vascular bundles, and many such bundles are scattered through the stem. The bundles are surrounded by a general matrix of undifferentiated parenchyma cells which are of the nature of both cortex and pith (Fig. 20). Lacking a cambium, these monocotyledon-

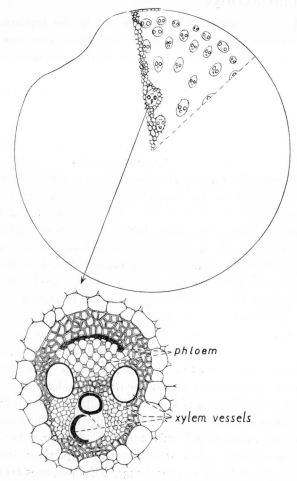

phloem

xylem vessels

Fig. 20.—The stem of the monocotyledon. *Above*, cross-section of entire corn stem, showing scattered vascular bundles. *Below*, enlargement of a single vascular bundle.

ous stems show little or no increase in diameter, although some, such as palms, get quite large. Actually the monocotyledon is a very successful plant both geographically and phylogenetically. Grasses, one of the most widespread of monocot families, occupy millions of square miles of the earth's surface, and from an evolutionary standpoint monocots are considered by many to be more advanced than dicotyledons.

STEM MODIFICATIONS

Considerable variation may be observed in the appearance and anatomy of some stems. Although these structures may superficially resemble roots or even leaves, they retain the morphological characters of stems and therefore are classified as such.

1. *Tubers.* The Irish potato is one example of a tuber. It is really a very much enlarged underground stem. Internally it has the tissue arrangement of the typical stem, except for a very much enlarged pith area. Externally the surface is marked at one end by a scar, which was the point of attachment, and by the "eyes" uniformly scattered over the surface. These "eyes" are in reality lateral buds with a tiny scalelike leaf developing from the ridge just below the bud.

2. *Corms.* Examples of corms are found in the gladiolus and crocus. The corm is a short, thickened, underground stem usually much broader than it is tall. In spring the aerial shoots develop from the central portion of the corm, which gradually shrivels as its food is exhausted. Later in the season, as food is manufactured in the leaves, it is transported to the base of the stem, which gradually enlarges, forming a new corm over the old exhausted one.

3. *Bulbs.* A bulb is usually short and much thickened, but instead of a solid center, typical of the corm, it has many fleshy, modified leaves which form a series of rings rising from a short fleshy base. If you cut an onion in cross-section, the rings of fleshy leaves are easily observed. Other examples of bulbs are lilies, hyacinths, and jonquils.

4. *Rhizome.* Rhizomes are more rootlike than those mentioned above, but the resemblance is only superficial. They grow horizontally in the ground, have nodes and internodes typical of stems, and also scale leaves and axillary buds. Large, fleshy rhizomes are found in the canna and iris, while slender, creeping rhizomes are found in strawberries and in many of the grasses, like Bermuda and quack

grass. The slender rhizomes, which often grow above ground, are frequently termed "stolons" or "runners."

Some stems develop **tendrils** which coil around supports or other plants and make it possible for a vine to carry itself up into the light. Often the entire stem of a vine will grow in an encircling manner as it grows upward, simply twisting itself around an object for support as it develops.

Most annual stems are green and therefore photosynthetic, but some perennials also have stems which remain green year after year and continue the production of food. Typical of this type is the **cladophyll,** a stem of the prickly pear cactus. These large, flat pads are really stems, but they have taken over the function of leaves on these plants, where photosynthetic leaves in fact do not exist.

ECONOMIC IMPORTANCE

It would be difficult to evaluate the significance of stems in dollars and cents, for the value of stems to our economy is enormous. The lumber industry alone is one of the nation's largest. Aside from lumber for various structural and finishing uses in the building industry, we use it for fuel, all types of paper, the manufacture of cellophane, rayon, and plastics. Some stems supply us with fibers, such as linen from flax, and rope from the hemp plant. Rubber is made from latex which comes from the stem of *Hevea brasiliensis.* Gums and resins are obtained from other trees. Turpentines come from a mixture of resins found in the resin canals of certain softwood trees. Various dyes and tannins are obtained from many different woods. One of our most important drugs, quinine, comes from the bark of the cinchona tree. The stems of many plants are also used directly as food. The Irish potato is one of our staples; cane sugar comes from the stem of an important tropical plant; other plants, such as broccoli and asparagus, are eaten in part for their stems.

V. The Root and Its Environment

SOIL

The word "soil" has different meanings for various individuals. To the uninformed it is just "dirt"; to the geologist it is disintegrated rock; to the farmer it is his livelihood; and to the botanist it is that portion of the earth's crust which supports vegetation. Actually, soil owes its qualities to a great variety of things. A sterile soil is mostly disintegrated rock, but a fertile soil is disintegrated rock with decomposed organic materials in it, brought about by the action of fungi, bacteria, protozoans, nematodes, and other minute organisms. A recent analysis of a fertile soil revealed the following poundage of microflora and microfauna in an acre-foot of soil (i.e., one acre in area and one foot deep):

Bacteria	500–1,000
Fungi	1,500–2,000
Actinomycetes	800–1,500
Protozoa	200–400
Algae	200–300
Nematodes	25–50
Other worms and insects	800–1,000

Most of the micro-organisms are found near the surface of the soil, usually within the upper six to twelve inches, and this is the portion we refer to as **topsoil.** Adequate moisture, optimum temperature, and aeration favor the growth of these organisms, which in turn cause the breakdown of the larger organic substances and build up the soil into a rich loam. Cultivation of the soil mixes these organisms and accelerates their work. Furthermore, cultivation brings up some of

56

the subsoil and mixes it with the upper layers, thus increasing the depth of topsoil and greatly enriching the substrata for the roots to grow in.

Soils are usually classified according to the size of their particles. Coarse sand varies from 2.0 to 0.2 mm. in diameter, a fine sandy soil from 0.2 to 0.02 mm., and in a clay soil the particles are below 0.002 mm. The physical structure of soil is important because it forms the substrate which makes the penetration of roots possible.

Yet soil structure alone is not sufficient to make a good soil. Soil must have organic matter. An enriched soil is one that contains an abundance of humus, which is really an aggregate of substances derived from the waste products of living organisms and from the decomposition of the dead bodies of plants and animals. Dark soils generally contain an abundance of humus, while the light-colored soils are relatively low in organic matter. Fertility of a soil is often governed by the amount of humus as well as the dissolved organic and inorganic compounds present. The disintegration and decomposition of organic substances, principally through the action of bacteria, fungi, and other soil organisms, produce and maintain in the soil a continuous supply of dissolved substances which the higher plants require. Soil organic matter thus becomes of paramount importance in soil fertility.

Soils owe much of their efficiency, so far as a plant is concerned, to their structure. We have classified them according to the size of particles, but, to break it down further, we see that a cubical grain of sand which is 1.0 mm. in diameter would have just 6 sq. mm. of surface. If this grain is divided into particles of colloidal size 0.1 micron on the edge, the total surface would be 60,000 sq. mm. Because of their platelike shape, clay particles have much greater surfaces than do cubes or spheres of similar diameter. Agronomists estimate that an acre-furrow slice (one acre in area and 6.6 inches deep) of sand contains 5,000 acres of surface, while an acre of clay would have 500,000 acres of surface.

In biology we are always concerned with surface relationships. Plant as well as animal bodies are designed either to increase the absorption of water and dissolved materials or to decrease absorption and water loss. The small but numerous red blood corpuscles in our blood have a much greater surface for the absorption of oxygen than if they were increased in size but decreased in number. Our kidneys are made up of thousands of tubules which offer tremendous surface area for the removal of toxic substances from the blood; similarly, the brain has many convolutions which increase the surface area and provide space for more nerve endings. We shall see later that a plant may have a vastly increased root surface for ready absorption, and yet this same plant may have a reduced leaf surface to retard the loss of moisture. Almost any organ in a plant or animal is constructed for maximum efficiency, and, since all substances that enter or leave the cells do so in solution, surface becomes a very important consideration. For this reason a soil of fine particles provides more air spaces for root growth and at the same time provides more surface for water and dissolved elements.

SOIL WATER

The growth of roots is dependent to a very large extent on the available water in the soil. Without it they cannot survive, and too much may cause them to die because of lack of oxygen. Of course, plants have varying degrees of tolerance for moisture content. Some prosper in the acid bogs, where they grow in standing water all the time. Others living in arid regions do very well where the soil is dry most of the time except for brief seasonal showers. No plant, however, can survive entirely without moisture, so water becomes a very important factor in the distribution of plants.

We usually classify soil water into several catagories. *Gravitational water* is abundant after a heavy rain. It descends through the soil in response to gravity, forcing out the air in a "percolating" sort of action. If the soil is sufficiently porous, the rain water soon reaches the water table and may remain in the subsoils as an underground reservoir. As this water flows downward through the soil interstices, it may leach many of the minerals from the upper soil layers. It also changes the soil atmosphere by removing carbon dioxide and oxygen from the pores. Ordinarily this is desirable unless the water stands too long and replaces too much oxygen.

A second category is *capillary water.* This is the water which is held as a loose film around the soil particles. It moves readily from place to place in the soil, governed only by the attraction of one molecule for another. It is the only important source of water for plant roots. The amount of movement of capillary water is determined largely by the size and compactness of the soil particles. In coarse soil capillary movement is not very far and is quite slow, while in a finely grained soil, such as clay, the capillary attraction is greater and the movement farther and faster. At best, the movement of capillary water is only a few feet. We find that a clay soil, because of the small size of its particles, actually has more total pore space between the numerous particles than a sandy soil and for this reason can take in a greater amount of water. However, because the particles are small and therefore closer together, a clay soil will lose most of its water by capillary action faster and more completely than a sandy soil, where the capillary chain is easily broken.

Hygroscopic water is held upon and within the tiny soil particles. It is held so tenaciously that plants are unable to absorb water of this type. As soil dries, some of this water becomes part of the water vapor in the soil and is ultimately lost into the atmosphere. We usually say that hygroscopic water is the water left in a soil after a plant wilts. This amount may then be determined by drying the soil in an oven. The weight before and after determines the amount of hygroscopic water in the soil.

EXTENT OF ROOT GROWTH

We have described something of the habitat in which roots grow; and this in a large measure determines the vertical and lateral distributions of roots, but it is not the only thing. Such factors as soil texture, moisture, temperature, and competition all have their effect, but heredity and the type of root system are at least as important. The pattern of root growth is almost as distinct as the branches and leaves above ground. For this reason it is often possible to identify a plant by the subterranean plant parts alone, and this certainly is a clue to their individuality.

Some years ago we made an effort to find out just how much root growth there actually is to a plant. A winter rye plant was grown in a box containing two cubic feet of soil; then after four months of growth the roots were washed free of all soil, and counts and measurements were made of the subterranean parts. This single rye plant, grown under ideal conditions, to be sure, had a total of 13,800,000 roots, including those of the main roots arising directly from the plant and all their branches out to the fourth or quaternary division. These roots, if placed end to end, would extend for a distance of 387 miles and have a surface area of 2,550 square feet.

Samples were also taken of roots growing in the field under natural conditions. Selecting an area from a row of oat plants, a core of soil three inches in diameter and six inches deep was removed. This is the area in which root growth was most abundant, and the sample included parts of several oat plants. It was found that in such a sample oat roots would number 110 per cubic inch, and for a similar sample of field-grown winter rye the number would be approximately 150 roots per cubic inch. The same volume of soil (one cubic inch) taken under Kentucky bluegrass would have approximately 2,000 roots.

Although these figures seemed unbelievably large, they did not include all the structures on these roots. Arising from the epidermal cells of roots are numerous *root hairs.* These hairs vary quite a bit in size on different species. Generally they are about 1/2,000 of an inch in diameter and usually vary from about 1/100 to 1/125 of an inch in length. Counting the number of oat root hairs, we calculated that the same cubic inch of soil that had 110 roots would also have about 150,000 root hairs growing from their epidermal cells. Winter rye would have about 300,000 from its 150 roots, and Kentucky bluegrass would have approximately 1,000,000 root hairs in a similar volume. This might end the story, but with such fantastic figures we felt we must include something on volume. It would seem that if a cubic inch had 110 roots and 150,000 root hairs there would not be much room for the soil in which they had to grow. When the volume occupied by these oat roots and root hairs was calculated, we found they took up only 0.55 per cent of the total volume; the large number of winter rye roots and root hairs occupied only 0.85 per cent of the volume, and the Kentucky bluegrass subterranean parts occupied only 2.8 per cent of the volume. Since the pores in soil take up about 50 per cent of the total volume, we can see that roots actually occupy a comparatively small amount of the total space available.

Figures in themselves are meaningless unless they have a purpose. It has been determined that a plant by its new growth of roots and root hairs each day can take care of its water needs. In other words, each day it is sending out new roots and root hairs to tap the film of capillary water lightly held by and between the soil particles. Furthermore, this method provides a means of estimating the potential absorptive capacity of the entire vast hair system. We also can determine a plant's potentialities in binding soil and retarding soil erosion by studying its root system. A plant with a long, deep root with few laterals would not hold much soil, but one with numerous fine roots, such as the grasses have, provides a fine network which closely holds the soil and prevents water from washing it away. You can prove this to yourself by digging up a plant like a carrot or a dandelion. How much soil stays on the roots when you pull it up? Now try to pull up some grass or dig it up and see if you can shake the soil off. The answer is obvious, and this is one of the reasons grasses are so important in soil-conservation programs.

CLASSIFICATION

When a seed germinates, the embryo pushes out its basal portion, which becomes the *primary root* of the plant. This is also known as the *seminal root,* a term reserved for those roots and their immediate branches arising directly from the seed. As the primary root develops and grows deeper in the soil, *secondary roots* develop from the primary, and in turn other lateral roots arise from the secondaries. In large plants the division continues throughout many categories. After the seed has established its primary root system, and as the entire plant grows larger, additional roots arise from the base of the stem. These are termed *adventitious roots.* In some plants they may even arise from leaves that make contact with the soil. Plants such as grasses have roots of adventitious origin. In fact, it is almost impossible to find the primary roots after the former are well developed. Adventitious roots also branch into many categories and, since they have the same structure as the primary roots, are quite similar in appearance. The prop roots of corn, wheat, and oats; those which arise from cuttings, such as geranium (Fig. 21); and those which form from trailing stems and runners, such as form on strawberries and Virginia creeper, are all adventitious.

Classification of roots is also made on the basis of their structure. *Taproots* are large fleshy roots, like those of radishes, turnips, and carrots (Fig. 22). They are of seminal origin and are used for storage of food and for anchoring the plant. *Fibrous roots* are those typical of grasses and are almost entirely of adventitious origin (Fig. 23). These fibrous roots form a fine network of interlacing roots which function admirably in binding soil, in addition to their primary function of absorption. *Fascicled roots* are of adventitious origin and become large storage organs (see Fig. 7). Dahlias and sweet potatoes have this type of root system.

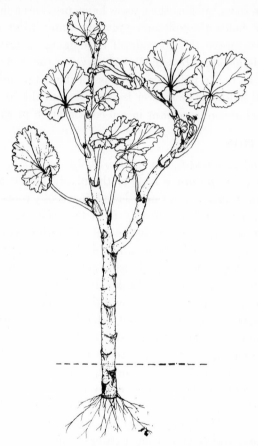

Fig. 21.—A diagram of a geranium shoot which has been rooted in sand. Note the development of adventitious roots at the base.

APICAL GROWTH

One important characteristic of plants is that they grow by means of very actively dividing cells at the tips of roots and stems. In roots, as in stems, the region of active cell division is the *apical*

meristem (Fig. 24). Just behind this meristem is a zone in which
the cells are enlarging but in which cell division has stopped. This
is called the **region of elongation** since the cells are becoming
much longer than their enlargement in di-
ameter (Fig. 25). Still farther back the cells
are beginning to differentiate into the various
tissues which will make up the mature root.
We call this area the **region of differentiation.** As the tissues mature, they are then
in the **region of maturation.**

The division of cells, elongation, and differentiation all take place within the first few
millimeters of the root apex, often within the
first millimeter. From then on all tissues are
formed, and in a grass root or similar plant
the tissues remain that way regardless of how
long the root may be. The broad-leaved plants
usually have additional growth in diameter
which alters the tissues somewhat and will be
discussed later.

The growing root tip has one other feature
we have not mentioned. As the root tip thrusts
its way through the soil, the abrasive action
caused by the soil particles endangers the only
part of the root capable of giving rise to new
cells and elongation. The little zone of dividing
cells at the root tip, while continuously laying
down behind itself those cells which are to be
incorporated into the root proper, at the same
time keeps producing a few cells which are
thrust out in front to form the **root cap**
(Fig. 26). The root cap acts as a buffer or
helmet for the root tip proper but is itself inevitably worn away as it thrusts through the soil,

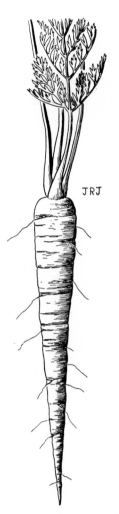

Fig. 22.—Carrot taproot

so that its cells must be renewed continuously
by the root tip. In a longitudinal section of a root tip, therefore, one
finds in order: the root cap at the very end; next, the meristem, the
very small zone of tiny, actively dividing cells; next, the region

of elongation, where the cells are enlarging to attain their adult size; and, finally, a zone where the enlarged cells are being differentiated to assume the adult characteristics of the various tissues.

INTERNAL ANATOMY

Except for the root cap, the most superficial tissue is the epidermis. As one might expect, this is the first tissue to be readily discernible

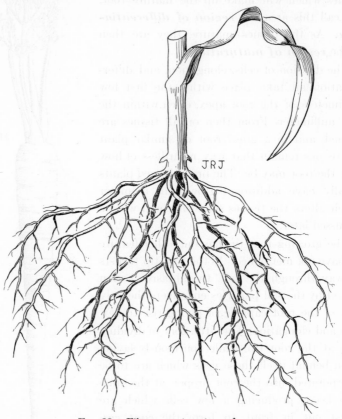

JRJ

FIG. 23.—Fibrous root system of corn

from the remaining cells in the root body. The root epidermis lacks the thick outer walls and waterproofing material that characterize the epidermis of the stem and leaves, for the total supply of water and mineral salts that the ordinary plant will ever get is that which enters through the epidermis of the root. Absorption is the primary function of the root, and to facilitate its work the epidermal cells give rise to numerous root hairs. In broad-leaved plants vast numbers of hairs occupy a comparatively narrow zone. They arise usually in the region of maturation and persist until the thickening, by growth in diameter of the root, forces off the epidermis and, of course, the root hairs with it. Roots of narrow-leaved plants, which increase very little in diameter once they are matured, may retain their root hairs for weeks, months, and even years. Root hairs on these plants may cover many feet of root length. Generally, however, the older root hairs become inefficient as absorptive structures because their

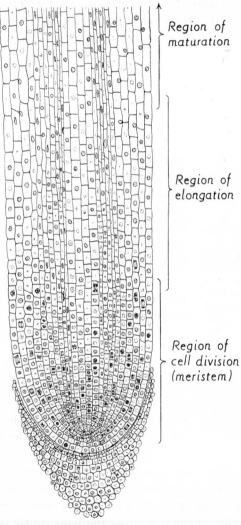

Region of maturation

Region of elongation

Region of cell division (meristem)

Fig. 24.—Much enlarged longitudinal section of a root tip

walls become thick and suberized, i.e., converted by a fatty substance called **suberin.**

In the cross-section of a young root there are three groups of primary tissues (Fig. 27).

1. Outermost is the **epidermis,** which is a single layer of cells from which root hairs arise.

2. The **cortex** is a layer, many cells in thickness, which begins just inside the epidermis and has as its innermost layer the **endodermis.** The cortex is composed mostly of thin-walled cells used for storage. These thin-walled cells are called **parenchyma.** They are distributed throughout all organs of the plant and make up most of the plant parts we eat. The root of a sweet potato is mostly parenchyma. So, too, is the potato tuber and the fleshy part of the apple fruit. The endodermis is generally quite conspicuous in the root of most plants. As the root matures, the walls of the endodermis become suberized. Apparently suberization of this ring of cells retards the loss of water from the inner vascular tissues. The endodermis thickens first over the food-conducting cells, then gradually completes its ring by suberization of all the cells.

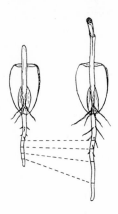

Fig. 25.—Experimental demonstration that the elongation of the root occurs near its tip. Evenly spaced markings were made on the root of the young corn seedling at the left. In the ensuing twenty-four hours the elongation of the root separated the markings in the manner shown on the right.

3. The **stele** consists of several tissues. Just inside the endodermis is a ring, one or more cells in thickness, which makes up the **pericycle.** Inside the pericycle we find a number of isolated patches of phloem, surrounded by parenchyma. The number of phloem areas varies in different species. The very center of the root is occupied by the xylem. Usually there are a number of radiating arms which have differentiated outward from the central xylem and which alternate with the phloem areas.

In many roots, particularly those of grasses and related plants, no other tissues are differentiated, but in the broad-leaved forms a final primary tissue has yet to be differentiated. This is the **cambium.** It begins as a few small brick-shaped cells which gradually differentiate from the parenchyma cells separating the phloem area from the xylem. As growth continues, the cambium cells divide to form a continuous one-celled layer between the xylem and phloem.

Thus far we have seen that all tissues in the root have differentiated from cells formed by the apical meristem and as such are known as *primary tissues.* Now, with the formation of cambium, we have a second meristematic region whose function is to increase the diameter of the root, and consequently it is known as a *lateral meristem.* The tissues which are formed from the cambium are known as *secondary tissues.*

The cambial cells begin to divide lengthwise, forming a series of brick-shaped cells. The inner band or strip of these cells continues dividing, forming more cells outside and also inside the cambial band. As new cells are added to the inside, the central area of the root becomes larger; consequently, the cambium must move outward with it. Gradually the cells outside the cambial ring differentiate into *secondary phloem* cells, and those inside the band differentiate into *secondary xylem* cells.

As the root gets larger in diameter, by the addition of secondary xylem and phloem, a new tissue appears. It is an embryonic tissue which originates from pericyclic cells and is called *cork cambium.* The cork cambium produces corky cells toward the outside of the root. These cells are highly suberized and take over the function of the epidermis

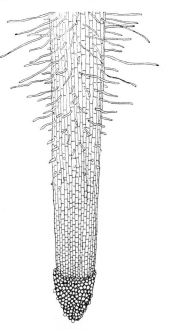

Fig. 26.—Enlarged surface view or root tip, including root hairs and root cap.

in retarding the loss of water from the root. As growth in diameter continues, the epidermis, cortex, endodermis, pericycle, and even the outer layers of the phloem are sloughed off. New cork cambium cells arise constantly, and eventually they are within the outer layers of the phloem and still continue to give rise to the cork cells which form the outer layers of bark. An old root therefore consists of a central xylem, cambium, phloem, cork cambium, and corky bark. These are the same tissues which we have found making up the anatomy of an old stem.

Branch roots are small replicas of the main roots; they have essentially the same internal anatomy and the same external features. These lateral roots do have a difference in origin. When the root is

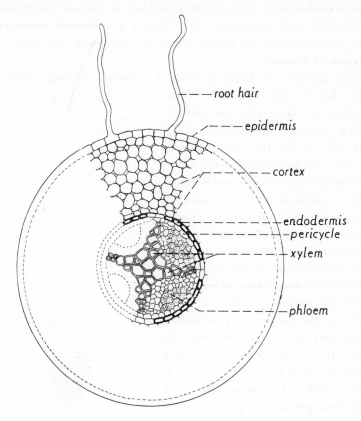

FIG. 27.—Cross-section of a root in the root-hair zone

still young, certain cells of the pericycle become embryonic and begin to divide at right angles to the main axis of the root. Usually the point of origin of a branch root is opposite a primary xylem strand. This often gives the lateral root a fairly distinct pattern and accounts in part for the differences in root systems in plants. As the young root develops from the pericycle, its tip pushes outward through the cortex and epidermis and finally emerges from the parent root as a distinctly new member. The tissues that it pushes aside are stretched and finally ruptured as a result of the mechanical pressure of the growing root. The xylem strand of the old root becomes continuous with the central cylinder of the new root, and the phloem areas on either side of the xylem strand become continuous with the phloem of the new root. The important vascular strands are now a continuous conducting channel, and it is up to the young root to give rise to its other tissues, including cambium, to continue its growth and become an important member of the entire root system.

FUNCTIONS

The functions of roots are *absorption, conduction, anchorage, storage,* and *vegetative reproduction.* Not all roots perform all these functions equally well, but most plants are capable of all to a degree. Roots absorb water, minerals in solution, and oxygen from the soil. They conduct these substances upward to the stems, leaves, and flowers, while the foods which are manufactured in the leaves are placed in solution and conducted downward to the roots for storage. Most roots are also anchoring organs which prevent the wind from blowing the plant away; they give the plant support to hold up a weight that might amount to many tons. Finally, some roots may give rise to new plants. This is a method of vegetative propagation typical of many plants which store large quantities of food in their roots. Unfortunately for us, the dandelion is capable of this type of propagation.

The manner in which living cells absorb water and dissolved substances is still not well understood. We usually speak freely of the ionic exchanges which occur between root hairs and the soil particles to which they adhere, but an unsolved question concerning the absorption of water by roots is whether osmotic or imbibitional forces are the more important in bringing water into the absorbing cells of roots. Ordinarily the osmotic concentration of the cell sap of root epidermal cells is higher than that of the soil solution, even when the concentration of the soil solution is increased. This would therefore provide a ready mechanism to insure the absorption of water by osmotic action, since water usually diffuses from a region of higher concentration to one of lower concentration.

This would answer the question of how water gets into the root, but apparently plants growing in hot, dry climates would lose water faster than they could take it up by osmosis. It is therefore the opinion of most botanists that with rapid evaporation plants probably depend on imbibition to replace water lost in this manner.

As the concentration of the soil solution approaches that of the cell sap, the rate of water absorption declines. When the concentration of the solutions inside and outside the plant is the same, water remains in balance. However, if the soil solution becomes more highly concentrated than the cell sap, water may be lost from the root cells. Generally when this happens, the plant wilts and often dies. Excessive applications of fertilizer may be a cause of this loss.

NUTRIENT ELEMENTS

Chemists tell us that today there are about 105 elements. Many of these are necessary for the growth of plants, and others may be taken up by a plant when in solution, even though they are of no apparent use to the plant. Still others are toxic. We would like to think that a plant could select only the beneficial elements necessary for its growth, but unfortunately it cannot reject those which are harmful. Consequently, plants are easily killed by a variety of chemicals. Of course, a plant is no different from an animal in this respect. If we drink a poison, it can be absorbed in the same way. The cells lining our intestinal tract are no more selective.

The elements of greatest importance to plants are carbon, hydrogen, oxygen, phosphorus, nitrogen, potassium, sulfur, calcium, magnesium, and iron. These are the so-called major elements, but a number of minor elements—including manganese, boron, and zinc—are occasionally taken in minute quantities by some plants. It is not our purpose to take each element separately and explain its use by the plant, but three of these elements are found in "complete" fertilizers. They are nitrogen, phosphorous, and potassium. When you buy a bag of fertilizer, you may note numbers on the bag like this: 6-8-4. This means that the bag contains 6 per cent nitrogen, 8 per cent phosphorous, and 4 per cent potassium. Different fertilizers contain different quantities of these elements, but the order of elements always remains the same.

These three elements are used in large quantities by plants and usually have to be supplied regularly to the soil because they are very soluble and frequently are leached out of the soil in water runoff. Nitrogen is a growth element necessary for the building of proteins. Lack of nitrogen results in poor vegetative growth and poor color in stems and leaves. Phosphorous is more important for the flowering of plants and the setting of fruit, while potassium is essential for maximum growth of roots; therefore, all root crops require an adequate amount of potassium in the soil for the development of their roots. Of course, we do not mean that certain plants use one element to the exclusion of others. There must be a balance of all elements for a plant's optimum growth, but some plants may use more of one element than of another.

ECONOMIC IMPORTANCE

Roots provide us with a smaller variety of products than stems, but many industries are built on the products obtained from them. Sugar beets produce thousands of tons of sugar annually. Horse-radish develops a very pungent glucoside, which is used as a condiment and flavoring. Sweet potatoes, carrots, beets, and parsnips are typical of the vegetable crops obtained from roots. Manioc is one of the most important crops in the tropics. The large fleshy roots of this plant provide a variety of starch products, including tapioca, with which we are most familiar.

VI. *Growth and Development*

Growth is a characteristic of all living things and of some that are not living. Yet it is a very difficult process to define. If we use the term "growth" to describe an increase in bulk—as when certain chemicals are united—we must say that increase in size is not enough. Growth is basically the production of new protoplasm. Therefore it includes all the metabolic activities concerned with repair and production of new cells. When an organism's powers of assimilation are such that it is constructing new cells in excess of the numbers that are destroyed in the normal activities of simply "living," then new tissue is being added and growth is taking place. In addition to increase in size, as a result of new protoplasm and new cell walls, growth is also said to result in permanent change, and once differentiation of tissues has taken place as the organism matures, it can no longer revert to its original form.

As we have already seen, growth in plants is different from that in animals. In the latter, growth occurs fairly uniformly all over. Different organs and tissues are all growing at about the same time and in about the same proportion. In plants, growth is largely terminal. The greatest amount of cellular activity takes place at *growing points,* which are located at the apex of all roots and stems and their branches. Of course, plants do get larger all over, but even lateral growth is the result of a single tissue, cambium, which gives rise to tissues forming the bulk of cells in the plant body. In leaves we have an exception to this principle. Here growth and enlargement are fairly uniform all over the organ (Fig. 28).

Growth in plants is also much more influenced by environmental conditions than it is in animals. Their activities may be affected by the seasons, but growth itself is not seasonal, as it is in plants. In temperate regions maximum plant growth occurs in the spring. Within the season, however, growth is also governed by temperature, light, humidity, growth regulators, minerals in the soil, carbon dioxide in the atmosphere, competition with other plants, and other related factors.

THE CELL AND ITS DIVISION

In any process of growth, for plants and animals, we are concerned primarily with the formation of new cells. Plant cells, as we have described them in chapter i, consist of a cellulose wall, within which is the protoplasm. The latter is divided into two portions, the nucleus and the cytoplasm. Both are concerned with cell division and growth, although in some plants at certain times nuclear divisions may occur without cell division. In every growing region three stages of growth may be observed: (1) *cell division,* in which each cell divides to form two, and these two divide into four, and so on through repeated divisions; (2) *cell enlargement,* in which the new cells expand rapidly to achieve their final size; (3) *cell differentiation,* in which the cells become modified in form and assume their function in the respective tissues.

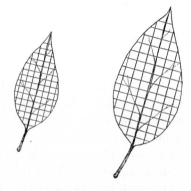

FIG. 28.—Experimental demonstration that enlargement of a typical leaf is not restricted to any particular zone. *On the left,* a young leaf to which "cross-hatching" has been applied with India ink. *At the right,* the condition of the same leaf a few days later.

Cell division in plants with nucleated cells is not a simple splitting in two but is a complex process involving and initiated by the nucleus. By now you have probably observed these embryonic cells in the process of division in the laboratory when studying the root tip. The nucleus in the mature cell is an opaque spheroid body occupying a rather large portion of the protoplasm near the center of the cell. Its contents are granular, occasionally fibrous, and often bearing

one or more tiny, darkly stained objects called *nucleoli.* Although
the cell at this stage is said to be in a "resting" condition, all the
processes of metabolism are very actively at work preparing for the
time of cell division, which in every embryonic tissue is imminent.
Actual nuclear division, called *mitosis,* begins with the granular
material in the nucleus clumping together to form elongated nuclear
strands, the chromosomes. Each chromosome is made up of two
slender threads, or *chromonemata,* which carry the hereditary units,
or *genes.*

In every species the number and shape of the chromosomes
are constant. Man, for instance, has 46, although the number was
thought to be 48 until recently; an onion has 16, the fruit fly, 8,
and a lily, 24. Furthermore, when each chromosome is formed in a
daughter cell, it retains its individual characteristics even though in
new cells it is broken down into granular and fibril material in the
maturing cell.

As mitosis progresses, the individual chromosomes split lengthwise
into two identical halves called *chromatids.* These structures now
move to the center of the cell and form a flat plane through the cell.
While the chromatids are forming, the nuclear membrane begins
to disappear, the nucleoli largely disintegrate, and delicate fibers
form at opposite ends of the cell. We consider the shape of a cell
to be much like that of the earth, and we term each end a *pole.* The
delicate massed fibers, which extend outward from the poles, are
collectively known as the *spindle,* since in outline they are spindle-
shaped. A spindle fiber is attached to each chromosome, but many
additional fibers extend from one pole to the other, seemingly without
any chromosome attachment whatsoever. The function of the spindle
is not well understood. It was thought that the fibers attached to each
chromosome contracted and pulled the paired chromosomes apart,
one member of each pair going to each pole. However this theory is
not universally accepted. In any case, it seems the spindle does facilitate the movement of chromosomes to the poles even though the
exact mechanism is not known.

When the chromosomes reach the poles, they elongate and form
a tangled mass around which a nuclear membrane is again formed.
Soon nucleoli begin to reappear, and the chromosome mass breaks
down into the granular and fibril material found in the original cell.
While the chromosomes are in transit to the poles, a new wall is being

laid down between these two nuclear areas. At first a delicate membrane, the **cell plate,** appears as a result of thickenings at the midpoints of the fibers or possibly by a proteinaceous material collecting at this point. This is the **_middle lamella,_** chemically composed of pectin, which serves as a binding material in holding the two cells together. Soon after the middle lamella is formed, a new cell wall is laid down on each side, thus completing cell division.

The time required for a complete mitotic cycle varies in different plants and different tissues. In addition the environmental conditions of temperature, moisture, and light have a very strong influence on the rate of division and consequently on growth. Once the cell has started to divide, in actively growing tissue, the two new cells will be formed in about one and one-half to three hours. However, the time that elapses for these two new cells, before mitosis again takes place, is usually from about twelve to twenty-four hours. In other words, most of the time is spent in the maturing stage, when the cell is said to be resting.

THE INFLUENCE OF LIGHT ON GROWTH

We have discussed the effect of light on photosynthesis in the chapter on leaves, but there is much more that should be considered in the over-all picture of growth. It has been observed that some plants grow better in dense shade or in light of low intensity, while other plants must be grown in direct sunlight all day, i.e., light of high intensity. It is very simple to show the extremes of this condition. We can place one potted plant out in the open, where it will get an adequate supply of light. Another can be placed in the dark. Assuming all other conditions are equal, we soon notice that the one in the light remains vigorous, carries on photosynthesis, and in general might be said to enjoy good health. The one in the dark begins to lose its green color; it begins to get taller but becomes spindly, and the internodes often become so elongated and weak that it no longer can hold itself up. Such a plant is said to be **etiolated.** If the two plants weighed the same at the beginning of the experiment, at the end we would see the one in the light would have a greater dry weight than the one in the dark, even though the latter might appear much larger. Light, of course, is essential for the formation of chlorophyll in addition to its function in photosynthesis.

The quality, or in other words the color or wave length, of light is of less importance than the total amount received, but it does have an influence on plant development. By means of colored glass it can be shown that when a plant receives only the red rays, or longer wave lengths of light, it tends to become etiolated, while blue light seems to check etiolation and causes an increase in the differentiation of tissue. The reds and the blues are both more important than the other colors for photosynthesis and growth, but maximum growth occurs only when plants are exposed to the full spectrum of sunlight rather than to any one part.

A third effect of light on growth is much more spectacular than either of the other two mentioned. This concerns the relative length of light and darkness to which a plant is exposed. The light period, or *photoperiod,* affects plants differently so far as vegetative development and time of flowering are concerned. Some plants such as sunflower, hibiscus, timothy, lily, and lettuce are *long-day* plants and will bloom only when the length of the *light* period exceeds twelve hours. *Short-day* plants are those which bloom only when the length of the *dark* period exceeds twelve hours. Typical examples include poinsettias, cyclamens, chrysanthemums, asters, and ragweeds. In temperate regions we find that short-day plants bloom early in spring or in late fall when the days are relatively short, while long-day plants flower in midsummer. Some plants, such as tomatoes and some marigolds, are very slightly affected by the photoperiod and will bloom under either a short or a long day. These plants are classified as *day-neutral.*

The economic significance of photoperiodism is quite apparent when we consider the problems of the commercial plant grower. Let us use the florist who is raising poinsettias for the Christmas season as an example. If he does not have these plants in bloom December 25 or shortly before, there will be no sale for them. If normal light conditions have been above average and his greenhouse rather cool, he will find his poinsettias flowering after Christmas. Knowing this, he will cover his plants with dark cloth several hours a day to shorten the photoperiod and hasten blooming. Lilies, on the other hand, prefer long light periods for blooming. Of course, the best time to sell the large white flowering lilies is during the Easter season. Since the date for Easter may vary from year to year by as much as six weeks, the problem of getting lilies in bloom at the right time for sale is much greater than that for poinsettias, with their dependable Christmas date. If Easter comes in March, the florist will probably have to expose the plants to additional light, either at the end of the day or earlier in the morning, to increase the length of the light period and force the plant into bloom. Fortunately artificial light is adequate, but it is important that the light period be continuous and not interrupted by even so much as a few minutes of darkness between the light periods. If Easter is late, possibly around the first of May, the florist may have to cover his plants for a few hours each day in order to shorten the photoperiod and thus delay flowering.

Most of us do not have to worry about the light period even though we may raise many different kinds of plants. The seed houses do it for us. If we raise plants, like lettuce and radishes, in which we are interested only in the vegetative parts, the nurseryman sells us long-day variety plant seeds which we raise in early spring or late fall when we have short days. If we were raising these same plants in summer, above the Arctic Circle, where the days are very long, we would soon have them blossoming and, of course, get poor vegetative growth. Therefore, if we were raising lettuce and radishes in the Far North—which we could—seed houses would sell us short-day variety plant seed so we would get good vegetative growth.

THE EFFECT OF TEMPERATURE ON GROWTH

Closely connected with all activities in the plant is the factor of temperature. Within limits, growth is stimulated by a rise in temperature and retarded when the temperature falls. Earlier in the chapter it was reported that the processes of cell division and mitosis were speeded up by an increase in temperature. This is true of all the other activities, including respiration, photosynthesis, assimilation, digestion, absorption, rate of movement of materials in the plant—in fact all physical, chemical, and physiological processes in the plant are affected by temperature.

Of course, different plants behave differently in response to temperature. Some reach maximum growth in a cool climate. Most evergreens do better in a cool climate than in warm or hot weather. Most of our melons do much better when the temperature is very high, typical of midsummer climate. In fact, people in Iowa sometimes say, "When the weather is hot and humid, hardly fit for man or beast, corn does so well you can 'hear' it grow." This is describing the effect of temperature to an extreme, but certainly there is an optimum temperature for the growth of every species of plant, and there are also maximums and minimums beyond which they cannot survive.

In considering environmental conditions which regulate in a large measure the growth of plants, it is almost impossible to show the effect of one factor without also noting that one factor may modify the effects of another. We find such to be true in the case of light and temperature. A plant may bloom when the length of the day reaches a certain photoperiod, but a higher temperature may have induced the plant to bloom a bit earlier than its scheduled time. Conversely, a lower temperature may delay flowering for some time after its usual blooming date. In other words, there is an exact time for flowering, provided that all environmental conditions are at their optimum for that specific plant.

In traveling from place to place, we observe that some plants grow in one type of environment and other plants find a different habitat acceptable, if not ideal. A cactus growing in our southwestern desert seems to have a very stark environment in which to make a living. Very scanty rainfall, blistering sun many months of the year, soil with a minimum of the necessary elements, and often with a maximum of others so that the alkaline reaction approaches the point of toxicity, make this type of habitat a poor one for most plants. Yet a cactus could not survive in the habitat a cranberry bush might call home. Here the rainfall would be heavy, the soil often saturated with water and very acid in its reaction, the temperature often cold, and the sun clouded over many days of the year. Obviously the habitat has a powerful influence over the success or failure of plant growth. But of course "it takes all kinds to make a world," and plants are no exception. Each ultimately finds its ideal habitat and remains there for one reason or another.

Life for a plant might be very much as it is for us. Each of us might wish to be a millionaire, with all the luxuries and material things that such an environment could provide. Yet we find we can get along with less, even though we might not wish to. Because of the challenge and the competition of many organisms in the same habitat, we succeed and excel far beyond what we might have done had we had nothing to work for. A plant thriving in the soil-bed of luxury might find survival impossible if its environment were slightly changed and it was unable to adapt itself to less luxurious surroundings. But a vigorous plant, able to grow on relatively poor soil, able to endure high and low temperatures, excessive transpiration, and varying light conditions, is the type that nature has brought down through the ages.

GROWTH REGULATORS

Growth is regulated not only by environmental factors but also by certain chemical regulating substances produced within the plant. These substances are the **plant hormones,** or **phytohormones,** which behave very much like the hormones produced by the endocrine glands in animals. In plants the hormones are mostly produced in rapidly growing embryonic tissues, whereas in animals there are special glands in which the substances are produced. The term **growth regulator** is a broader concept than "hormones," since a number of synthetic organic compounds have been produced that exert the same effects on growth as do those naturally produced in plants. Consequently, we usually refer to all such growth substances as growth regulators.

Of all the various growth regulators **auxin** has been most widely studied. It was first observed in the **coleoptile** of oat seedlings. The coleoptile is a tiny sheath that surrounds the stem growing point within the seed. As the seed germinates, the coleoptile elongates and emerges above the ground. It serves as a protective cover for the apical meristem, but after a time the closed end of the coleoptile is ruptured by the first foliage leaf.

From experiments, which now have become classic in botanical research, the effects of auxin on the growth of the oat coleoptile have been noted. When light is provided on one side of the tip, the coleoptile bends toward the light. If the very tip is covered with a small cap of tin foil, there is no curvature. If the lower portion is illuminated but the tip remains covered, there is no curvature. But if the lower portion is shaded and the tip is illuminated, the curvature occurs in the normal way. From these simple experiments it was concluded that, when the tip of the coleoptile was exposed to light, some influence was transmitted from the upper portion to the lower which caused the latter to bend.

We now know that the bending of the coleoptile, as well as all other types of bending in plants, is the result of more rapid elongation of those cells on the shaded side than those on the illuminated side. Many additional experiments have shown that the substance produced in the tip is transmitted on the shaded side from the tip toward the base. If a transverse cut is made just below the tip on the shaded side and a tiny piece of mica inserted to prevent translocation of the auxin, curvature does not occur. If, however, the incision is made on the illuminated side and the mica inserted, curvature does occur. This has been further demonstrated by removing the tip and placing it on a gelatin block. The block receives the auxin and, if placed on the cut end of the coleoptile, will permit normal curvature with side illumination. Furthermore, if the block were placed on one side of a decapitated coleoptile, curvature would result in the direction opposite to the side on which the block was placed. This is, of course, just one example of a hormone affecting the growth of plants, but there are others.

In the apical bud of plants there is produced an inhibiting hormone. When pruning trees, we find that if we cut off the terminal bud, the lateral buds develop into branches, but in many plants if the terminus is left on, the lateral buds do not produce branches. This results in strong apical dominance in those plants with apical buds. Most conifers have a spirelike form which results from strong apical dominance.

Many plants are rather difficult to root from cuttings, but, by treating the cut ends with such synthetic growth regulators as indoleacetic acid, indolebutyric acid, and others, it was found that the rooting of such plants was greatly enhanced. We also find that the use of these substances in transplanting various plants not only assures us greater success but also hastens their growth to a large extent. Usually "watering in" the roots with a very dilute hormone of the types mentioned is all that is necessary.

Tomatoes will develop fruit without seeds if growth substances are brushed on the ovary before pollination. These substances apparently provide the same stimulation for the ovary to develop into the fruit as the developing seed would have provided had fertilization taken place. Many seedless fruits have been produced in this way, including watermelons and cantaloupes, but the operation must be performed on each flower. Those seedless fruits which need no special treatment, such as seedless grapes and seedless oranges, have been produced in nature quite by accident. Man observed these new fruits, recognized them as desirable varieties, and continued their propagation by cuttings, grafting, and layering. Changes in fruits such as these are the result of chromosome alterations and are inherited from one generation to the next.

All plants do not respond to growth regulators in the same way, nor will the same plant respond to a hormone the same way each season. Usually if a plant has an adequate supply of the growth regulator, the addition of more will have no effect. Recently gibberellin, a growth-promoting drug, has been widely advertised. In some cases it greatly hastens growth and may also increase the ultimate size of the plant, but in other carefully regulated experiments no effects were obvious.

TROPISMS

Movements resulting from external stimuli in plants are classified as either *tropisms* or *nastic* movements. In tropic responses the movement is toward the source of the stimulus, which may include such factors as light, gravity, water, and contact. Nastic movements are more rapid and usually quite fascinating. They involve changes in turgor pressure, for the most part, and some plants, like the sensitive plant, respond immediately to touch by folding their leaves back on the rachis.

Phototropism is a response by a plant to light. We often observe that plants, when growing in the house, tend to lean toward a light source. If left to grow by a window for several weeks, a plant would grow very much out of its normal upright habit. The leaves are pushed toward the light by the petioles, and the stem may grow in that direction also. Again this is an example of more rapid growth on the shaded side than on the light side. In general we say that leaves and some stems are positively phototropic because they grow toward a light source, while roots are negatively phototropic because they invariably grow away from light. A few stems, such as prostrate vines, do not grow upward in response to light, nor do they seem to grow toward shade; they can best be described as **transversely phototropic.**

Gravity also exerts a pronounced effect on the growth of plants; this response is **geotropism.** By planting a bulb upside down, one can readily demonstrate that roots are positively geotropic and stems negatively geotropic. If we germinate seeds on a soil surface, similar geotropic responses are readily observed (Fig. 29). Some structures, like branch roots, which grow horizontally from the main root, and leaves that take a position at right angles to the force of gravity, are **transversely geotropic.**

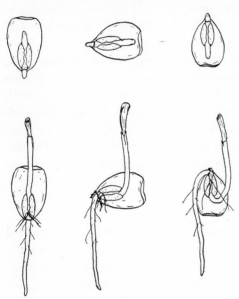

Less easily demonstrated is **hydrotropism** —the response to water. Although roots are positively hydrotropic, they have no way of knowing where a water source is unless there is a little seepage in their direction. If this occurs, we find that roots will grow rapidly toward the water source. However, if adequate water were but a few inches away and roots had to grow through dry soil to get to it, most of them would never make it. The positive hydrotropic response most roots have is a constant source of revenue for plumbers hired to ream roots out of sewer lines.

FIG. 29.—Experimental demonstration of the negative geotropism of the stem and the positive geotropism of the root. Sprouting corn seedlings were oriented in the manner shown in the top row. About forty-eight hours later they had reached the condition represented in the bottom row.

Thigmotropic responses are those a plant may make in response to contact. This is much less obvious, and most plants have little or no reaction to contact, but a few climbers grow up on structures when they touch them. A few have tendrils which become wound around trees or lattice supports; others simply grow in a spiral manner around and around a pole or tree that they manage to make contact with. Morning-glories have the spiral type of growth in response to contact, and many legumes, such as garden peas, produce tendrils and in this way hold the main plant body to a support.

Much more spectacular than any other type of movement in plants are the **nastic movements**. Their direction of movement is not related to the direction from which the stimulus comes. The most remarkable case of rapid response is shown by the "sensitive plant," *Mimosa pudica*. If the tip of a branch is but lightly touched, the leaflets begin folding together progressively down the rachis to the base of the leaf. Often other leaflets on the same leaf continue to fold up, and finally the leaf itself falls down against the stem as if on a hinged joint. After a number of minutes, depending on the humidity and how often the plant has been touched recently, the leaflets begin to unfold, and in a short time the leaf is open and back in position again. The response made is the result of a small nodule (**pulvinus**) at the base of each leaflet and each leaf. The pulvinus is a very spongy little organ made up chiefly of parenchyma cells. It responds to contact by quickly losing its turgidity, causing a consequent change in position of the leaflet. Apparently the closing of one leaflet is stimulus enough for the closing of the ones next to it, and so on. After a short time, turgor returns to the pulvini, and the leaflets assume their open shape.

Venus's-flytrap is an example of an insectivorous plant that operates on this same principle. The leaf is modified into two hinged halves with a ring of spines around the outside border. The leaf lies flat most of the time, but if a fly or other insect should alight on this leaf, the stimulus is enough to cause the turgor to change, and the two halves snap shut, trapping the insect. After a time digestive juices are secreted into the two closed halves, the insect is digested, and the leaf again opens up, ready for another insect.

VII. *Plant Classification*

The classification of plants undoubtedly goes back to very early man. He depended upon them for food, shelter, and probably clothing. He fashioned weapons from them for his protection and to capture animals for food. He found that some plants were better than others for his different purposes. They undoubtedly became a major subject in conversation as he described their uses to his family and members of his tribe. It became necessary to give them names so that he could distinguish among them in his oral communication. Finally, he must have devised a simple system of classification so that he could more readily identify and name them.

Possibly he classified them into groups based upon their uses, such as those for food, fiber, weapons, medicine, and religion. Those tried as food were probably classified, through trial and error, into edible, inedible, and poisonous. He probably observed that some shrubs and trees produced curved branches or straight shafts that made ideal weapons and that some woods were much harder than others, were more durable, more workable, and consequently could be used for better tools than others. Similarly, by experience early man undoubtedly found medicinal plants which seemed to cure his ailments and others which brought quicker death to his enemies or aided in the slaying of animals for food. All primitive peoples also had a number of plants which played an important part in their religious ceremonies and superstitions. Even today certain plants are used in religious ceremonies, not only in present-day Christian ceremonies but in other contemporary religions as well. From these humble origins there slowly emerged a branch of biology known as *taxonomy.*

For the organization of any branch of science, a primary essential is some serviceable system of classifying the materials which that science proposes to study. For biology this has been a tremendous task—a task which has not as yet been completed down to its last detail and never will be so completed. In remote quarters of the globe, many types of plants and animals are still waiting to be classified, and, even in our very backyards, evolution continues slowly but surely to bring new types into existence. No, there will never be a time when the taxonomist (classifier) can close his books with the statement that the last plant and the last animal have been identified, described, and assigned to the proper categories. On the other hand, the past accomplishments of thousands of taxonomists, taken together, constitute an amazingly large contribution to human knowledge and provide a substantial foundation upon which the other branches of biology can build.

Most of us get experience with some sort of classification, from the boy who assembles his stamp collection to the administrative officer who attempts to organize the machinery of his institution into some sort of workable hierarchy. In the main, this experience consists of arranging materials into categories of various magnitudes. Materials with much in common are put into the same small category. Small categories with somewhat less in common are assigned to a still larger category, and so on—until all the various materials or entities are grouped in a manner that reflects our opinion of their degrees of resemblance or difference.

If the materials to be classified are few, any one of several systems of classification may be adequate. If the materials are many, it is important to seek out the most understandable, workable, and serviceable system of classification and to adhere to that consistently throughout. In the early days of classification the several taxonomists used systems that were inconsistent, cumbersome, and not readily understood by their colleagues. Theophrastus (370–285 B.C.) made the first deliberate attempt to classify all the plants known at that time. He based his classification on habit or form, e.g., trees, shrubs, undershrubs, and herbs; the latter were also classified according to longevity into annual, biennial, or perennial. In addition, he pointed out certain flower characteristics which have been used in many systems since that time, although usually in a different way.

Tournefort in 1700 followed Theophrastus in dividing flowering plants into two categories of trees and herbs. He then subdivided these groups into flowers with petals and those without; he also used the character "petals separate or united." About the same time, John Ray, an English botanist, classified about eighteen thousand species, in which he recognized the differences between dicotlyedonous and monocotyledonous plants.

There were other taxonomists before Tournefort and Ray who made contributions, and there were many who followed, but the dominant figure in systematic botany was Carolus Linnaeus (1707–78). He classified all flowering plants into twenty-three different *classes* based on the number and arrangement of stamens and then subdivided the classes into *orders* on the basis of styles in each flower. His twenty-fourth class included all plants without flowers, namely, ferns, mosses, fungi, and algae.

Between 1735 and 1758 Linnaeus published various classified lists of plants and animals. These were of some importance in themselves, being the best and most complete lists that had been published up to that time. Even more important, however, was their influence in establishing standards which were adopted by taxonomists all over the world. Casting aside the cumbersome descriptions that were employed by his predecessors, Linnaeus introduced a brief, graphic method of formal description for each type of plant and animal. (The description was written in Latin, which was agreed upon as the international language of science.) To each type he attached a formal Latin title which was to be regarded as the official scientific name of that type of organism all over the world and for all time to come. The title was a double one, and this system of *binomial nomenclature* has been employed ever since. The name of the genus is written first (and always capitalized), the name of the species second. This combination of generic and specific names makes it readily possible to assign to each known species a title that is absolutely distinctive. Thus *Homo sapiens* can refer to only one thing, i.e., the species *sapiens* of the genus *Homo*, which happens to be the species to which all living men belong, while *Trillium grandiflorum* refers only to a particular species of flowering plant that grows in the woods of North America.

Systematic arrangement of categories within categories is quite possible on the basis of any arbitrary criteria. One taxonomist, for example, might delimit great groups on the basis of flower size, smaller groups on the basis of flower color, and still smaller groups on the basis of number of floral parts. Another taxonomist might delimit great groups on the basis of number of floral parts, smaller groups on the basis of floral size, and still smaller groups on the basis of floral color. The final results of the two classifications would be conspicuously different. To a large extent this very state of affairs did exist until the biological world was provided with an underlying concept which helped to standardize the method of delimiting groups. The concept was that of organic evolution, effectively brought to the biological public by Darwin in 1859.

The guiding concept which evolution gives to classification is the concept of "blood relationship" or "common ancestry." An effort is made to have classification represent degree of "blood relationship." All species thought to have descended from a relatively recent common ancestor are put into the same genus; all genera thought to have descended from a somewhat more remote common ancestor are put into the same family; and so on.

In making this effort, the following evolutionary considerations are kept in mind. It is clear that, in general, different lines of descent have diverged, not with respect to just one of their characters at a time but simultaneously with respect to many. It is equally clear that the rate of divergence is less for certain "conservative" characters than for other less conservative, more "fluctuating" characters. The classifier judges relationship in terms of the totality of characters but weighs more heavily those that his experience tells him are the more conservative. Thus the presence of an embryo is a very conservative character, and all plants with this character are thrown into the great subkingdom of EMBRYOPHYTA, while such characters as color of flower, size of flower, or size of entire plant are known to be so highly fluctuating that they are used merely to distinguish the several species of the same genus or perhaps merely several varieties of the same species.

The point has already been made that the great groups of the plant kingdom are not equally represented in the vegetation of modern time. In most habitats the picture is overwhelmingly dominated by seed plants belonging to two classes—Gymnospermae and Angiospermae. Even here there is a big difference in the total number of species. The gymnosperms, which inhabit most of the mountain ranges thoughout the world and in general are able to survive on very shallow soils, number only about 550 species, while the much more diversified angiosperms number close to 250,000 species.

In the chapters which follow, descriptions of the various plant groups will be presented. It is sufficient at this stage for the student to visualize the essence of the system employed in classification. Memorization of the title of the different groups can be more easily accomplished when each group is studied in detail. Actually there are some inconsistencies in all systems of classification and certainly many between different systems. It is much more important for the student to know the characteristics of the plants in a certain group and to know where it is placed in plant phylogeny than to be greatly concerned as to whether that category is a class or a subclass.

For almost seventy-five years the dominant system of classification in North America was that outlined by Engler. This system utilized four "divisions" of the plant kingdom, i.e., thallophytes, bryophytes, pteridophytes, and spermatophytes, and is outlined below merely for comparative purposes.

Division I. THALLOPHYTA—thallus plants
  Subdivision 1. Algae
  Subdivision 2. Fungi

Division II. BRYOPHYTA
  Class 1. Hepaticae—liverworts
  Class 2. Musci—mosses

Division III. PTERIDOPHYTA
  Class 1. Lycopodineae—club mosses
  Class 2. Equisetineae—horsetails
  Class 3. Filicineae—ferns

Division IV. SPERMATOPHYTA—seed plants
  Class 1. Gymnospermae—conifers and allies
  Class 2. Angiospermae—flowering plants
    Subclass A. Dicotyledonae
    Subclass B. Monocotyledonae

equisetum — horsetail

This system is only a partially natural one; many of the forms placed in these groups have only the most superficial relationship to others in the same group. In other words, it is also a system for convenience. Nevertheless, it served its purpose well and is superseded now by a system that shows greater relationship.

In 1942 Tippo proposed a classification system for the plant kingdom based largely on anatomical and morphological criteria. In this system the plant kingdom is divided into two **subkingdoms** and these in turn into **phyla.** Succeeding categories were divided as before in classes, orders, families, genera, and species. This is the system now most widely accepted by systematists and is the system we will use in this book.

It will be noted that THALLOPHYTA is now called a subkingdom and is comprised of ten phyla. These phyla, formerly considered classes, comprise a very heterogeneous group of plants that show slight relationships. They are so distinctive that we can only conclude that they must have had a number of different origins.

The second subkingdom, EMBRYOPHYTA, dominates the plant world today. The plants themselves are larger and therefore much more conspicuous, but, more than that, they have come to occupy most of the terrestrial habitats and for that reason are our most familiar plants. The embryophytes are divided into two phyla and these into four subphyla, as listed below.

CLASSIFICATION OF THE PLANT KINGDOM

Subkingdom THALLOPHYTA—thallus plants

(The plant body is undifferentiated; it has neither roots, stems, nor leaves; the reproductive cells are inclosed only by a cell wall; the zygote does not develop into an embryo while still within the female sex organ.)

The Algae

Phylum CYANOPHYTA—blue-green algae

Phylum EUGLENOPHYTA—flagellates

Phylum CHRYSOPHYTA—yellow-green algae, golden-brown algae, and diatoms

Phylum PYRROPHYTA—cryptomonads and dinoflagellates

Phylum CHLOROPHYTA—green algae

The Algae—*Continued*

Phylum PHAEOPHYTA—brown algae

Phylum RHODOPHYTA—red algae

The Fungi and Bacteria

Phylum SCHIZOMYCOPHYTA—bacteria

Phylum MYXOMYCOPHYTA—slime molds

Phylum EUMYCOPHYTA—true fungi

Subkingdom EMBRYOPHYTA

The Liverworts and Mosses

Phylum BRYOPHYTA

    Class Hepaticae—liverworts

    Class Anthocerotae—hornworts

    Class Musci—true mosses

Vascular Plants

Phylum TRACHEOPHYTA

  Subphylum Psilopsida

    Class Psilophytineae

      Order Psilophytales

      Order Psilotales

  Subphylum Lycopsida—"club mosses"

    Class Lycopodineae

      Order Lycopodiales

      Order Selaginellales—small club mosses

      Order Lepidodendrales—giant club mosses

      Order Pleuromeiales

      Order Isoetales—quillworts

  Subphylum Sphenopsida—horsetails

    Class Equisetineae

      Order Hyeniales

      Order Sphenophyllales

      Order Equisetales

  Subphylum Pteropsida

    Class Filicineae—ferns

      Order Coenopteridales

      Order Ophioglossales

      Order Marattiales

      Order Filicales

Class Gymnospermae—cone-bearing plants and allies
  Subclass Cycadophytae
    Order Cycadofilicales—seed ferns
    Order Bennettitales
    Order Cycadales—cycads
  Subclass Coniferophytae
    Order Cordaitales
    Order Ginkgoales—maidenhair tree
    Order Coniferales—conifers
    Order Gnetales
Class Angiospermae—flowering plants
  Subclass Dicotyledoneae
  Subclass Monocotyledoneae

For convenience, the algae will be considered under two separate chapters. In chapter viii ("The Ubiquitous Algae") the forms are in general small, and the vast majority are unicellular and widely dispersed in habitat. In chapter ix ("The Higher Algae") we find, for the most part, much larger, multicellular species. However, the chlorophytes of the latter group include some very primitive species which may actually have been the ancestors of certain algae groups in the earlier chapter.

VIII. *The Ubiquitous Algae*

Subkingdom THALLOPHYTA

    Phylum CYANOPHYTA—blue-green algae

    Phylum EUGLENOPHYTA—flagellates

    Phylum CHRYSOPHYTA—yellow-green and golden-brown algae

    Phylum PYRROPHYTA—dinoflagellates

These are the simplest and most primitive members of the plant kingdom. There are about 110,000 species in all, with a great variety in form and structure. Some of the groups appear related, others do not; but, because they all have a vegetative body with very little differentiation into the organs found more typically in the higher plants, we call them **thallus plants** or, more technically, THALLOPHYTA. The last part of this word comes from the Greek *phyton*, meaning "plant." It reappears in titles of the other groups. The first part is derived from *thallus*, which signifies a plant body in which there is little or no differentiation of vegetative parts. Actually the title is not quite definitive since a few members of this group show a greater differentiation of body regions than do a few of the members of the EMBRYOPHYTA.

The diversity we find in the ten phyla of the THALLOPHYTA points to many divergent lines of evolution. This variation is shown in many different ways, one of which is size of plants. They may vary from unicellular forms to some several hundred feet in length; they differ also in the degree of differentiation of both vegetative and reproductive organs; physiologically they vary in the type of food they manufacture and store and also in the manner in which they live. Some are photosynthetic, while others are saprophytic and still others are parasitic. In the simplest forms there is no nucleus as such, but soon it is evolved and continues throughout the remaining phyla.

The methods of reproduction are particularly diverse. In the simpler forms *asexual* reproduction is the only method known. Usually this is accomplished by *fission,* which is merely a pinching-in-two of the individual cells, or reproduction may be by the production of unicellular *spores.* When *sexual* reproduction was evolved, it also took a great variety of forms. At first it was *isogamous,* in which the individual sex cells, the *gametes,* had no distinguishing sexual differences. As sexual reproduction progresses through the phyla, the gametes become unlike (male and female) and are termed *heterogamous.* In some of the THALLOPHYTA individual plants may look alike and have similar gametes, but it can be shown that they actually belong to two sexual types. In such cases it requires two gametes from different plants in order to accomplish fertilization. Since there are no apparent morphological differences between gametes of this type, they are designated by neutral symbols like + and − rather than male and female. Such species are termed *heterothallic.* Plants which are all alike, and in which two gametes from the same individual may unite, are termed *homothallic.*

The thallophytes are divided into two major groups: the *algae,* which contain chlorophyll or an allied pigment which makes it possible for them to live independently; and the *fungi,* which lack chlorophyll and exist only as saprophytes or parasites, and which will be considered in chapters x and xi.

The algae are among the most primitive of the thallophytes. Nearly all algae live in water, although a few may live in soil or on rocks, trees, or other structures. Some live on the backs of turtles, on the fur of aquatic animals, and on birds, or almost any place where they can find a reasonably moist habitat and enough light for photosynthesis. Most of the species living in water are in the sea, but some are restricted to fresh water. Most of the forms are attached to some substrate for anchorage, but a vast number of very minute forms live as free-floating species in the sea or in fresh water and, along with other small, drifting animals, make up the *plankton* which constitutes the chief source of food for many small aquatic animals and even much larger ones, including the whale. Other algae are used by man for different purposes. Some we use directly as food; others are used for fertilizer, building material, and certain chemicals. We will consider the economic importance of algae later.

Phylum Cyanophyta. The blue-green algae are among our most widely distributed organisms. They are of common occurrence in ponds, running and stagnant water, in lakes and reservoirs, in brackish and salt waters, and they are even found growing in hot springs where the water temperature is as high as 185° F. Some of the most colorful habitats of blue-greens are those around the hot springs of Yellowstone National Park. Here they are found in great abundance around the edges of the hot pools, where they aid in the deposition of the mineral substances dissolved in water to make the spectacular terraces formed in that park.

Blue-greens form a large portion of the free-floating population of microscopic organisms in our lakes and oceans. Many species live in damp soil several inches beneath the surface; others may be found on the moist bark of trees or other supporting structures; and many live upon or just beneath the epidermis of larger plants and even animals.

In structure the Cyanophyta are as varied as their choice of habitats. Some are unicellular; others have many cells joined together in a colony. These colonies may take the form of flat plates, grapelike clusters, much-branched filaments, or unbranched filaments.

The simplicity of the blue-greens is best exemplified in their lack of a distinct nuclear body. The protoplast within the cell wall is differentiated very slightly into a more densely colored peripheral area and a central, lighter colored area. In many of the species the central, lightly colored area has a relatively dense mass of material, the **central body.** This central body is considered by some phycologists as nuclear material, but it is without the nuclear membrane and nucleoli. Partially for this reason, other investigators claim that this material is not nuclear.

Another very primitive characteristic concerns pigmentation. In the other algae chlorophyll and the other pigments are contained in distinct plastids or chromatophores. In the Cyanophyta the pigments are not localized in definite plastids; they appear uniformly distributed throughout the protoplasm. Furthermore, in the blue-greens the dominant pigment is **phycocyanin,** a blue pigment; the other pigments, chlorophyll and the carotinoids are also present, but in most species they are secondary to phycocyanin.

Photosynthesis in blue-greens undoubtedly occurs in the same manner as in other plants, but, because of the predominance of the blue color, more of the yellow, orange, and even green wave lengths of light are used than in the very green plants. The storage product in blue-greens is also starchlike, but it is somewhat different from that of green plants. In addition, many of the blue-greens store reserve foods in the form of oils.

Reproduction in the blue-greens is of the simplest type. No gametes, motile spores, or zygotes, or any type of conjugation which might be construed as sexual reproduction, has been found in this phylum. Increase in number of individuals is simply brought about by cell division. There is no mitosis involved; the cells simply split in two to produce two new cells by a process appropriately called "amitosis." There are several different types of immobile spores produced. They are usually formed within a filament by a vegetative cell which becomes filled with reserve foods and develops a thick wall. This spore eventually becomes separated from a parent filament and may then or at a later time develop into a new filament of vegetative cells. In some species vegetative cells develop very thick walls, but the cellular contents seem to break down and become transparent. These sporelike cells are called **heterocysts.** They apparently do not germinate into new cells but may serve as a breaking point in the filament, thus forming two shorter filaments where originally there was one. The cells in these filaments then divide by fission and soon restore each filament to the size of its parent.

The blue-green algae probably had some representatives living on this planet fully two billion years ago. At first there was doubtless just the one very simple type, but some of its descendants must have been modified as time rolled on, thus giving rise to new types and in some instances perhaps "better" types. Today we recognize hundreds of existing species of blue-green algae, and there is no knowing how many additional species may be living their lives in such inconspicuous crannies as to have escaped the attention of the scientists. Furthermore, there may well have been thousands of species that were evolved in the past, only to be exterminated without leaving a trace.

In the first chapter we discussed, at considerable length, the blue-green *Gloeocapsa* (see Fig. 1). There we considered it as a primitive plant, which it is. Now it would be advisable to again read that chapter, considering the characteristics of *Gloeocapsa* as typical of a blue-green alga. Many of the Cyanophyta fall into the non-filamentous category, but in the laboratory it is often easier to study the filamentous species. *Oscillatoria* is one of the most widely distributed of the filamentous genera (Fig. 30). Usually we find it in water or growing on damp soil. It gets its name from a very distinguishing feature which sets it off from other algae. The tip of the filament frequently waves slowly back and forth, and occasionally the entire filament may move backward and forward for short distances. Just what the mechanism is which causes these movements is unknown.

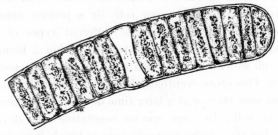

Fig. 30.—*Oscillatoria,* a filamentous blue-green alga, showing dead cell in filament.

Nostoc is another rather widespread filamentous genus of this group (Fig. 31). It is usually found in gelatinous colonies about the size of a marble. Within this gelatinous matrix are thousands of tiny filaments. The individual cells are spherical or beadlike in appearance, quite different from the rectangular cells of *Oscillatoria.* *Nostoc* also produces spores and heterocysts in the filament, in addition to the usual method of fragmentation of the filament.

Phylum Euglenophyta. The euglenoids, found most frequently in fresh water, consist of a small phylum of 25 genera and about 235 species. Zoologists, observing certain characteristics, often consider them as animals and call them "flagellates." Botanists, giving greater weight to other characteristics, study them as plants. Whether we consider them as plants or animals is not important. We are sure it makes no difference to them. It is, however, important for us to know something of their characteristics and why we place them in a separate phylum.

Members of this phylum possess a definite nucleus and chlorophyll localized in definite chloroplasts. In this respect they resemble the Chlorophyta. Furthermore, the chlorophyll is green and is not combined with other pigments except for the usual carotinoids associated with chlorophyll. The euglenoids differ from the green algae in that the reserve food is *paramylum,* a substance similar to starch, but it is not the same type of starch stored in the green algae. A few of the genera ingest solid food, do not have chlorophyll, and thus resemble animals in their nutrition. Most of the genera are naked,

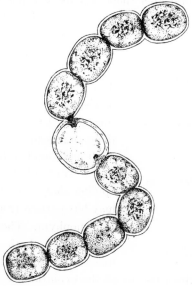

Fig. 31.—*Nostoc*, a filamentous blue-green alga, with heterocyst in center of filament.

unicellular flagellates. The motile vegetative cell stage usually has one flagellum, occasionally two or even three. The lack of a rigid cell wall is an animal characteristic, since most plants have fairly rigid cellulose cell walls.

Reproduction in the euglenoids is usually by longitudinal cell division, a type of asexual reproduction similar to fission in the blue-green algae, except that in this case nuclear division is also involved. Some species form thick-walled resting cells which may withstand unfavorable weather conditions for lengthy periods. Upon the return of optimum conditions of moisture, temperature, and oxygen, the resting cells germinate into the usual flagellated vegetative cells.

The type genus of this phylum is *Euglena,* a spindle-shaped organism which propels itself through water by means of an anterior flagellum (Fig. 32). The cell membrane is quite pliable, and this permits *Euglena* to take a variety of shapes when moving about. The nucleus is centrally located, and the cytoplasm is well filled with numerous small, green chloroplasts. At the anterior end there is a **gullet** through which solid foods may enter the organism's body. In the same general area there is a red eyespot which probably is

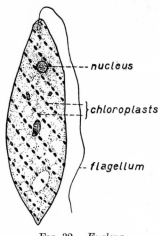

FIG. 32.—*Euglena*

sensitive to light. Reproduction is like that of the other euglenoids. The nucleus divides mitotically, following which the cell divides longitudinally to produce two new individuals. In a colony of *Euglena* it is quite common to see thick-walled resting cells which enable these organisms to withstand periods of drought and unfavorable temperatures. Most phylogenists are of the opinion that several lines of evolution may have arisen from members of the Euglenophyta. They probably have given rise to both plant and animal lines of evolution, but it is doubtful that they have given rise to *all* the evolutionary lines.

Phylum Chrysophyta. Members of this phylum are as diverse as those of the Chlorophyta and with as many lines of evolution. There are about 300 genera and close to 5,800 species now classified in the group. For convenience, the phylum is usually divided into three classes chiefly on the basis of the color of the pigments in the chloroplasts, and on the form of the individual cells. Most of the species are yellow-green or golden-brown, with the brown and carotinoid pigments more prominent than the chlorophylls. A large number of the species live in fresh water, a few are terrestrial, and a good many, especially diatoms, live in the ocean.

The walls are usually composed of cellulose, but in many of the species, chiefly diatoms, they are often impregnated with silica. They store their food in the form of a starchlike substance, **leucosin,** and in the form of oils. Many of the species bear two laterally attached flagella, a characteristic of brown algae, while other species have no flagella. Reproduction is usually asexual, generally by simple cell division; but in some forms motile spores are freely produced, and in others, various types of non-flagellated spores are common. Sexual reproduction is often absent, but where present it is usually isogamous, although a few species are heterogamous.

Most of the species in this phylum live as single-celled individuals, but the usual variation exists, as in most of the THALLOPHYTA. Some are filamentous, others form variously shaped colonies, and a few are multicellular organisms.

It is not our purpose to consider the three classes and the large number of genera in this phylum, but an example or two are worthy of mention. *Botrydium* is a terrestrial alga which grows abundantly on damp soil (Fig. 33). The thallus consists of a balloon-shaped aerial portion, often one or two millimeters in height, and a mass of branched **rhizoids** which anchor the plant to the soil. The entire plant consists of but one cell with many nuclei. It has the characteristic siphonaceous body of an alga similar to a few green algae, but it produces motile spores

FIG. 33.—*Botrydium,* a member of the Chrysophyta, showing balloon-shaped thallus and branched rhizoids.

which bear two unequal flagella typical of the brown algae. The gametes are also biflagellated and isogamous.

Recent study of one very important alga, *Vaucheria,* has demonstrated that it has certain affinities with some of the members of this phylum. Although it is quite green in appearance, careful examination of its pigments, its photosynthetic storage products, and the flagellation of its zoospores has shown that *Vaucheria* should be placed in the Chrysophyta rather than the Chlorophyta.

The plant body of *Vaucheria* consists of an elongate, sparingly branched tube which is divided into very few, but large, cells. Numerous nuclei and plastids are quite uniformly distributed throughout the filament. A large compound zoospore is produced from a terminal cell and soon germinates into a new siphonaceous filament. Sexual reproduction is heterogamous, with the production of a single large, non-motile egg in the specialized female sex organ and numerous sperm formed in a variously curved and unique male sex organ (Fig. 34). The sperm are unequally biflagellate. Fertilization occurs in the female sex organ, which may then break away from the filament. After a dormancy period the zygote germinates into a new filament.

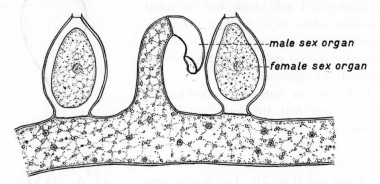

male sex organ

female sex organ

FIG. 34.—Fragment of *Vaucheria*, showing coenocytic body and differentiated sex organs.

Possibly the most unusual of all algae are the ***diatoms*** (Fig. 35). There are many genera and over 5,000 species which live in both fresh water and salt water. A small spoonful of bottom ooze taken from a pond, lake, stream, or ocean will usually yield hundreds of diatoms and often many different species. They are considered unicellular but may appear in filamentous colonies or in variously branched and unusual clusters. The individual cells may be disk-shaped, boat-shaped, rodlike, or even shaped like a wedge. They are often called "jewels of the sea" because the individual cells often appear like perfect stones for an expensive ring or locket.

Each cell of a diatom consists of two halves called "valves." The valves fit together like the two halves of a Petri dish. Since the walls are composed of silica, the protoplasm of a diatom is covered by a glassy exterior. The protoplasm is made up of a single nucleus and one to many plastids. The color of the plastids varies in different species from green or yellow to golden-brown, depending on the dominance of the pigments. The most distinguishing characteristic of the diatoms is the marking in the walls. There are tiny dots which appear as sculptured lines in the walls so uniformly placed that they are sometimes used to test the resolving power of microscope lenses. Reproduction is also rather different in diatoms and will not be

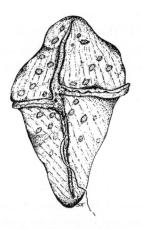

FIG. 36.—A variety o *Gymnodinium*, a dinoflagellate found along our southeastern seaboard and associated with "red tide." Another, more rounded form, *Gymnodinium brevis*, causes even greater havoc with the fishing industry in the Gulf of Mexico.

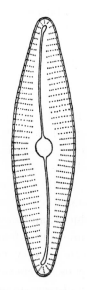

FIG. 35.—A diatom

considered in detail here, but in general it is asexual. Where sexual reproduction exists, it is usually isogamous, but in some forms gametes of unequal size have been observed.

Diatoms are of considerable economic importance both directly and indirectly. The silicified cell walls do not decay after the death of the organisms; consequently, great numbers accumulate at the bottom of waters in which diatoms live. Layers of fossil diatom walls, deposited over the years, are known as "diatomaceous earth." This material is mined in a number of places throughout the world, such as in Lompoc, California, where the deposits are over 3,000 feet thick. The material is used as a heat-insulating substance in high-temperature ovens, in the manufacture of lightweight cement, as a filtering material, and as a source of fine abrasives in tooth pastes, silver polishes, etc. In addition to these and other uses, diatoms form a great deal of the plankton in oceans, which is used as food by many fishes. The oils of diatoms are believed to find their way through the digestive tract of a fish to the liver, where they are stored. This oil is the basis for some of our vitamin products obtained from fishes—such as cod-liver oil. We also believe that vast deposits of diatoms in the past provided us with the oil now being brought up from the earth by workers in the petroleum business.

Phylum Pyrrophyta. Members of this phylum are usually called **dinoflagellates,** although a few of them are non-flagellated. There are about 135 genera and about 1,000 species. They are usually colored yellowish-green or golden-brown, depending on the dominance of the pigments found in the plastids. Food may be stored as oils or starches. In some, cell walls are absent, but in others they are very conspicuous and composed of cellulose. Some of the members are placed in the animal phylum Protozoa by zoologists; however, botanists now place them in the Pyrrophyta because of their photosynthetic characteristics, cellulose wall, and similarity to other plantlike organisms.

Reproduction in the Pyrrophyta is accomplished mostly by cell division; in a few, zoospores are freely produced; and in some, non-motile spores. Sexual reproduction is not common but is found in some of the species. The rate of cell division can be very rapid when conditions are ideal. One dinoflagellate genus, *Gymnodinium,* has caused great havoc to the fishing industry and recreational pursuits along the south Atlantic and Gulf coasts (Fig. 36). For unknown reasons it suddenly increases in vast numbers and causes the death of thousands of fish along these coasts. In some areas it may cause some damage every year, but it has reached serious proportion only about once every two or more years. Members of this genus secrete a red pigment which has resulted in its sudden appearance being called "the red tide." A good many research workers in our marine laboratories are devoting years to the study of this problem in the hopes that we can prevent the periodic plagues to our coastal fish.

IX *The Higher Algae*

Subkingdom THALLOPHYTA
   Phylum CHLOROPHYTA—green algae
   Phylum PHAEOPHYTA—brown algae
   Phylum RHODOPHYTA—red algae

Phylum Chlorophyta. The Phylum Chlorophyta (green algae) has the largest number of genera of any algal group. There are approximately 360 genera and 5,700 species living in a variety of habitats. The term "habitat" refers to a particular complex of environmental conditions. Accustomed as we are to the versatility of man, it surprises us to find that most lower organisms can succeed in only one habitat (or a very few). The earth's surface may provide this particular ideal habitat at many points. All such points will be occupied by the species in question, provided (1) that the species has been distributed to that location and (2) that the spot has not been effectively pre-empted by other forms of life. The bulk of green algae grow submerged in fresh water, most of them anchored at the bottom by their holdfasts, but some float free at or near the surface of stagnant waters. A few are found in the ocean (e.g., *Ulva* or "sea lettuce") and some in air which is continuously or frequently very humid, as in a moist soil surface or the bark of forest trees (e.g., *Protococcus*, Fig. 37).

Green algae, as the name implies, possess the green pigment, chlorophyll, as their most prominent pigment, but they differ from the blue-greens in other characteristics as well. The most significant advance is in the differentiation of cell organs. No longer do we find the cell composed of homogeneous protoplasm; instead it is differentiated into three distinct parts which may be called **cell organs** or **organelles** ("little organs"). In the center of the cell is a denser, spherical region of the protoplasm, sharply delimited from the rest by a definite membrane. This cell organ is the **nucleus.** It carries the critical materials of heredity and exerts a governing influence over the rest of the cell.

One genus we might consider in some detail is *Protococcus.* This organism is found growing very abundantly in temperate regions. Although it is simple in appearance, and sexual reproduction has never been observed in it, certain advanced characteristics, such as its manner of cell division and cell-wall formation, lead us to believe that it deserves a fairly high position in the phylum.

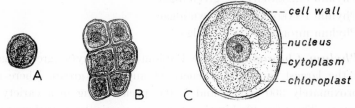

FIG. 37.—The green alga *Protococcus.* *A*, single-celled individual; *B*, colony; *C*, highly magnified single cell.

In *Protococcus* the green chlorophyll, which was diffused throughout the entire cell of *Gloeocapsa*, is contained within a single **chloroplast.** Hence the chloroplast alone is endowed with the power to manufacture food. Surrounding both the single nucleus and chloroplast, and forming the more dilute matrix of protoplasm in which they lie, is the **cytoplasm.** It is the business of the cytoplasm to use the food manufactured by the chloroplast for maintenance and growth of the cell and to regulate the interchange of materials between the cell and the medium in which it lives. In short, the homogeneous protoplasm has been superseded by three specialists, each an expert at its own particular line of work. This type of change is usually regarded as a step in evolutionary progress.

We commonly think of progress as being any change in which the organism (individually or as a member of some group) achieves a more efficient adaptation to the conditions of life. This result may be brought about in any one of a great many ways. One of the most common ways is by a change from the relatively "generalized" to the more "specialized" condition. History assures us that progress in human societies has frequently involved this very thing. In the primitive social group—as, for example, in a pioneer community—those composing the group are likely to be doing pretty much the same work. As time passes, some usually come to devote themselves to certain tasks, and others contribute in a different manner. By this concentration of attention upon one task, this freedom of responsibility from all other duties, a man may become quite expert. The social group as a whole, by co-ordinating the work of its several experts or specialists, will thus get the sum of its tasks performed more efficiently than before. Increased efficiency means a better adjustment to the requirements of life. It makes possible a discharge of necessary duties with comparative ease, leaving a comfortable margin of available strength which may be called upon in time of stress.

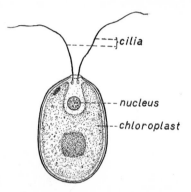

Fig. 38.—*Chlamydomonas,* a single-celled, motile green alga.

Such considerations make us regard transitions from generalization to specialization as steps in progress (though there may be exceptions to this principle in special situations). Accordingly, *Gloeocapsa,* the blue-green alga, with its generalized protoplasm, appears to be quite primitive, while *Protococcus,* the green alga, with its differentiation of cell organs, appears to have taken a step in evolutionary progress.

Of the thousands of known species of green algae, all possess this same differentiation of cell organs. Size and shape of cell vary tremendously among the different species, as do also the size, shape, and number of chloroplasts, and other characteristics as well. Yet all species retain the same fundamental organizations of the cell into nucleus, chloroplast, and cytoplasm, and this makes us believe that they have all inherited this organization from a common ancestor.

One of the most primitive members of the Chlorophyta (Fig. 38) is a common alga known as *Chlamydomonas.* The plant consists of a single cell which is egg-shaped. The cell contains a single, large, cup-shaped chloroplast, with a centrally placed nucleus, an **eyespot,** and one or two **contractile vacuoles.** The latter are located near the anterior end. The cell wall is composed of cellulose. Zoologists often consider *Chlamydomonas* as a primitive flagellate in the Phylum Protozoa, while botanists consider it a very primitive alga. It has some characteristics in common with the Euglenophyta, but in general it is placed in the Order Volvocales in the Phylum Chlorophyta. But plant or animal, it is one of our most primitive of nucleated organisms.

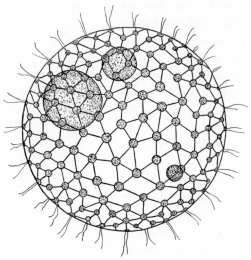

Fig. 39.—A *Volvox* colony, with its ciliated vegetative cells arranged in the form of a hollow sphere. Some of the cells have the power to enlarge and divide to form new colonies; three such are shown within the interior of the sphere. The eggs and sperm are not shown in this particular specimen.

Was the common ancestor of the green algae *Chlamydomonas?* This question, like the innumerable similar questions that are asked in biology, cannot be answered with any assurance. The best that one can ever say is something like this: "Probably all the green algae have been derived from a single progenitor, and probably this progenitor resembled *Chlamydomonas* in having a body composed of a single, spherical cell and in showing a simple form of the differentiation of cell organs." One genus, *Volvox* (Fig. 39), has carried the *Chlamydomonas* cell into a highly complex colony. The vegetative cells of *Volvox* are similar in every respect to those of *Chlamydomonas,* but they have become arranged into a hollow sphere and vary in their degree of differentiation sexually as well as vegetatively.

In at least one respect *Chlamydomonas* differs from the ideal, hypothetical ancestor of the green algae, and that is in its method of reproduction. We would assume that the earliest ancestor of the green algae would simply divide in two to form new individuals, but *Chlamydomonas* shows a higher degree of differentiation than this. It has been experimentally shown that vegetative cells in some species of *Chlamydomonas* will differentiate into gametes when there is a low supply of nitrogen in the culture medium. In other words, nutritional conditions favor the formation of gametes. These gametes may swim about for a short time, then fuse in the water to form a zygote. A thick wall usually develops around this structure to form a zygospore, which may then overwinter in this stage. At the time of germination of the zygospore, reduction division occurs to produce two daughter cells, and then a second division occurs to form four daughter cells, all within the old zygospore wall. Four new individuals are thus produced, which soon emerge from the old spore wall and take up independent existences.

Protococcus, on the other hand, differs from the ideal, hypothetical ancestor of the green algae in another way. One would infer that this ancestor grew submerged in water, which *Chlamydomonas* does. *Protococcus* most commonly grows not actually submerged in water but in places that are moist or usually moist. One recalls seeing a thin green coating over parts of the surfaces of bricks, stones, and flowerpots that have been kept for a long time in a moist greenhouse. One may also recall a similar green coating on the bark near the base of trees in a moist forest. These coats commonly consist of nothing but innumerable microscopic bodies of *Protococcus* crowded together. Of course, a few raindrops or a minute film of dew will effectively submerge these plants and enable them to carry on their life processes in the manner that is customary for their group. But this submergence occurs only at intervals. *Protococcus* is unique among green algae in being able to survive the intervening periods of comparative drought, owing perhaps to some special quality of the cell wall or the protoplasm itself.

A *Protococcus* cell, which is at the same time a *Protococcus* individual, grows to a certain size and then divides. In this case, division is not accomplished by the simple process of pinching in two that is employed in blue-green algae. The protoplasm of *Protococcus*, with its several organelles, is a heterogeneous system, such that any rather crude bisection of the cell might often yield two daughter cells with significantly different contents. Since actually the characteristics of *Protococcus* appear to be rather perfectly perpetuated from one cell generation to the next, the organism must be endowed with some more accurate method of division. As a matter of fact, the cells of *Protococcus*, like practically all the cells of higher plants and animals, divide by the process of mitosis. Mitosis involves a series of events that bring about a remarkably accurate division of the contents of the nucleus, so that each daughter cell receives a nucleus qualitatively like that of the mother cell. Apparently it is the nuclear contents that are of most critical importance in deciding the characteristics of the cell. While the nucleus is being accurately divided by mitosis, chloroplast and cytoplasm are being pinched in two in a less accurate way, and a wall comes in to separate the two resulting daughter cells.

These daughters usually remain attached to each other along the line of division, and, since such attachments may persist through many cell divisions, a single cell may at last yield an irregular clump that is composed of scores or hundreds of descendants. Perhaps this attachment is due to the fact that *Protococcus* lives in moist air and has no power to move its body. Most of the one-celled green algae live in water and are endowed with means of locomotion, so that after division the two daughter cells become separated. Even in *Protococcus*, however, these cells appear as two functionally distinct individuals, for, if they chance to become separated, they continue to carry out their life processes in the same way as they did when they were attached.

The size attained by the cell at the moment of division varies somewhat—varies more, in fact, than in some other unicellular forms that might be cited—and yet one is impressed with the fact that *Protococcus* cells are all pretty much the same size at the time they divide to form two daughters. Not that there is anything unique about this, for one is equally impressed by the corresponding phenomenon in many other organisms. Why these fairly uniform size limits?

If we can answer this question for a one-celled organism, we may thereby be suggesting at least one part of the answer for such a complex organism as man. Biologists have usually guessed that the answer is to be found along one or both of the following lines:

1. Normal life activity depends upon the diffusion of materials in and out through the cell surface, to and from the mass of protoplasm. The more the surface, the more the possibility of exchange of materials. Double the diameter of the cell and you square its surface. But at the same time you cube its mass. Hence, with increase of size, surface keeps diminishing relative to mass, and a ratio is finally reached where the cell is presented with the alternative of continuing to grow and reducing its life activities, or dividing and maintaining the life activities at their normal rate.

2. The nucleus governs the cell as a whole. Growth of a cell is growth of the general cytoplasm (and chloroplast) only, the nucleus maintaining essentially its original size. When the "domain" reaches a certain size, effective government requires two governors instead of one.

These two suggestions concerning the division of the cell when a certain optimum size limit has been reached should not be regarded as genuine explanations, for they tell us nothing of the causal mechanics involved or the actual physical or chemical forces that are responsible for initiating the division at this stage which is advantageous to the living cell.

In the study of biology, one is repeatedly encountering these two types of interpretation of the structures and functions of living organisms: (a) statements as to how the structure or function may be advantageous to the organism; (b) descriptions as to how materials and energy have been applied to the production of the structure or the discharge of the function. In the interests of clear thinking, students should form the habit of distinguishing these two types of interpretation and of regarding only type b as constituting a genuine explanation. With a view to the clearest possible understanding of biological phenomena, biologists are constantly searching for such genuine explanations. In many cases, however, where the genuine explanation has not yet been reached, the biologist feels that he has at least advanced a little in his understanding of the phenomenon by providing an interpretation of the a type.

The contributions which the earliest green algae have made to the evolution of the plant kingdom lie in the differentiation of organelles and in a new method of cell division that is associated with that differentiation. Most of the green algae, however, have taken still further steps in evolutionary progress. On the stones that lie in shallow, rapidly moving, fresh water one sometimes encounters green growths that have a rough resemblance to human hair. Such growths may consist of any one of a number of types of green algae, one of them being the genus known as *Ulothrix* (Fig. 40). Under the microscope *Ulothrix* is revealed to be a long filament, composed of a single line of cells attached end to end.

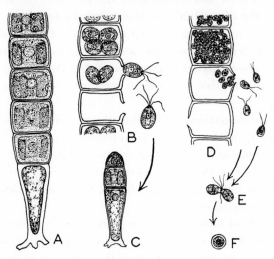

Fig. 40.—*Ulothrix. A,* vegetative filament with holdfast cell; *B,* production and discharge of spores; *C,* young filament recently produced by a spore; *D,* production and discharge of gametes; *E,* fusion of gametes; *F,* zygote.

When growing conditions are good, each cell contains a nucleus, cytoplasm, and a single large chloroplast, shaped like a bracelet, surrounding the bulk of the cytoplasm and the nucleus.

All cells of the filament are essentially the same, with two conspicuous exceptions: (1) The cell at the upper or free end is dome-shaped rather than cylindrical. A living cell normally takes in enough water to exert a strong outward pressure upon its retaining wall. It follows that when the wall is elastic (as is commonly true of the cellulose cell walls of plants), and equally elastic in all places, the cell will assume the shape of a perfect sphere. In *Ulothrix* mutual pressure of adjoining cells flattens out their end walls and converts the sphere into the barrel shape. The terminal cell, however, being unconfined above, becomes a dome. (2) The lowest cell of the filament, known as the "holdfast cell," is longer and narrower than the others, and its lower surface, conforming to irregularities on the surface of some submerged rock or other object, adheres thereto and thus serves as an anchor for the entire filament. By virtue of the holdfast, *Ulothrix* is able to maintain itself in a medium of rapidly moving water. Through evolving forms, equipped with holdfasts, the green algae have been able to exploit a range of habitats that would otherwise have been unavailable.

Food manufacture by the individual cells and their resulting growth lead to cell division. In *Ulothrix*, cell division is restricted to a single plane, and it is this which maintains the filamentous form of the entire body. Simple cell division of this sort does not effect reproduction of the entire body but merely increases its length.

The plant body is reproduced by a somewhat more involved program. Under certain conditions the entire protoplasm of a cell will shrink slightly away from the cell wall and divide several times. The result is anywhere from two to thirty-two tiny protoplasmic bodies, each being actually a small cell equipped with nucleus, chloroplast, and cytoplasm, but all contained within the confines of the old cell wall. After a time the cell wall breaks and these bodies are released into the water. Each one is pear-shaped and equipped at the more pointed end (anterior) with four long and extremely thin extensions of the protoplasm that are called *flagella.* At this stage the protoplasm is relatively "naked," lacking the cellulose wall which ordinarily surrounds plant cells and being held in shape merely by the "protoplasmic membrane," i.e., the stronger and less fluid outermost layer of the protoplasm itself. All cells of the filament commonly produce and discharge these bodies at about the same time, and the many filaments in the same vicinity act in the same way almost simultaneously.

The bodies that have been discharged are zoospores, the motile type of reproductive unit that appears in all THALLOPHYTA except a few of the lowest. The zoospores of *Ulothrix* swim about very actively for a time, being propelled by the lashing action of their flagella. At the same time, of course, they are usually being carried along in currents of water. At last they quiet down; their flagella rapidly disappear; and a few of the multitude of spores may chance to be lodged in situations that will permit them to produce new plants. The successful spore, still a naked bit of protoplasm, fits itself like a tiny drop of jelly into irregularities in some substratum at the bottom of the water and by this act establishes the holdfast cell.

The zoospore is now on its way to becoming a young plant. Equipped with a chloroplast, it commences food manufacture and has soon grown to the size which evokes cell division. From here on it is merely a story of continued growth and cell division until a full-sized filament results. By means of these spores *Ulothrix* may run through quite a number of generations in a single growing season.

It appears, then, that the spore can accomplish reproduction of the many-celled body where ordinary cell division fails to do so. But, beyond the matter of reproduction itself, or the simple bringing into existence of new individual bodies, there are two other functions that spores discharge.

The ultimate success of any species depends not merely upon how well its body may be adapted to the environment but also upon its reproductive efficiency. Of the many elements which enter into reproductive efficiency, a very obvious one is the reproductive ratio. In simple organisms, such as *Gloeocapsa* and *Protococcus*, the reproductive ratio is two, meaning that one parent individual gives rise to two offspring. Other things being equal, the more successful species will be the one with the higher reproductive ratio. The spore reproduction of *Ulothrix*, in which the scores or hundreds of cells of the many-celled body may yield several spores and each spore has the power of producing an entire many-celled body, provides a very high potential reproductive ratio. The actual reproductive ratio will depend, of course, upon how many of the spores succeed.

Another function of the spore is that of distributing the species. Those species which have made the most successful conquest of the earth's surface are those which have had effective means of scattering themselves to new locations. In many plants the spore is practically the only agency that can bring about this result. The better to insure it, spores of *Ulothrix* and of most other water forms are equipped with flagella which scatter them through the medium even in the absence of water currents.

Spores, however, are not the only means of reproduction in *Ulothrix*. Conditions which exist toward the end of the normal growing season are apparently responsible for stimulating the vegetative cells to a new activity. As in zoospore formation, the protoplasm withdraws from the wall and starts to divide. In this case, however, a greater number of divisions occurs, so that the final product is likely to be sixty-four or more tiny protoplasmic bodies within the old cell wall. Here, too, each of these products is a complete cell, with its nucleus, cytoplasm, and a tiny bit of chloroplast. As before, these bodies are discharged with the breaking of the cell wall; as before, they are equipped with flagella (two, in this case); and, as before, they swim around quite aimlessly for a time. It appears, however, that these tiny bodies are incapable of producing new filaments by their own independent action. Only through another type of action can they be instrumental in bringing about reproduction. With such a great swarm of these bodies swimming at random in the same small region, it is inevitable that occasionally two will collide. Though many of these collisions come to naught, there are some that bring a startling result, the two tiny cells fusing together to form one.

This is clearly a sex act, here revealed in what is probably its most primitive form. The fusing bodies are called **gametes** and the fusion product a **zygote.**

The flagella of the gametes have disappeared in connection with the fusion, so that the zygote soon settles down and lodges at the bottom of the water. Surrounding itself with a heavy, protective wall, the zygote passes into a period of dormancy. In this condition it usually lasts through winter, to be awakened by the more favorable conditions which arrive in spring. At that time the zygote divides internally to form four zoospores, which escape through the broken zygote wall and are capable of producing new filaments by their own independent action.

A consideration of such forms as *Ulothrix*, in which the gametes are similar (rather than differentiated into male and female gametes), comparatively simple, and apparently little more than small editions of the zoospores, has suggested that sexual reproduction originated from spore reproduction. It would appear that the first sex acts ever to occur were nothing more than purely accidental fusions on the part of undersized spores. There is nothing unprecedented in such a view, since most biologists trace back the origin of all the structures and modes of behavior of higher organisms to "happy accidents" in the first instance.

The accident which brings a benefit to the species is usually perpetuated by inheritance. So we must conclude that some benefit resulted from sex. An exact understanding of the function of sex demands a knowledge of the machinery of heredity. Even without such knowledge, however, one can catch the general import of the following considerations. For evolution to occur there must be variation in the population; i.e., some individuals must possess hereditary characteristics different from the rest. The amount or rate of evolution will depend, among other things, upon the amount of variation that occurs. Sex is conducive to a greater amount of variation than would otherwise occur, since sex is the only form of reproduction that can combine hereditary characteristics from two different parents and thus open the way to a series of new combinations of characters in the individuals of the following generations. Thus the advantage of sex is in encouraging evolution and in this way favoring the production of species that are better adapted to their environments. One can see from this that the real benefit of sex is realized only when the two gametes come from parents of a somewhat different hereditary constitution. Even in *Ulothrix* this is at least a possibility, since many *Ulothrix* filaments are ordinarily releasing gametes into the water at the same time; and one recent investigator claims to have demonstrated that the only successful fusions are those of gametes from different filaments.

Practically all the green algae include some form of sex among their methods of reproduction. Many of them are like *Ulothrix* in having similar gametes (isogamous), but more of them have taken a further evolutionary step and possess gametes of two distinct types (heterogamous), male and female. This may be illustrated by a fairly common form known as *Oedogonium* (Fig. 41).

Oedogonium, like the majority of green algae, has a simple filamentous body that is anchored to the substratum by a holdfast cell, but it is usually found growing in quieter water than is *Ulothrix*. The vegetative cell is longer and the chloroplast of a more irregular shape, but the more significant differences lie in the reproductive structures. Under certain conditions one or more cells of the filament will each discharge a single large zoospore, pear-shaped and equipped near the more pointed end with many cilia in a crownlike arrangement. In its behavior, however, this swimming spore is like the smaller and structurally simpler zoospores that we see in *Ulothrix.*

It is in connection with the gametes that we see a pronounced change. Under conditions favoring gamete production, an occasional vegetative cell in the filament will enlarge, bulging outward and becoming more spherical than its neighbors. This is no more than

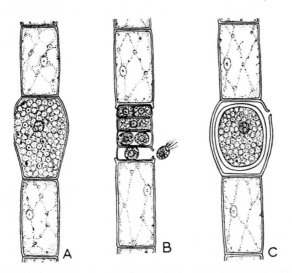

Fig. 41.—*Oedogonium.* *A*, portion of filament containing unfertilized egg; *B*, production and discharge of sperm; *C*, a zygote with its newly formed, heavy wall. Note aperture in original wall through which sperm entered.

the superficial consequence of a transfer of some of the nutritive materials from neighboring cells to the cell in question. The result is a very large gamete, well filled with food but with no power of motility. This large passive gamete is the female gamete, or egg, and is contained within the specialized **oögonium.**

Elsewhere in the same filament, male gametes are being formed at the same time. In this case a vegetative cell will divide into a series of smaller cells separated by walls. Each of these smaller cells, now termed an **antheridium,** then divides internally to form two small, active gametes, the male gametes or sperm. When the retaining walls break, the sperm, structurally small replicas of the spores of the same species, swim actively and, for a time, at random. Some of them, however, are soon directed in their swimming by a chemical that is exuded from a neighboring egg. As a result of this guidance, they swim toward a small aperture in the oögonium which retains the egg, and through this the first sperm to arrive makes its entry. The ensuing fusion of sperm and egg, often referred to as the act of fertilization, produces a zygote. Almost instantaneously the protoplasmic membrane (not the wall) around the egg changes in such manner as to prohibit the entrance of any sperm that might arrive subsequently.

The *Oedogonium* filament, which now carries, here and there along its length, several fertilized eggs or zygotes, is destined soon to disintegrate, releasing the zygotes from their previous confinement. By this time, however, each zygote has laid down around itself the heavy wall which is to provide protection during the ensuing period of dormancy. The rest of the story duplicates that of *Ulothrix.*

Ulothrix possesses similar or undifferentiated gametes. With the differentiation of gametes *Oedogonium* has made a significant evolutionary advance, for this same distinction between large passive egg and small active sperm is preserved among all higher forms. The biological value (i.e., value to species) of differentiation of gametes is readily seen. Whether or not an individual is to survive depends in large part upon what sort of a start it makes, for it is the period of infancy that is the most defenseless, the most susceptible to adverse environmental influences. *Oedogonium*, through the food that is stored in the egg, furnishes its young with a greater nutritive capital than does *Ulothrix*. In this way they are, in effect, "fed by the parent" until they have had ample opportunity to establish themselves. So the differentiation of gametes is an improved provision for the young. Further steps in this same general direction are taken by still higher plants, while the same evolutionary trend appears even more impressively as we pass from the lower to the higher members of the animal kingdom.

With the differentiation of gametes there is established a reproductive program in which it might appear that the maternal parent contributes a great deal more to the offspring than does the paternal parent. This is true in only a limited sense. The female parent does indeed contribute more nutrition than does the male, and nutrition is highly important in deciding whether the young will survive the early critical period of life. But this nutrition has no more effect in deciding the specific and varietal characteristics of the organism than does the soil in which a plant grows. The physical basis for the truly hereditary characters lies in the nucleus. In any case of differentiation of gametes the difference is in the cytoplasm, while the nuclei of egg and sperm are of the same magnitude and importance. Experiments in heredity have amply demonstrated that (with negligible exceptions) male and female parents contribute equally to the hereditary constitution of their young.

Vegetatively, the green algae made little evolutionary progress. In some the body is merely a single cell, stationary as in *Protococcus;* more often it is free-moving in the water by means of cilia, as in *Chlamydomonas.* Most commonly, however, the body is a filament, one-celled in caliber. This filament may be unbranched, as in *Ulothrix* and *Oedogonium,* or may be divided into a series of filamentous branches, as in *Cladophora* (Fig. 42). A very few have platelike bodies in which a single layer (occasionally a double layer) of cells is spread out in two dimensions, as in the marine form, sea lettuce (Fig. 43).

In reproductive devices the group made more progress. Already we have noted that the green algae added to the vegetative multiplication, which they must have inherited from their ancestors, the new methods of spore reproduction and sexual reproduction which were to mean so much to their descendants. In addition they introduced the differentiation of gametes, a further step in the advancement of sexual reproduction. Beyond this, two more refinements in the program of sexual reproduction are added by some of the higher green algae.

The term "sex organ" is applied to any container of gametes. Among thallophytes the simple structure which contains the egg is technically referred to as the oögonium and that which contains the sperm as the antheridium. In a form like *Oedogonium* the sex organs appear at random along the filament, being nothing but transformed vegetative cells.

The other refinement consists of the "differentiation of sexual individuals." As has been pointed out before, sex brings an advantage to the species only when the two gametes have been derived from bodies which differ somewhat in their hereditary characteristics.

It is not surprising, therefore, to find that nature is full of devices which favor and in some cases insure cross-fertilization. One guaranteed method is that of sexual differentiation of individuals. If one plant can produce only sperm and another plant can produce only eggs, any fertilization that occurs will be cross-fertilization.

Best known of all the green algae is the picturesque *Spirogyra* (Fig. 44)—picturesque not for its habitat, which is stagnant water, but for its unique chloroplasts, which are coiled like green ribbons

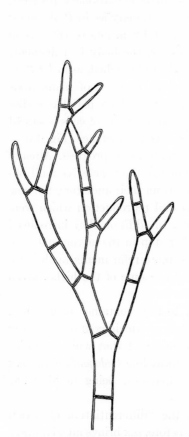

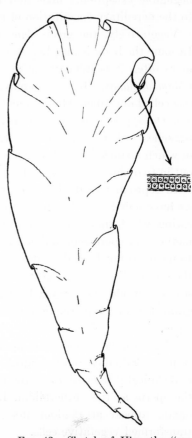

FIG. 42.—Outline sketch of the common green alga *Cladophora* as an example of the branching filament.

FIG. 43.—Sketch of *Ulva*, the "sea lettuce," rather commonly found washed up on the New England coast. The enlarged fragment, shown in section, reveals the two-layered condition of the body.

within the walls of the cylindrical cells that make up the filament. *Spirogyra* produces no spores but relies upon sex for its reproduction. Among the more common species of this genus, male and female filaments exist. Indistinguishable in the vegetative state, the two filaments reveal their sexes when they chance to float side by side. Under those circumstances tubes grow out from the cells of each filament—tubes which join at their tips so that the two filaments are now connected all along their length in a ladder-like arrangement.

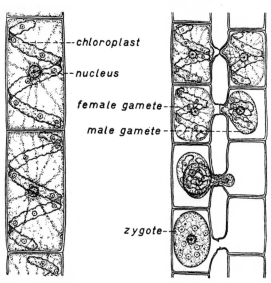

Fig. 44.—*Spirogyra. On the left,* an enlarged portion of the vegetative filament, showing the striking ribbon-like chloroplasts. (Some species of *Spirogyra* contain within each cell several of these chloroplasts in parallel, spiral arrangement.) *On the right,* conjugation of male and female filaments, with the successive stages in the process shown in sequence from top to bottom.

After a time the adjoining end walls of the tubes are dissolved away, creating passageways which lead from each cell of one filament to the neighboring cell of the other. At this stage the entire protoplasm of each cell—spiral chloroplasts and all—pulls away from its wall and rounds up. The two sexes can be distinguished not by size but only by their activity. All the rounded protoplasts of the female filament remain quiescent, while those of the male filament force themselves through the narrow connecting tubes to fuse with the female gametes on the other side.

Spirogyra provides merely one example of the sexual differentiation of individuals, which appears, as well, in some of the species of *Oedogonium* and in still other green algae. It appears regularly in an interesting group known as the "desmids." Desmids are beautiful little single-celled plants that occur in an amazing variety of sizes and shapes. In every one, however, the cell is organized into two perfectly symmetrical halves, each half with its chloroplast and the nucleus in a position midway between the two. Desmids reproduce by cell division or by a sexual fusion. Two individuals, coming to lie side by side, produce a single zygote through a fusion of the contents of the two cells.

So far we have discussed only the blue-greens and members of the green algae. Before looking at any additional members of the THALLOPHYTA, we would do well to pause and consider the matter of the evolutionary transition from one-celled to many-celled bodies. Mere increase in size of an organism (or of an institution) is not a truly progressive step. Progress results only insofar as the many-celled body can accomplish certain things that the one-celled body fails to accomplish, or can discharge certain functions more efficiently. To a limited extent this may be true even when all the cells of the many-celled body are alike. (We shall consider an example of this in the chapter on the acquisition of the land habit.) For the most part, however, the advantage of the many-celled condition lies in the fact that it opens up the possibility of specialization on a new level. If one cell, or preferably a whole "tissue" of cells, is specialized to discharge a certain function (and if many such cells or cell groups are co-ordinated in their activity), the body as a whole may constitute a more efficient working unit than does the one-celled body.

The higher algae must have become many-celled ages ago, but apparently they never made much of the possibilities of the many-celled body. Some advantage is derived from a specialized holdfast at the bottom of the filamentous body, for in this way algae can maintain themselves in a range of habitats that would otherwise be impossible. Some advantage is gained in combining food that is derived from several cells into the large egg of *Oedogonium*, for in this way the young are given a better start in life. Some advantages, too, are derived from the somewhat more complex body organization that we shall see among brown algae. It was not until much later in evolutionary history, however—not until life had emerged from the water and started to spread over the land surface—that plants really capitalized upon the possibilities of the many-celled body.

Man, who is forever classifying things, finds it convenient to put living organisms into the two great categories of one-celled individuals and many-celled individuals. No doubt such a treatment is convenient, but at the same time it is in danger of being misleading. It seems to suggest that the delimitation of the two categories is sharp, corresponding to a sudden, radical evolutionary change that occurred in the past; and this is far from the truth. If we look, on the one hand, at the simple one-celled body of *Gloeocapsa* and, on the other hand, at a human being with his several billion cells, highly interdependent but co-ordinated into the single functional unit which provides our best example of "individuality," we may well be impressed with the profound difference between one-celled and many-celled organisms. These, however, are the extremes; and, if we give our attention to some of the intermediate cases, we find great difficulty in determining just where the condition of the one-celled individual leaves off and the condition of the many-celled individual begins. For actually there is no sharp delimitation of the two great categories in nature, and such evolutionary change along these lines as has occurred in the past must have occurred very gradually indeed.

There is no plant in existence that possesses anything like the full development of individuality that appears in man or in any of the higher animals. At their very best, many-celled plants are but feebly individualized. Even so, such a thing as an oak tree can, with justification, be referred to as a many-celled individual; for its numerous cells are living an interdependent life, and each one is playing a role in the economy of the larger organization. Between this condition and that of *Gloeocapsa* there are many transitional levels.

The mere fact that the cells of *Gloeocapsa* or the cells of *Protococcus* are usually found growing in groups is not enough to qualify them in our minds as many-celled individuals. The group does not act as a unit, and there is no evidence of interdependence on the part of the component cells. We say, therefore, that such a group is merely a "colony" of single-celled individuals. Then what of *Ulothrix* and of *Oedogonium?* In the botanical literature these forms are referred to in both ways, both as colonies of single-celled individuals and as many-celled individuals. The writers prefer to think of them as colonies of single-celled individuals that have taken a few small steps in the direction of the many-celled individual, for such a diagnosis helps to keep alive the undoubted fact that in nature the transition has been a gradual one. The higher algae have taken further steps in the same general direction, but there is not a single alga and not a single thallophyte that has achieved any very convincing many-celled individuality.

Phylum Phaeophyta. The brown algae owe their name to the presence of a brown pigment, *fucoxanthin,* which partially masks the chlorophyll and carotinoid pigments. As a result, these algae vary in color from olive-green to a rather deep shade of brown. With very few exceptions these brown algae live in the oceans and seas throughout the world. Many of them live in the intertidal zones, freely exposed to the atmosphere at low tide but often covered by several feet of water when the tide is in. Species of this type are usually rock-weeds since they grow attached to rocks. Others grow much farther out from shore and have long stripes which enable the leaflike thalli to float on the surface while their large holdfasts anchor them to the bottom. There are about 190 genera of brown algae with about 900 species. Most of these algae thrive in cool water; hence we encounter the greatest abundance of them along the northern stretches of both our Atlantic and Pacific coasts. *Sargassum,* however, is a rather unorthodox genus. Popularly spoken of as "gulfweed," it is commonly found free-floating on the surface of the warmer waters in and near the Gulf of Mexico. Here it forms extensive tangled mats of vegetation, which are said to have been quite a menace to the old sailing vessels, as recorded in the experiences of the Ancient Mariner and of Christopher Columbus.

In published accounts one can find amazing reports of the size attained by some of the larger brown algae, lengths of up to 1,500 feet being cited. Most of these reports can be traced back to the stories of the old sea captains and other travelers who have always had a weakness for impressing the stay-at-homes with descriptions of monsters of the deep. Reliable records place the maximum length at about 150 feet, but even this is a rather impressive figure, especially when compared with the body size of the other algal groups.

No single-celled brown algae are known. At its simplest the body is a branched filament, one cell in caliber, which in size and contour is similar to the body of many green algae. The majority, however, are much larger and coarser than this, many-celled in caliber, and with a certain amount of differentiation of body tissues (Fig. 45). Usually there is a strong, many-celled holdfast at the base, by means of which the alga is anchored in comparatively shallow water along rocky stretches of the seacoast. The rest of the body may fall into any one of a great many patterns. Stretching upward from the holdfast is a tough, leathery stalk of a length suitable to carry the upper portions of the body near to the surface of the water. These upper portions are more or less broken up into flat blades, which stretch out horizontally near the water surface and conduct most of the food manufacture. To maintain this position they may be assisted by one or more "air bladders" or "floats." Those forms which are best equipped with long, ropelike stalks and floats can keep their blades in the surface position at both high and low tides. Those which lack this flexibility may be deeply submerged at high tide. The whole body is of an exceedingly tough consistency, adapted to resist the pounding of the waves—an adaptation that frequently fails, as testified by the great numbers of "seaweeds" cast up on the shore after a storm. These larger brown algae are known as "kelps," and they are of considerable economic importance.

When it comes to reproduction, we find that most of the brown algae employ the ciliated swimming spore, similar in function to that of the green algae but different in structural detail. In addition, most of them imitate *Ulothrix* with a sex program which involves similar, swimming gametes. As in the green algae, however, one could arrange quite an impressive series of brown algal types to show a steady increase in size and loss of motility by the female gamete. This culminates in forms like *Fucus*, the most common of the rockweeds of our New England coast, in which the discrepancy in size between the two gametes surpasses anything found among green algae. *Fucus* has the additional peculiarity of discharging its enormous, non-motile eggs into the water. The *Fucus* egg, bombarded by a halo-like swarm of diminutive sperm and set into rotation thereby, is a very impressive sight under the microscope (Fig. 46).

Ectocarpus is a simple marine alga which grows in tufts attached to rocks (Fig. 47). The thallus consists of a main filament from

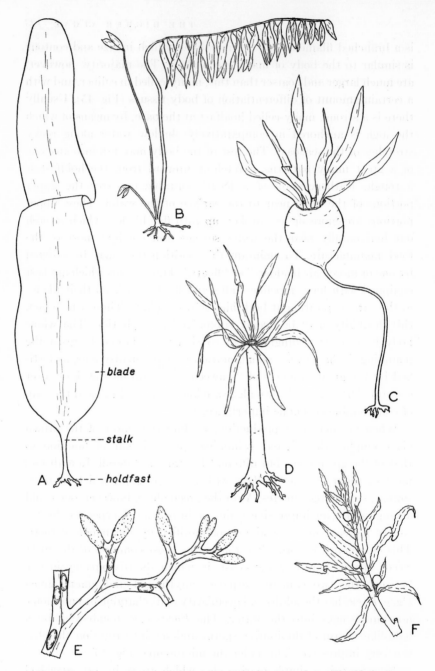

Fig. 45.—An assortment of the coarse-bodied brown algae. The "kelps" are represented by *A, Laminaria; B, Macrocystis; C, Nereocystis;* and *D, Postelsia* ("sea palm"). *E,* a rockweed, *Fucus; F,* the "gulfweed" *Sargassum.*

which develop many branches. All the individual cells are uninucleate and contain a number of small discoid plastids. The life cycle of *Ectocarpus* is somewhat more complicated than that of the forms we have considered thus far, although *Ulva* in the green algae has a similar arrangement. Two types of plants are produced in *Ectocarpus;* both are alike vegetatively, but each produces its own type of reproductive organs. The sexual plant produces a number of multicellular elongated organs called **gametangia.** Each cell in the gametangia gives rise to a biflagellated gamete. These isogametes escape from the gametangia, swim about in the water for a time, then fuse in pairs to produce zygotes. The zygote, upon germination, produces the asexual plant, which forms on its branches two types of sporangia. One type, and by far the most common, is a **plurilocular zoosporangium,** which closely resembles the gametangium of the sexual plants. This type of sporangium produces zoospores which will germinate directly into new asexual plants. The second type of sporangium is unicellular, oval in outline, and is called a **unilocular zoosporangium.** Zoospores produced in this sporangium have the reduced number of chromosomes, following a reduction division at their origin in the sporangium, and consequently, are **haploid.** These zoospores germinate into the sexual plants, which consequently are also haploid.

Fig. 46.—*Fucus* egg and sperm. (The actual size difference between the two gametes is greater than indicated in the illustration.)

The asexual plant is diploid, which completes for us a life cycle. The two types of plants produced here thus form an alternation of generations. The sexual plant is called the **gametophyte** since it produces gametes; the asexual plant is the **sporophyte** since it produces spores. Parts or organs of the gametophyte cycle are always haploid, while those of the sporophyte are always diploid. Reduction division marks the beginning of the gametophyte generation, which, as we shall see, usually begins with the formation of the gametes; but in *Ectocarpus,* as in many other thallophytes, reduction division may occur in the formation of certain spores or even in the germination of the zygote. The sporophyte in all higher plants, and in most members of the THALLOPHYTA, begins with the fusion of the haploid gametes to form the diploid zygote.

The kelps have a similar alternation of generations, except that the gametophytic plant is very small, often consisting of but a few cells. Generally the sexual organs are produced on separate plants.

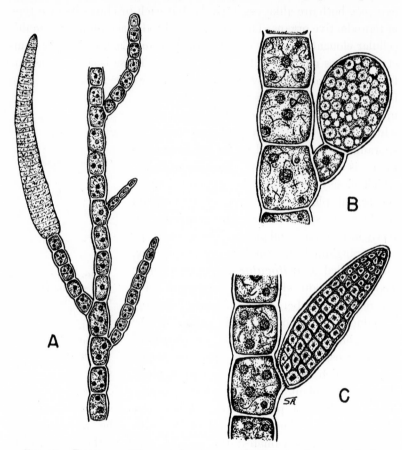

FIG. 47.—*Ectocarpus*. Filament showing reproductive structures. *A*, plurilocular zoosporangium; *B*, unilocular zoosporangium; *C*, gametangium.

The male plants bear antheridia which produce one biflagellated sperm apiece, while the female plants produce oögonia which bear one egg in each. After fertilization the zygote germinates to produce the sporophytic plant. The latter is the one we commonly associate with brown algae because of its immense size. The leaflike thalli bear patches of zoosporangia which produce thousands of zoospores, and they in turn germinate into the male and female plants.

The relationships of the group are still rather obscure. There is a general impression among botanists that they have been derived from the green algae. Along with this hypothesis goes the notion that life may have originated in fresh water and that salt-water habitats were invaded later by some lines of descent. It is quite possible, however, that both brown and green algae were derived long ago from some common ancestral stock, with parallel lines of development that has since become extinct. Some of the brown algae do indeed resemble the greens in more ways than one, but the same forms include little structural peculiarities which differ rather sharply from the corresponding features of green algae. Some of the browns are close to the primitive vascular plants in vegetative organization, but the sex organs lack the protective layer of cells characteristic of the higher groups.

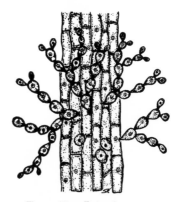

Fig. 48.—*Batrachospermum.* Short section of filament showing dwarf branches.

Phylum Rhodophyta. The red algae comprise a much-varied group containing some 400 genera and over 2,500 species. They are almost entirely marine, although a few species are found thriving in inland fresh-water streams far removed from the oceans. Most of them live in warmer water, such as around islands of the South Pacific, off the coast of southern California and southward. The dominant pigment is usually **phycoerythrin,** which is red, although the blue pigment, **phycocyanin,** commonly associated with the blue-green algae, is also often present. Chlorophyll is of course present, but it is generally masked by the red pigment. Most of the Rhodophyta are reddish-purple in color, but a few are olive-green—such as *Batrachospermum*, a genus occasionally found in fresh water (Fig. 48).

Red algae are much smaller than the kelps, seldom exceeding three feet in length, but their vegetative body is often beautifully shaped (Fig. 49). They may have flat, leaflike thalli, much-branched feathery filaments, or coarse, stemlike bodies. Most of them are multicellular, but a few unicellular algae have been placed in this phylum. Since the body is usually rather delicate, the red algae are poorly adapted to the turbulent habitat of the brown algae. Instead, we find most of the reds living at quite a depth, some as much as 300 feet beneath the surface, where waters are quiet and where the more serious problem is to obtain enough sunlight for food manufacture.

The reproductive structures of many of the red algae reach a

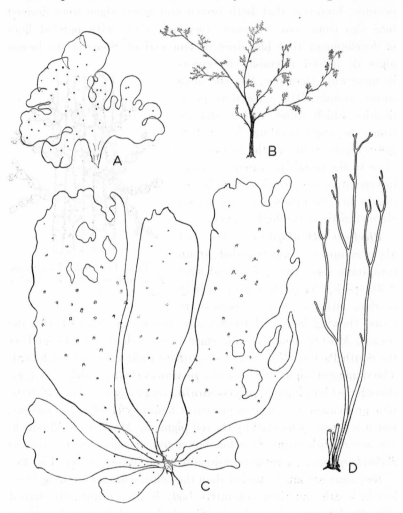

Fig. 49.—An assortment of red algae. *A, Pugetia; B, Polysiphonia; C, Gigartina; D, Nemalion.*

complexity surpassing that of any of the other groups. The group as a whole is characterized by the absence of any flagellated reproductive cells, either sexual or asexual. Consequently, the gametes and spores are quite at the mercy of water currents.

In *Nemalion*, one of the simplest red algae, the thallus is a much-

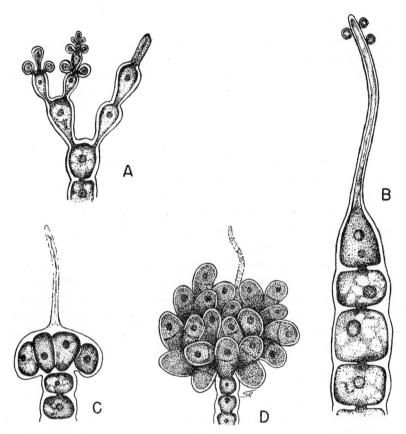

Fig. 50.—*Nemalion*. *A*, young male branch, with antherids near tip; *B*, young female branch with swollen carpogonium and elongated trichogyne, to which three sperm are attached; *C*, cystocarp beginning to develop, trichogyne gradually disappearing; *D*, matured cystocarp with carpospores formed.

branched filament bearing numerous tiny antheridia, each of which produces a single sperm, and a female sexual apparatus called the **procarp** (Fig. 50). The procarp consists of an enlarged basal portion, known as the **carpogonium,** which bears an elongated terminal hair, the *trichogyne.* Sperm are carried by the currents to the trichogyne; they adhere to its surface and discharge their contents into it. The nucleus descends to the carpogonium, where it fuses with the nucleus of the egg to form the zygote. The resulting zygote passes into a long program of cell divisions, including a reduction division, which yields a mass of short filaments. At the tips of the filaments tiny spores, known as *carpospores,* are produced. This entire structure, consisting of carpogonium, filaments, and carpospores, is known collectively as the *cystocarp,* and in *Nemalion* it is a very loosely organized mass.

Polysiphonia has a more complicated life cycle and is more typical of the higher reds. The general pattern of the life cycle is the same as that of *Nemalion,* but there are three separate plants: (1) a male plant, producing antheridia; (2) a female plant, producing procarps; (3) an asexual plant, producing sporangia, in each of which spores are produced in clusters of four called *tetraspores.* In general the structures are somewhat more complex. The thallus consists of a central core surrounded by a jacket of filaments, from which it gets its name *Polysiphonia.* The procarp contains a group of auxiliary cells which help to make the cystocarp a more distinct and well-formed structure than in *Nemalion.*

Finally, we see that the life cycle of *Polysiphonia* consists of three phases. One phase consists of the haploid plants with their sex organs; a second phase begins with the diploid zygote and continues through the formation of the diploid carpospores in the cystocarp; and the third phase consists of the asexual plant, which is diploid, producing the haploid tetraspores by reduction division.

RELATIONSHIPS

The red algae are a specialized group unique among the algae in a number of ways. The absence of flagella places them apart from every other algal group except the blue-greens; furthermore, some of the red algae possess the blue pigment phycocyanin, while some of the blue-green algae have a red pigment similar to phycoerythrin, found in the blue-greens. It is possible that the red algae arose from some type of blue-green ancestor; it is also possible that both groups came from some non-flagellated common ancestor. In any event, the red algae developed their own system of sexual reproduction, quite different in the structure of the organs and cells from those in the greens and browns and certainly much beyond that found in the blue-greens, since the latter have no type of gametes or sexual reproduction.

The characteristic sex organs of the reds have a striking similarity to those found in some of the fungi, particularly to those of the Ascomycetes. For this reason some phylogenists are of the opinion that the red algae may have given rise to some of the higher fungi by becoming saprophytes or parasites with the accompanying loss of chlorophyll. This is the opinion often expressed by those who have studied red algae taken from the deeper recesses of the ocean, where light is at a minimum and where the stimulus to take over another type of existence seems to be present.

ECONOMIC IMPORTANCE OF ALGAE

Seldom do we think of algae as plants of great economic importance, and yet the products obtained from them are almost as varied as is their morphology. Furthermore, the potential they offer, in their world-wide distribution and speed of growth, assures us that they will be of even greater importance in the future. Sometimes their importance is negative; that is, we must place the result of their growth on the debit side of the ledger—blue-greens, particularly, fall into this category. They may grow in such numbers in ponds and lakes as to use up the oxygen in the water, causing the death of thousands of fish. This means loss not only in revenue from the fish but also in fishing licenses, equipment, and recreational pursuits. The oil stored by the blue-greens decomposes after death of the plants, resulting in a "fish odor" or "marsh odor" which soon drives vacationists from the lakes back to the cities. We have previously discussed a similar effect created by the "red tide," when certain dinoflagellates increase to prodigious numbers in our southern coastal waters.

Most of the green algae that provide food for fishes are unicellular, but many of the filamentous species provide protective cover for protozoans, crustaceans, and small fishes. It has been reported that *Oedogonium* and *Spirogyra* are dried, put up in small packets, and sold on the market in India to be made into soup. Some of the marine greens, such as sea lettuce, are cooked with fish in Hawaii, Japan, and other Asiatic countries.

Studies which have been made of inland lakes in the United States emphasize the food prospects of algae. In the 200,000 acres of inland waters of Ohio there are about 100,000,000 pounds of algae grown annually. If these algae were regularly harvested to provide greater turnover, the total amount would be much more. Most of these algae are free-floating forms growing as plankton and used by fish either directly or indirectly as food. It has been shown that fertilization of the waters with nitrates and phosphates greatly increases algal production. One Iowa farmer raised fish in a pond located on his farm and harvested 333 pounds of fish per acre. Compare this figure to hogs raised from corn grown on the rich Iowa soil. In the corn-hog program a farmer produces about 240 pounds of pork per acre per year. It can readily be seen that ponds and lakes offer us great possibilities in food production.

FIG. 51.—*Chondrus crispus* ("Irish moss"). A small fragment of the algae separated from the usual compact cushion to show branching.

The tremendous importance of diatoms has been discussed under the Phylum Pyrrophyta. We might add that world production of diatomaceous earth is over 100,000 tons annually.

More red and brown algae are used for human food than any other groups of THALLOPHYTA. One red alga, "Irish moss" (*Chondrus crispus*), is the most important single seaweed in the United States (Fig. 51). It grows abundantly along the Atlantic coast from Maine to the Carolinas. Irish moss is used in making desserts such as puddings and jellies because of its high agar content. Of greater importance than food and drug products made in part from agar is its use in the preparation of bacteriological media. Agar is extracted mainly from red algae, on both our east and west coasts, by a process of bleaching, cleansing, freezing, and milling. The dried product is then made up as a gel in practically all bacteriological laboratories in the world. In China, Japan, and elsewhere agar is used as a thickener for soups, sauces, ice cream, and other desserts.

The large brown algae (kelps) are rich in some of the necessary elements used as soil fertilizers. From about 400,000 tons of fresh seaweeds collected annually in Europe about 175 tons of iodine, 10,000 tons of potassium salt, 3,000 tons of crude salt, and 7,000 tons of washing soda are extracted. Many farmers living in seaside areas use kelp, which they rake up at low tide, as fertilizer.

The iodine content of eggs and milk is increased by feeding marine algae to hens and cows. The stipe of *Nereocystis* is made up into an imitation citron which is called "seatron." In Hawaii seaweeds are wrapped around fish, shrimps, pigs, and dogs before roasting. Often you will find small chunks of seaweeds in various Chinese food dishes you may order at authentic Chinese restaurants.

X. *Plants without Chlorophyll*
Lower Forms

Subkingdom THALLOPHYTA
  Phylum SCHIZOMYCOPHYTA—bacteria and related forms
    Class Schizomycetes
    Class Actinomycetes
    Viruses
    Bacteriophages
  Phylum MYXOMYCOPHYTA—slime molds

The spread of mankind over the face of the earth has been made possible by the repeated establishment of pioneer communities in previously uninhabited regions. These pioneers have usually been hardy souls, capable of maintaining an independent existence, of wresting their livelihood directly from nature without the assistance of any human beings outside their own community. After these early settlers have established themselves successfully, and the local community has commenced a thrifty growth, men of a different stamp almost inevitably begin to appear. These newcomers proceed to support themselves not independently but dependently, not by exploiting nature directly but by exploiting their fellow men.

In most cases the newcomers are dependent individuals who have migrated to the pioneer settlement from older communities. In other cases they are of local origin, for a few of the pioneers themselves (or their descendants) may have changed to adopt dependent habits. In either event, the new, dependent individuals must have been derived from an ancestry which was at one time independent.

In the conquest of the earth by living organisms, the pioneers in any region were probably some form of green plants. For today we find that, save for a few types of bacteria, the only organisms that are able to live independently are the green, food-manufacturing plants. Their green pigment, chlorophyll, enables them to take energy from the sunlight and use it in manufacturing organic food from inorganic compounds that individually have no food value.

We have seen how the algae played the role of pioneers in the conquest of the various regions of the sea and of the fresh waters. Later we shall see how higher green plants, descendants of the algae, were pioneers in the conquest of the various regions of the dry land. On countless occasions the same general sequence of events must have occurred, involving the gradual establishment of a thrifty community of green plants in a previously uninhabited locality.

In each case, the first main act in the drama was followed with deadly certainty by the second. Given a new community of green plants, dependent organisms were certain to appear. These organisms, which did not manufacture their own food, by one device or another appropriated some of the food that had been manufactured by the green plants. Time after time, dependent organisms were evolved from independent ancestors and proceeded to prey upon their independent relatives. And in the course of time secondarily dependent organisms were evolved—organisms which preyed not directly upon their independent relatives but upon their dependent relatives. Today our organic world consists of a broad foundation of green plants supporting a towering superstructure of other organisms, some of which are only remotely, but nonetheless certainly, dependent on the food-manufacturing power of the green plants.

In the course of time, three great groups of dependent organisms have succeeded in establishing themselves. Each is today widely distributed over the earth, and each is represented by tens or hundreds of thousands of distinct species.

The most conspicuous of these groups consists of the **animal kingdom**. This vast assemblage of a million or more species is bound together by the common property of dependency. Animals work out their lives on the basis of an exploitation—and usually a direct exploitation—of other living organisms. The history of the animal kingdom has been characterized by a series of triumphs for those types most successful in this matter of exploitation. Man's own supremacy has depended upon his unusual success as an exploiter of other living things.

Another great dependent group is the **bacteria.** Judged by structural characteristics, these are relatives of the blue-green algae. In bacteria we find the same microscopic, one-celled bodies, with no clear differentiation of a nucleus and with simple cell division as the only method of reproduction. Again we find amazingly high resistance to extremes of conditions—in some bacteria even higher than in the best of the blue-green algae—and a corresponding ubiquity. The conspicuous difference lies in the absence of chlorophyll among the bacteria. (Recently a substance very similar to the chlorophyll a of higher plants has been identified in certain bacteria and has been given the name of bacteriochlorophyll.)

From these considerations one might well conclude that bacteria are dependent offshoots from the blue-green algal line and that here we had identified the earliest of all adventures in dependency. Such may, indeed, be the truth, but there is another interpretation which is, perhaps, equally plausible. Perhaps some still more primitive group, with independence of a different type, gave rise on the one hand to the green and independent blue-green algae, and on the other hand to the non-green and dependent bacteria.

Whatever their origin, the bacteria are today the real rivals of the animal kingdom. Man himself, at least in civilized communities, has firmly established his dominance over the rest of the plant and animal kingdoms; but the bacteria, while actually serving man's interests in many ways, continue to be a serious menace to his health and welfare.

A third great group of dependent organisms is the *fungi*. Although this group does not dominate the organic world to the same extent as do the animals and the bacteria, it is nonetheless a vast assemblage and one of great economic significance. This consideration, together with the prominent place occupied by fungi in the plant kingdom, justifies our devoting considerable space to them in the next chapter.

Most, but not all, of the known dependent organisms fall into these three groups—animals, heterotrophic bacteria, and fungi. In addition, dependency is exhibited by a few scattered members of the highest plant group, the seed plants.

Schizomycetes. Bacteria are regarded as plants by biologists, largely because of their apparent similarity to the blue-green algae.

These similarities include: (1) rigid cell wall, (2) ability to obtain food in a soluble form, (3) multiplication by simple transverse binary fission, and (4) capability of food synthesis. Occasionally uninformed individuals classify bacteria as animals because most of them derive their food from the tissues of other living organisms and are therefore parasites, or because some may obtain food from non-living organic matter and live as saprophytes. Actually bacteria more closely resemble fungi in their habits of growth and preference of environment, but other characteristics are sufficiently different to place them in a separate phylum. If, as some biologists do, we divide the entire organic world into three great groups—the plant kingdom, the animal kingdom, and the fungus kingdom—bacteria would certainly fall in the last group. But if we are more conservative and consider all organisms as either plants or animals, we must classify bacteria as plants.

Like the blue-green algae, bacteria may be unicellular, and many of them tend to form colonies—most commonly filamentous colonies. Like the blue-green algae, they all possess a rather generalized protoplasm, with no clean-cut differentiation of cell organelles. Many, but by no means all, are able to swim through a liquid medium with the assistance of minute flagella. As in the blue-green algae, the only method of reproduction is by simple cell division. In rate of reproduction, however, many of them excel the best of the blue-greens. Under favorable conditions some bacteria may grow to full size and divide every twenty minutes, and it is largely this feature that accounts for the appearance of serious and large-scale symptoms in a host that has been infected a few days or a few hours before. One organism, *Escherichia coli*, which inhabits our large intestine, could produce about 5 (with 21 zeros after it) offspring in a twenty-four hour period. This number would weigh about 1,000 tons. Obviously such a rate of reproduction is only theoretically possible, because the accumulation of waste products and lack of readily available food prevent such rapid multiplication.

Bacteria are the smallest known living organisms, if we exclude the filterable viruses, whose nature is still uncertain. Decidedly smaller even than the blue-green algae, they range in size down to the limits of visibility under our best microscopes. Roughly speaking, an average-sized bacterium would be about 1/25,000 of an inch in its shortest dimension and two or more times that in its longest.

In cell shape there is more variation than among the usually spherical blue-greens. Spherical bacteria are spoken of as "coccus" forms, rod-shaped bacteria as "bacillus" forms, and curved or corkscrew-shaped bacteria as "spirillum" forms (Fig. 52). Thousands of species are known; their classification takes cognizance not only of shape, size, and the types of colonies formed but also of their staining characteristics and of the reactions produced in non-living nutritive media and in living hosts.

Bacteria are, in general, even more resistant to extremes of conditions than are the blue-greens. Even in their active vegetative state, many of them are able to withstand degrees of heat, cold, and acidity that are fatal to most organisms. Beyond this, there are some of the rod-shaped forms that can strikingly increase their powers of resist-

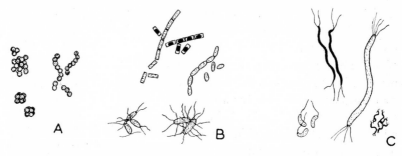

Fig. 52.—An assortment of bacteria. *A*, coccus forms. *B*, bacillus forms; "spore" formation is exhibited by one of these specimens. *C*, spirillum forms.

ance by forming spores. The term "spore," as used by the bacteriologist, is not an agent of reproduction but merely a dormant condition of the ordinary cell. In spore formation the protoplasm rounds up more compactly than before and usually surrounds itself with a thick wall, within which it may remain dormant but viable for a prodigious length of time (see Fig. 52, *B*). In this state some bacteria have been known to withstand extreme dryness for many years, only to reawaken and return to the active vegetative state when conditions of moisture and warmth were provided. Many bacteria will resist long freezing in ice, and this includes the typhoid bacillus. At the other extreme are some which, as spores, will resist boiling for several hours. Complete sterilization, therefore, demands boiling under pressure or the thoroughgoing application of strong germicidal fluids to every spot in which bacteria might be lurking. The strength of the germicide required to kill bacteria in their spore forms is often more than ten times that needed to kill them in their ordinary vegetative phase.

It is a very fortunate thing for man that most of the bacteria responsible for his more serious diseases are incapable of forming spores. Were this not the case, the continuous warfare that has been going on between man and the bacteria might well have ended long ago in overwhelming victory for the latter.

In view of these record-breaking powers of resistance, it is not surprising that bacteria also hold the record for wide distribution. All ordinary soils are teeming with bacteria, particularly those upper layers of the soil that are rich in organic matter. Natural streams and sea water contain many; small lakes, ponds, and puddles contain many more. The number of bacteria present in every drop of water at popular bathing beaches is shockingly high. The air is full of them. In the comparatively pure air of the mountain tops they are quite rare, but in the air of crowded cities the bacterial population is enormous. This appears to be due in part to the fact that bacteria "ride the dust particles" in most of their sustained journeys through the air.

Bacteria are almost always present on and in the bodies of other organisms. Man is no exception. On his skin, in his mouth, and particularly throughout the lower stretches of his alimentary tract, he harbors millions of bacteria. Most varieties of these intimate companions of man are not at all harmful under ordinary circumstances, but many become so when there is any serious upset in the structural and functional defenses with which nature has provided man's body.

Earlier, in citing differences between bacteria and the blue-green algae, we mentioned the absence of chlorophyll which results in most of the bacteria being dependent organisms. Among these are the *sulfur bacteria,* which inhabit waters and soils high in sulfur compounds. They oxidize hydrogen sulfide to free sulfur, then sulfuric acid—thereby obtaining energy which they utilize in synthesizing organic compounds from carbon dioxide and other inorganic substances. Iron bacteria oxidize ferrous compounds in a similar manner from the iron-bearing waters in which they live. Organisms—in this case bacteria—capable of synthesizing their own food are classified as *autotrophic;* those which are dependent on other organisms for their food are *heterotrophic.*

On the basis of both structure and physiology, the autotrophic bacteria appear to be the simplest of living things, but whether they represent an approximation of the original ancestral condition or the product of retrogressive evolution remains an open question. The vast majority of bacteria are heterotrophic, and the exploitations of some of them are such as to carry them into the field of man's interests.

A good many bacteria parasitize both plants and animals, including man's cultivated plants, man's domesticated animals, and man himself. Infection of a host depends upon the kind of bacteria and the kind of host, and upon whether the existing conditions favor the defenses of the host or the penetrating power of the bacteria. Some bacteria enter man's body through tiny scratches in his skin that he has not taken the trouble to disinfect, some through his alimentary tract, some through his respiratory tract. Even when they have entered, the bacterial hordes are, more often than not, defeated by the various defense mechanisms with which man's body is provided. But there are many humans in which the defenses against certain bacteria are either permanently or temporarily weak. In these cases the bacteria gain a foothold, with ultimate consequences that are more or less serious.

It is not through a simple devouring of tissues that bacteria work their greatest havoc. It is more through the poisons that they liberate as a by-product of their own life processes. When the poisons are in significant concentration only in the immediate locality occupied by bacteria, an abscess or local destruction of host tissues results. Other bacteria release powerful poisons into man's circulatory system. The results are fever and weakening of the host at many points. Further description of the nature of bacterial disease is obviously beyond the scope of this small book on plants.

In addition to this destructive attack upon the body of man himself and upon those other organisms in which he is interested, bacteria (together with some of the fungi) are responsible for the spoilage of his foods. It is a far-reaching principle of chemistry that the rate of a reaction increases with an increase in temperature. Since life processes are in large part merely chemical reactions, it follows that the rate of the life processes will increase with an increase in temperature. At low temperatures bacteria may continue to live, but they grow and reproduce slowly if at all. Store the foods in a warm place and bacterial spoilage will proceed apace. Store them in refrigerators and the spoilage may be so slow as to be negligible.

It is another principle of chemistry that the rate of many reactions is strikingly expedited by putting the reacting substances into solution. The most generally effective solvent is water, and it is the medium to which protoplasm is adjusted. For this reason, another very effective method of reducing bacterial spoilage is to dry out ("dehydrate" or "desiccate") the food that is to be stored, making sure that the material is kept dry throughout the storage period.

Dozens of industries have been founded because of the action of bacteria. The dairy industry is dependent upon bacterial action for many dairy products, but it also must guard against them to prevent souring. Transportation and storage industries are regulated in part because of bacteria. Sewage disposal plants operate as they do because of these micro-organisms, and of course the refrigeration industries, dehydration plants, frozen-food-processing plants, and even leather-tanning factories use bacteria or operate against them in some way.

The "negative economic significance" of bacteria, particularly in disease production, has been increasingly publicized since the days of Pasteur and has gone far to clear man's understanding of the world in which he lives. The general public, however, little realizes that there is another side to the picture—that bacteria are man's friends as well as his enemies. The student of biology knows this and knows that it is no small matter. It would be no overstatement to say that man could not exist on the earth as it is today were it not for the useful activities of some bacteria.

This "positive economic significance" of bacteria is due largely to a certain dependency which the green plants have upon bacterial action. For its proteins and its protoplasm the green plant must have nitrogen. Approximately 80 per cent of our atmosphere is free nitrogen gas, so that a sea of nitrogen not only bathes the aerial parts of the green plant but also percolates through the air spaces of the soil and bathes the roots. This limitless supply of nitrogen is of no more value to the green plant than is sea water to the thirsty shipwrecked sailor. The green plant cannot use nitrogen in this form. In general, to be available to the green plant, nitrogen must be in the form of *nitrate,* in which one nitrogen atom has been combined with three atoms of oxygen.

Some nitrates are present in most soils. Throughout their lives, green plants are continuously drawing upon this supply. If there is no

replacement, a time will arrive when the nitrate supply is reduced below what is necessary to support plant growth. Some nitrate may be
added to the soil by non-living agencies such as lightning, but this is
negligibly small in amount. Were it not for living agencies, green
plants would soon perish from nitrogen starvation.

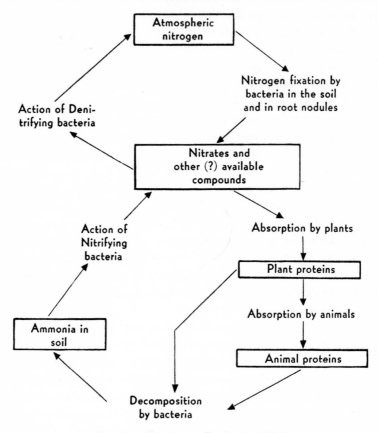

FIG. 53.—The nitrogen cycle, simplified

Nature works out a partial solution for this problem by a *cycle*
(Fig. 53) which serves to feed new generations of green plants with the
same nitrogen that has already served the needs of pre-existing green
plants. The dead plant or animal body gradually decomposes as it lies
upon the ground. This phenomenon recurs so frequently and so copiously that most mortals have perceived it, but those who have thought

about it at all have usually attributed it rather vaguely to the action of some non-living agency of nature. As a matter of fact, a corpse would break up very slowly indeed under the attack of wind, rain, and the like. Were these the only agencies of decomposition, the ground surface would today be hopelessly cluttered with the accumulated corpses of many generations past. Actually, it is the bacteria of decomposition that take care of all this debris, gradually breaking it up and returning its component materials to the soil (and to the air). Through the action of these bacteria of decomposition, plant and animal proteins are converted into ammonia in the soil; other bacteria (the *nitrifying bacteria*) then seize upon the ammonia and convert it into nitrates. These nitrates may then serve the needs of new generations of green plants and of the animals that eat the plants.

Here, then, is a complete cycle which might seem to provide for the living organisms for all time to come. By itself, however, it is not a perfect solution to the problem. Through the action of rain and soil water, some nitrates are usually leached out of the soil and carried away. Worse than that, there are some bacteria, known as the *denitrifying bacteria,* which act to break up soil nitrates in such manner as to return free nitrogen gas to the air. Due to these steady losses, the system would inevitably run itself down were there not some agency for the reconversion of atmospheric nitrogen into soil nitrates.

Exactly this role is played by the *nitrogen-fixing bacteria.* Without these humble, microscopic organisms, man would soon pass out of the picture, along with most other forms of life. Of the nitrogen-fixers there are two categories. Some exist here and there in the soil in a free state, having no intimate connection with other living organisms. More nitrogen is fixed, however, by those of the other category which live in the root *nodules* ("tubercles") of *leguminous plants* (e.g., beans, peas, clover, alfalfa). The presence of these bacteria in the roots acts as a stimulus to growth, so that the local root tissues enlarge to produce a tumor-like swelling that may be several times the diameter of the normal root (Fig. 54). It is within these nodules that the bacteria make their homes and carry on their peculiar work of nitrogen-fixing. The result is an ample supply of nitrate for the host plant.

The farmer usually relies upon the nitrogen-fixers to rejuvenate his exhausted soils. After a series of ordinary crops has brought the local nitrate supply to a dangerously low level, the farmer may allow that field to lie fallow for a season, so that the free-living nitrogen-fixers may have opportunity to replenish the supply. If he wishes a more copious replenishment, he sows leguminous plants in the field and at the end of the season plows their bodies back into the soil. The nitrate supply will not be replenished, and the leguminous plants will not

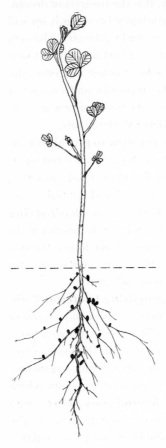

themselves thrive, unless the proper nodule-forming bacteria are present. If these are known to be in the local soil where legumes are to be planted, the roots will be infected. If not, the farmer can buy bacterial cultures from the seed house with which to inoculate the seeds before sowing. This is usually done by mixing the seeds and a bacteria-containing carrier together. As the seeds germinate, the bacteria will enter the young roots, usually through the root hairs, when they appear.

One can see, therefore, that the oft-mentioned **nitrogen cycle** in the organic world is really a compound of two smaller cycles. Given nitrates in the soil, we may have a cycle which involves successively the following organisms:

$$\text{green plant} \rightarrow (\text{animal}) \rightarrow \text{bacteria}$$
$$\text{of decomposition} \rightarrow \text{nitrifying}$$
$$\text{bacteria .}$$

In the other cycle we have the denitrifying bacteria and nitrogen-fixers continuously working at cross-purposes, the former changing nitrates into free nitrogen and the latter effecting the reverse change. The two cycles feed

FIG. 54.—Root nodules ("tubercles") produced by nitrogen-fixing bacteria on the roots of a clover plant.

into one another at the point of the soil nitrates.

Actually there is a cycle for every one of the "essential elements" in plant and animal bodies, and in each cycle the bacteria of decomposition play a role. Most significant, however, are the nitrogen and carbon cycles.

In large part the **carbon cycle** has been described already. Atmospheric carbon dioxide is incorporated by photosynthesis into plant carbohydrates. Some of these later become fats, and some enter into the protein molecules. The cycle is completed without the intervention of other organisms when plant respiration returns carbon dioxide to the atmosphere.

The carbon cycle becomes longer when herbivorous animals (or other dependent organisms) enter the picture, and still longer when the herbivores are, in turn, devoured by carnivores. Thus the carbon of plant carbohydrate, fat, and protein may become the carbon of animal carbohydrate, fat, and protein. Much of this carbon, in the form of carbon dioxide, is steadily poured back into the atmosphere by animal respiration.

The cycle is longer yet for those carbon atoms that remain a part of undevoured plant and animal corpses. At this point the bacteria of decomposition get in their work, breaking down the various body materials into simpler forms, such as organic acids. These organic acids do not exist for long in the soil, however. They still contain some chemically stored energy, and this energy is soon exploited by a second crew of bacteria, which oxidize the organic acids and return the carbon, in the form of carbon dioxide, to the atmosphere. Graphically, the carbon cycle is represented in Figure 55.

Actinomycetes. For many years these organisms were placed among the higher fungi, but recently it has been conceded that their rightful place is with the bacteria. Morphologically the Actinomycetes are generally larger than most bacteria and usually filamentous. Spores are produced singly or in clusters at the tips of specialized units on the branched filaments. A few members of the group cause diseases in plants and animals.

A very intensive study of the Actinomycetes is now under way because of the discovery of antibiotics. It was observed that one of the soil-inhabiting forms (*Streptomyces*) was found to contain a substance, since known as streptomycin, capable of combating certain infectious diseases of man and other animals. Many of these soil organisms have since been found, isolated, and their properties observed in connection with disease. Among the antibiotics found in other members of the Actinomycetes are aureomycin, chloromycetin, and terramycin.

Viruses. With the development of the field of pathology, it was found that a number of diseases which appeared to be infectious and transmissible could not be blamed on bacteria, fungi, or any other known micro-organism. It was possible to make an extract of tissue from a diseased organism, pass it through a filter too fine to permit the

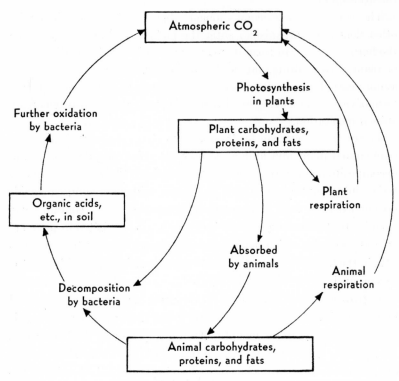

Fig. 55.—The carbon cycle, simplified

passage of the smallest bacteria, and yet cause that same disease in a healthy individual by introducing the filtrate into his blood stream. Furthermore, the agent in the filtrate seems able to reproduce in numbers or quantity since it may be diluted to the extent of one part in a million and still cause the disease when injected into the specific host. With the aid of the electron microscope some research workers claim to have seen tiny organisms of ultra-microscopic size which are able to grow and multiply in their host's cells. Certainly the electron microscope has given us the visual evidence that at least some viruses have a definite organization. It has also been demonstrated that some viruses can be crystallized and that when these crystals are dissolved and introduced into a healthy individual the specific disease develops. Viruses are all obligate parasites, which means that they can grow and reproduce only in the tissues of living organisms.

Some plant diseases caused by viruses are the mosaic (a mottled, often blighted, condition) diseases of tobacco, squash, cucumber, and potato. Human diseases caused by viruses include infantile paralysis, smallpox, mumps, and yellow fever.

Bacteriophages. In the early part of the twentieth century it was observed that bacteria were subject to viral infections similar to those observed in higher plants and animals. The causative organism was recognized as a virus and given the name **bacteriophage.** For many years the bacteriophage was thought to be a toxic substance or a solution rather than a distinct organism. However, with the aid of the electron microscope we have been able to demonstrate that at least some of these bacteriophages resemble a coccus bacterium with a single flagellum. Still, it is questionable whether they are true cells or merely small protein bodies. In any case, they are very widespread in nature; they are found in the digestive tracts of animals (including man), in bodies of water, in most soils, and in sewage. Their potentialities in the control of bacteria were first observed in 1917 by D'Herelle, who filtered liquid cultures of dysentery bacilli through very fine filters and found that the filtrate checked the growth of other bacteria. Furthermore, he noticed that material from colonies of bacteria killed in this manner killed other healthy colonies when mixed with them. Just how the bacteriophage acts upon the bacteria is not definitely known, but the end result is complete dissolution of the susceptible bacteria— hence the name "bacteriophage," which literally means "bacteria eater."

Myxomycophyta. The slime fungi, or **slime molds,** are a group of organisms that lie on the border line between the plant and animal kingdoms. Those who consider them animals assign them to a class in the animal phylum Protozoa. Most biologists, however, consider them very unique plants and assign them to a phylum in the plant kingdom, the Myxomycophyta. When one studies the slime molds, he is quite impressed with the weird combination of simple and complex traits that appears in the group and with the remarkable plasticity that characterizes their life cycle. It is no wonder that the biologist finds difficulty in placing them with certainty in either plant or animal kingdom. But if they are plants, it is much safer to regard them as fungi on the grounds that they lack chlorophyll. Yet because of their habit of growth and life cycle, we are still safer in putting them in a separate phylum rather than considering them as true fungi.

The majority of slime molds are **saprophytes,** which grow in moist places, such as rich soil and decaying wood. A few, however, are aquatic, and some are parasites. One parasitic form is *Plasmodiophora brassica,* which causes a disease known as "club root of cabbage." Here the slime mold, which may persist for years in the soil, enters the subterranean plant parts of cabbage and stimulates the roots to a disorderly overgrowth which results in an enlarged but malfunctioning development of these organs. Most of the slime molds, however, live on moist soils rich in decaying organic matter and on fallen tree trunks in well-shaded damp forests.

The remarkable working body of the slime mold, and the structure from which it gets its name, is the **plasmodium,** a formless, naked mass of protoplasm containing thousands of nuclei. This body is strongly suggestive of such simple animals as *Amoeba.* The entire body moves like an animated mass of jelly, the plasmodium flowing forward by pushing out irregular protrusions of protoplasm and having the rest of the body flow into them from behind. Like *Amoeba,* the slime mold moves in response to certain stimuli, such as light, retreating from sunlight until it reaches some shaded place. Again like *Amoeba,* the slime mold flows around organic particles and engulfs them into its body, where they are gradually digested and assimilated. The plasmodium is rather viscous and slimy to the touch, often several inches in diameter, and it varies in color from colorless to yellow, orange, red, violet, and other colors, depending on the species and the mineral content of the substrate.

It is in its reproductive features that the resemblance to plants is most prominent. While in the plasmodial stage the organism moves about, ingesting food, but under adverse conditions, such as increasing dryness or inadequate food supply, the plasmodium becomes quiescent and often forms a protective crust around itself. In others, **sporangia,** resembling tiny mushrooms, are produced. The shape and size of these sporangia are used in identifying the various species. Each plasmodium will form hundreds of tiny sporangia, which in turn produce thousands of spores on the elaborate network that is developed within the wall of the spore case.

When the sporangial wall breaks, the spores are released and distributed by the air currents. If the spore reaches a suitable substratum, such as moist tree bark or damp decaying leaves, and environmental conditions are optimal, the spore wall breaks open and a uninucleate mass of protoplasm emerges. Each spore will produce one to four *swarm cells,* each bearing two flagella. Usually these swarm cells will divide several times, forming more swarm cells. After swimming around or moving about on the substrate for a time, the tiny cells fuse in pairs to form zygotes. In some species the zygotes grow directly into a new plasmodium; in others, many zygotes coalesce into larger and larger groups, forming at last a plasmodium with its continuous cytoplasm and numerous nuclei.

XI. *Plants without Chlorophyll Higher Forms*

Subkingdom THALLOPHYTA
   Phylum EUMYCOPHYTA—true fungi
      Class Phycomycetes—algal fungi
      Class Ascomycetes—sac fungi
      Class Basidiomycetes—club fungi
      Class Deuteromycetes—imperfect fungi
      Symbiotic Organisms
         Lichens
         Mycorrhizae

The Phylum Eumycophyta, the *true fungi,* consists of about 75,000 species of very diverse form, size, and methods of reproduction. All but a very few of the simplest species have a vegetative thallus termed a *mycelium.* This consists of a mass of tiny filaments called *hyphae.* In some species the hyphae are elongated unicells; in others a hypha is a many-celled structure. In general the four classes have rather distinctive hyphae which contribute to the uniqueness of their vegetative bodies and make them fairly easy to recognize as members of one class or another.

All species of true fungi produce some type of spore, often several types, in their reproductive cycles. Sexual reproduction has been observed in most of the species. Exceptions are the *imperfect fungi,* representing a large number of organisms. (Their popular name refers to our imperfect knowledge of them rather than to some shortcoming of the organism.)

150

Of the two great groups of plants without chlorophyll—bacteria and fungi—we find that parasitic bacteria more commonly attack animals, while fungi usually parasitize green plants. In the notorious "ringworm," in "athlete's foot," and in a few rare diseases of the throat, we have examples of parasitic fungi that make direct attacks on man's body. Similarly, there are a few that attack the bodies of other animals. But the vast majority of the victims of parasitic fungi are green plants, and, when the green plant happens to be an important food source for man, the fungus may be of tremendous economic importance.

The manner in which fungi attack their hosts is quite variable. Some confine their attack to the skin, while others attack internally. Those parasites which attack externally have no serious problem of penetration. Once they become lodged on the surface of the host, they are in direct contact with the tissues which are to provide their food. The skin diseases which such parasites produce may be moderately destructive but are seldom fatal. It is the internal parasite which is usually more to be feared.

In the case of the internal parasite, mere presence of the spore on the surface of the host is no guarantee that infection will result. For true disease, penetration must be effected; and this is usually no simple matter, for nature has endowed most plants and animals with skin tissues which are highly efficient in preventing the entrance of internal parasites. Penetration may occur through one of three avenues, depending on the nature of the fungus and the nature of the host. (1) Some fungi enter only through wounds. Knowing this, the tree surgeon, after pruning off a branch, hastens to coat the exposed surface with some substance which is physically or chemically an effective obstruction to the entrance of wood-destroying fungi. (2) Other fungi make use of the natural openings in the plant host, the tiny breathing pores (stomates) which are scattered over most of its surfaces (Fig. 56). In such cases it is not necessary that the original placement by the wind be in, or even very near to, the breathing pore, for the young hyphae which emerge from the spore can grow along the surface for some distance before reaching a stomate. (3) Unfortunately for the prospective hosts, there are still other fungi capable of producing strong digestive fluids with which they eat their way directly through intact surfaces (Fig. 57).

Although it is probably most common for a fungus to be endowed with only one of these three devices for penetration, there are some fungi that evidently can rely upon more than one, and the reports are that the fungus producing late blight of potato can penetrate by any one of the three methods. Once within the tissues of the host, a fungus, having by this time pretty well exhausted the food that was stored within the spore, must immediately tap a new food supply. The main mycelium of the parasite usually grows not in, but between, the cells of the host. In leaf tissue this presents no problem, for there is already established in the leaf a connected network of air spaces between the cells. But the main mycelium is not all. Just as the main mycelium of some saprophytic fungi pushes nutritive branches into the substratum, so also does that of the parasite branch out with tiny processes which actually enter the host cells to digest and absorb much of their living contents.

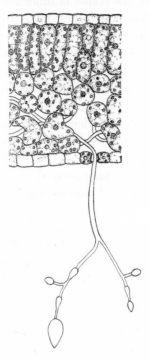

FIG. 56.—Spore-bearing branch of the fungus responsible for "late blight of potato," emerging through a breathing pore on the lower surface of a leaf of its host.

Parasitic fungi are surprisingly specific in their tastes. Very commonly a given fungus will confine its attack not merely to a single host species but often to only one or a few varieties of that species. Furthermore, its attack is usually restricted to a particular type of tissue within the host. Other tissues may be traversed by the main mycelium but are not exploited as a source of food.

A fungus may grow through all parts of a plant, but for the most part it attacks and destroys only those rather soft cells of the leaves that contain the chloroplasts. Pushing on rapidly from one leaf to another, it may thus wreck the food factories of the entire plant within a week or so after the time of the original infection.

The parasitic fungus is a serious enemy of man whether or not it completely kills its host plant. Usually the green plant is so weakened by the attack of the parasitic fungus that it becomes prey to secondary invaders. Furthermore, in economic plants the yield of the crop is often cut down to such an extent that it is impractical to harvest. Ordinarily a plant manufactures much more than enough food to supply current needs, and most of this excess is stored in the roots—as in sweet potatoes, or the tuber of Irish potatoes, the fruits of apples, and grains of wheat. But a blighted plant will lose so much of its food-manufacturing tissue that there is little or no excess food to be stored.

Thus a large and important chapter in the story of man's conquest of nature is that which deals with his warfare against the diseases of his crop plants. In part these diseases are due to bacteria, in part to the mysterious filterable viruses, occasionally to animal parasites, and at times to no parasites at all, being apparently nothing more than functional or nutritional diseases. The majority of serious plant diseases, however, are attributable to parasitic fungi. In man's fight against plant disease, there is usually no such effort to save the individual patient, as in the case of diseases of man himself or his more

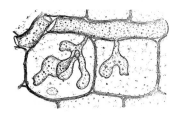

Fig. 57.—Portion of an internal parasitic fungus, showing main mycelium wedging between the cells of the host and nutritive branches actually penetrating the host cells.

valuable domesticated animals. Man stands quite ready to sacrifice an individual plant or so, if only an epidemic can be prevented and the bulk of his crop saved. The two most common tactics which man uses in this warfare are the **application of fungicides** and the **breeding of resistant varieties.**

As the name implies, a fungicide is a fungus killer. First, experimentation must demonstrate that a certain chemical or combination of chemicals will kill the spores or young mycelia of the fungus without at the same time working any serious injury on the superficial tissues of the host plant. A solution of the chemical, mixed with some adhesive substance, is then sprayed upon the surfaces of the crop plants. Because of rain and other agents, the coating of fungicide gradually disappears, so that several sprayings are often necessary during the growing season. The spore of the fungus, lodged on the surface of its host, puts out the mycelium only in the presence of moisture. On a sprayed surface, this moisture also dissolves a little of the fungicide, and the result will be a poisoning of the young mycelium. Of course, this procedure confers no benefit upon the plant that is already infected, but it usually prevents new infections.

For some crops, such as wheat, the plantings are so thick and so extensive that a program of spraying has proved difficult. Control of diseases of such crops has been sought through the breeding of disease-resistant varieties. Proceeding on a knowledge of the laws of heredity, breeders have in some cases been able to separate out, from a mixed population, a variety with a combination of hereditary characteristics that makes it immune to the disease in question. In other cases they have succeeded, through crossing (hybridization), in breeding into a resistant variety the desired fruiting qualities of a susceptible variety. Both procedures involve breeding programs that must be arranged and guarded with extreme care through several generations before the breeder can put on the market a new variety which, while possessing desirable commercial features, at the same time is able to grow without succumbing in a region in which the parasitic fungus is prevalent. Already man has developed varieties of cereals that completely or almost completely resist the attacks of some parasitic fungi. It should not be thought, however, that the entire problem has been solved or is ever likely to be solved once and for all. Many parasitic fungi are prevalent in this country, and new ones are frequently added to the list, some arriving as unwelcome immigrants from other parts of the world and others apparently being evolved anew from fungus ancestors of a different type. From this it can be seen that, though progress has indeed been made in the past, there remain plenty of practical problems to be solved by the plant breeders of the future.

The development of disease-resistant varieties has not been limited to cereal crops. In many other crops, such as our potato, spraying is arduous, not altogether certain, and needs to be repeated annually. The development of disease-resistant varieties is a far more satisfactory method of control, for the results are relatively permanent and relatively foolproof. So we find repeated instances in which the temporizing methods of spraying have been succeeded by a more lasting solution of the problem through the production of resistant varieties.

Though spraying of dusts and solutions and the production of disease-resistant varieties are the control measures that are most widely employed today, there are others which play quite significant roles. One is by *quarantine.* This is an obvious method of attempting to prevent introduction into a region of a new and dangerous parasite that has been working its havoc elsewhere. The government spends a great deal of money in establishing quarantine barriers around, and even at points within, the country. Planes coming from foreign countries in which a serious plant disease is prevalent are sprayed before taking off from that country and again when they land here. The same sort of inspection takes place at all our ports of entry; a few states, such as California, have inspection stations also at points where main highways enter the state.

Another attempt at control of plant disease is by *removal of alternate hosts.* As we shall see later, rust is a serious fungus disease of wheat and many other grasses. By removing the alternate host, which in this case is the American barberry, the fungus cannot complete its life cycle on the wheat and barberry plants. Other fungi having similar life cycles but with different hosts are the cedar apple rust and the white pine blister rust. Unfortunately, certain spore stages may perpetuate the parasite, so that, although removal of one of the alternate hosts may curb the activities of the fungus, it does not wipe it out completely.

Seeds coming from plants growing in infected fields are often either burned, so that the next crop is not infected, or else they are soaked briefly in fungicides, a process which usually kills the spores and mycelia and prevents further growth of the parasite.

A good practice, followed especially in small gardens where plants have become infected, is to *burn the infected plants and weeds.* This is a method of sanitation which destroys fungi capable of overwintering in the dead tissues of the previous year's crops.

Particularly elusive are those parasites that overwinter in the soil itself. In a limited number of cases, chemical treatment of the soil has proved of some value. In most cases, however, soil treatment is exceedingly dangerous, for it destroys or seriously alters the population of soil organisms, such as beneficial bacteria, fungi, algae, and protozoans which have been working steadily, putting the soil into condition for good crop growth. Such problems can be solved to some extent by *crop rotation.* Here the soil which is known to harbor a particular parasite either is allowed to lie fallow or is planted with some other crop for as many years as are needed to cause the parasite to die out in the soil.

In some cases a disease can be curbed by **removing the carrier.** Insects are known to carry bacteria and fungi. Eliminating or greatly reducing the number of these insects deprives the fungus of its means of transmissal. This method is effective against the Dutch elm disease, which is caused by a fungus and carried by a beetle.

CLASSIFICATION

The Eumycophyta are divided into four major classes, based upon their vegetative features and particularly upon their methods of reproduction. The four classes are: (1) Phycomycetes, or algal fungi; (2) Ascomycetes, or sac fungi; (3) Basidiomycetes, or club fungi; and (4) Deuteromycetes, or imperfect fungi.

Phycomycetes. Members of this class are usually called **algal fungi** or alga-like fungi, because a comparative study of the filamentous bodies, their manner of spore production, and particularly their sex structures and behavior gives them not only a morphological similarity but apparently a phylogenetic relationship to the algae. Most Phycomycetes have **coenocytic** filaments, which, of course, means that there are no cross walls in the mycelium and that the protoplasm is continuous, with numerous nuclei in the various hyphae. The coenocytic condition likewise occurs in one of the orders of green algae, which the Phycomycetes most closely resemble.

The Phycomycetes are divided into several fairly large orders and several others of lesser importance which we will not consider here. The most primitive group, the **Chytridiales,** infect various plants and may also live saprophytically. Most of them are very small, consisting of nothing more than a single cell with rhizoids or a body composed of small hyphae with irregularly placed bulbous swellings. They reproduce asexually by zoospores and sexually, being either isogamous or heterogamous.

The **Peronosporales** are nearly all plant parasites. They are often called **downy mildews** because many of them form a soft, downy growth on the surface of the host they infect. A few members of the order live in water or moist soil. These forms produce zoospores, which greatly aid in their distribution. The more typical parasitic species, like *Phytophthora infestans,* which causes the disease "late blight of potato," although terrestrial, produce tiny zoospores that are able to move about on a thin film of water on the leaf surface. They then send out small hyphae that penetrate host tissues and bring about new infections. These tiny zoospores are asexual and are produced by **sporangia,** which in turn have been produced by **sporangiophores.** Infection may take place by the sporangia blowing from one plant to another susceptible to that fungus.

A third order, the **Saprolegniales,** consists of water molds which attack algae as well as fish and other aquatic animals. In water and in moist habitats we sometimes see a whitish ring or "halo" around a dead insect. This halo is actually composed of sporangia and spores, discharged forcibly by the fungus, which has already consumed many of the internal organs of the insect without affecting its external appearance. Most of the water molds are distributed by flagellated spores, similar to those of certain algae, which enable them to attach themselves to the scales of fish and other organisms.

The fourth and last order that we will consider in the Phycomycetes is the **Mucorales.** This is the order in which the very common and abundant **bread mold,** *Rhizopus nigricans,* is found. The general characteristics of most fungi are rather simply and clearly displayed by this fungus, which usually grows as a saprophyte on stale bread, jelly, and manure piles. Many a housewife, planning to salvage the remainder of a three-day-old loaf, has been distressed to find parts of it covered with fine white "whiskers." In fact, most of us have doubtless eaten bread in this condition without realizing that we were getting more than we had bargained for. Since the microscopic spores are being produced copiously and released into the air by the almost innumerable patches of mold that are growing somewhere in the neighborhood, and since the spores are so light as to be readily carried by the slightest of air currents, it follows that a goodly number of them are circulating in the atmosphere of every household. Repeatedly they are lighting upon objects of all sorts. It is only, however, when they chance to light upon a favorable nutritive medium (under the proper conditions of humidity and temperature) that they germinate to produce the mycelium body of the fungus.

During the first few minutes of its exposure on the kitchen table, the loaf of fresh bread is likely to receive one or more of these *Rhizopus* spores. Lodged on this relatively warm and moist nutritive medium, the spore will, within a few hours, germinate to produce the first microscopic filament of the new mycelium. Growth is rapid, but the mycelium is so minute and colorless that it is usually only after two or three days that it has reached proportions discernible by the naked eye.

The main mycelial body grows only along the surface of the bread, branching repeatedly and spreading in an ever widening disk from the point of its origin. Here and there, for nutritive purposes, it sends down into the substance of the bread little rootlike processes, called

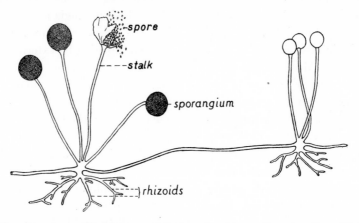

Fɪɢ. 58.—A magnified diagram of the bread-mold mycelium, together with the structures involved in spore production.

rhizoids (Fig. 58), that are of smaller caliber and more copiously branched than the main mycelium. Through the surfaces of these little branches, water and organic material are absorbed from the bread and passed upward to provide for growth of the main mycelium. Thus the purely vegetative life of the fungus is simple enough, since there is no problem of food manufacture or of the building of a complex body and no particular difficulty involved in the transport of materials within the body.

Reproductively, however, the bread mold is more complex, illustrating all the three major types of reproduction that occur in the plant kingdom. Simplest of the three is reproduction by vegetative multiplication, in which the unmodified vegetative body itself may split up into a number of individuals. If one were to detach a fragment of the mycelium and transplant it onto a new nutritive substratum, this fragment would constitute a separate individual and would soon develop to whatever size was permitted by the amount of food available in that locality. Even when left to itself, the spreading fungus mycelium often becomes a series of detached individuals through the starvation and death of intervening parts.

If such vegetative multiplication were the only method of reproduction, however, this fungus would be rare. Fragments of mycelium are ineffective as agents of distribution; any very lengthy trip through the air tends to dry and kill them. Such a conspicuously successful species must possess a more efficient means of distribution.

Usually, when the fungus is only a few days old, numerous vertical branches will arise from scattered points on the mycelium. Each of these branches is at first a very simple affair, uniform in caliber throughout its entire length. Very shortly, however, a spherical swelling appears at the tip of each branch. This sphere continues to enlarge until it is eight or more times the diameter of the branch that carries it. Up to this point the sphere contains merely the pigmentless cytoplasm and nuclei that are characteristic of the mycelium itself. At such a stage the growth of mold would appear under the hand lens as a miniature thicket of delicate stems tipped by snowy white balloons. These, of course, are the sporangia.

Within another day the sporangia turn black. This is because the contents are cut up into hundreds of tiny spores, each equipped with nucleus and cytoplasm and surrounded with a dark brown wall. Now our loaf of bread advertises its moldiness to the naked eye, for the black color of the ripe spore cases, tiny as they are, makes them stand out clearly against the white background of the bread. It is because of this fact that the popular name of "black mold" is applied to this fungus almost as frequently as is "bread mold."

In these reproductive organs, as in those of all higher plants and animals, we can distinguish "fertile" and "sterile" elements. In the case at hand, the spores are the fertile elements, for they are the cells which actually develop into the individuals of the next generation. Purely accessory elements are the spore case (i.e., the wall surrounding the entire group of spores) and the vertical stalk which bears it. Though these are sterile, they nonetheless contribute to the efficiency of the program of spore reproduction. The spore case surrounds and protects the spores in their tender developing stages. The stalk elevates the sporangium and thereby increases the likelihood that the spores, when released, will be caught up and carried away by the breeze. Throughout the fungi (most of which live and release their spores in a medium of air) these two sterile elements recur in a variety of forms, sometimes quite elaborate.

When the spores are ripe, an upward pressure of the watery protoplasm within the stalk comes to bear upon the contents of the sporangium. This pressure, transmitted through the mass of spores, stretches the outer wall (i.e., the spore case proper) until at last it reaches the limit of its elasticity. At this point it bursts, forcibly ejecting most of the spores and thus catering further to their effective distribution. Similar devices appear among higher plants, providing for an active discharge of spores or other reproductive units.

Unlike the spores of the water-living algae, those of the bread mold are light and provided with a wall which resists desiccation. In other words, they are adapted to distribution in a medium of air. The tiny bit of protoplasm within the spore wall is in a state of dormancy. Animation is not completely suspended, but life goes on at an extremely slow rate, so slowly that even the meager supply of nourishment present will maintain the viability of the spore for several years. Whether it is a day or a year after the time of discharge, that spore which lights on a suitable substratum will germinate to produce a new mycelium.

The third method of reproduction is sexual. In their general vegetative characteristics, all bread mold mycelia are alike, but the manner of sexual reproduction reveals that actually there are two types of mycelia, commonly referred to as the + (plus) strain and the − (minus) strain. Neither strain by itself will ever initiate sexual reproduction, for here there is clearly a sexual differentiation of individuals, and the two strains must co-operate in the production of zygotes. When a strand of mycelium from the plus strain grows close to one from the minus strain, the two put out tiny side branches which come into contact at the tips. At a short distance behind the tip of each branch a wall is laid down. The two small masses of protoplasm which are thus cut off at the tip of each branch act as gametes. In this case, however, there is nothing in the relative size or activity of the gametes to betray which is male and which is female. Both stay where they are, but the contiguous end walls of the two dissolve away and allow the two little masses of protoplasm to fuse into one. This fusion product is, of course, the zygote. Soon it enlarges and lays down about itself a rather irregular, heavy black wall (Fig. 59).

Ordinarily this zygote remains dormant for months, later to be awakened if moisture and warmth are provided. Under such conditions the zygote wall is softened, and the contained protoplasm pushes

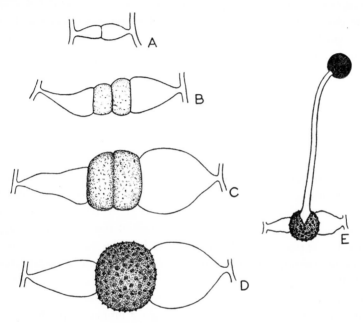

Fig. 59.—Sexual reproduction in the bread mold. *A–D*, successive stages in zygote formation; *E* (taken from a related fungus), germination of zygote to produce stalk and spore case.

through. At once it produces a vertical stalk and spore case. Each of the many spores released from this spore case has the power to produce a new mycelium.

The three possible life cycles shown by this fungus represent the three fundamental types of reproduction for living organisms in general.

In the first and simplest type there is no setting-aside of specialized reproductive cells. Instead, a part of the ordinary vegetative body is transformed directly into the individual of the next generation. Vegetative multiplication is at its simplest in the unicellular organism, where ordinary cell division is, at the same time, an act of reproduction. In the multicellular organism it is usually not one alone but a group of vegetative cells which becomes the new individual. In this case, too, the new individual owes its origin to a series of cell divisions. The difference between such a case and that of the unicell lies more in the matter of separation from the parent body. In the unicell, cell division itself functionally separates the body of the new individual from that of the parent. In the many-celled organism, a group of new cells which may result from a series of cell divisions remains functionally a part of the parent individual and continues to co-operate with the rest of the body until such time as it becomes separated through the action of some other agency, such as accidental severance or the death of intervening parts. If, then, the isolated group of cells has not already become too highly and irrevocably specialized as a subordinate part of the parent body, it will itself continue to grow as a separate individual. Hence many of the lower plants, whose body parts are not highly specialized, have a large capacity for vegetative multiplication. As we pass to the higher and more specialized plants, we find fewer cases of vegetative multiplication; but even among the highest of plants we often find that certain of the body parts, apparently less specialized and subordinate than the rest, are capable of effecting vegetative multiplication if separated from the parent body and placed in appropriate conditions. Specialization and subordination of body parts has, of course, been carried much farther in the animal kingdom, so that among the highest animals reproduction by vegetative multiplication is a practical impossibility.

In the second of the fundamental types of reproduction, spore reproduction, we encounter a characteristic combination of several features: (1) Though the body of the individual may be many celled, the spore is a single cell, capable by its own independent action of producing a new individual. (2) Some device is present for the regular release of ripe spores into the surrounding medium of air or water. (3) Spores are more or less specialized as agents of distribution, being equipped in such manner as to encourage their wide dispersal through the medium. (4) In most cases a single parent individual produces its spores in large numbers.

Sex, the third of the fundamental types of reproduction, is readily characterized by the feature of fusion. The details of sexual reproduction vary tremendously in the plant and animal kingdoms, but these details are merely accessories to the fusion of two cells (and, most significantly, of the two nuclei within those cells), commonly from different sources.

Ascomycetes. The *sac fungi* as a group are characterized by the possession of an *ascus,* or sac. The ascus, at first a simple cell, undergoes a characteristic series of nuclear and cytoplasmic divisions which yield at last a group of (usually) eight ascospores, the spores being retained within the old saclike cell wall (Fig. 60). At one stage of botanical knowledge, though this development of the ascus itself was pretty well understood, antecedent events remained obscure. Now it is known that the single nucleus, which is the progenitor of the eight spore nuclei, has been derived (directly or indirectly) from a sex act, i.e., from a fusion of male and female nuclei. The sex organs which are responsible for this are often so similar to ordinary wefts of the vegetative mycelium and are usually so well buried within the tissues of the host and of the fungus itself that only an expert can identify them. Even today there remain quite a number of Ascomycetes in which certain identification of the sex apparatus has not been made. In addition to the spores within the ascus, most Ascomycetes also produce other spores by simpler methods at some stage of the life cycle.

FIG. 60.—A typical ascus, the saclike spore container that characterizes the Ascomycete group.

In terms of the number of species, Ascomycetes are the largest of the three fungus groups. One family of Ascomycetes, the so-called **powdery mildews,** is responsible for an amazingly large number of "skin diseases" in plants. Here the fungus is strictly an external parasite, the mycelium spreading over the surface of the host and exploiting for nutrition merely the skin layer of the latter. A very common example is the **lilac mildew,** in which the mycelium produces what are apparently dusty patches on the leaves, patches which the uninitiated owner of the lilac bush often attempts vainly to rinse off with water (Fig. 61). Other Ascomycetes are responsible for more serious skin diseases, as in the "scabs" and resultant splitting of the skin which we so often see in apples and pears.

The group also furnishes many internal parasites: forms which cause the rotting of fruits and vegetables, either before or during their transit to the market; forms which destroy whole plants by plugging up their vessels for water conduction or by actually rotting away their entire root system; and a form that is responsible for the notorious

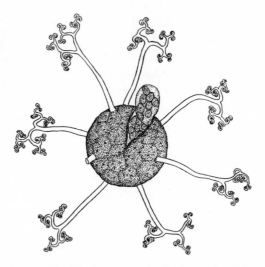

Fig. 61.—Lilac mildew. The "dusty patches" seen on the surface of an infected lilac leaf are composed of the mycelium of the fungus together with spores, which are produced in chains at the end of short stalks. Here and there on the dusty patches one may notice black bodies, barely large enough to be identified with the naked eye. These black bodies are ascus containers. One of them is shown above, with its remarkable "appendages" and the ovoid asci starting to emerge through a crack in the wall.

"chestnut blight," a disease which has wiped out practically all American chestnut trees in the United States during the past fifty years.

There is one disease-producing ascomycete which has been turned to advantage by man. ***Ergot*** (Fig. 62) is a disease of rye and some other cereals in which the grain becomes enlarged and virtually supplanted by a hard mass of fungus mycelium that contains a unique alkaloid chemical with medicinal properties. Though this chemical is quite dangerous to cattle and horses, and to humans as well when they accidentally eat the ergot in uncontrolled quantities, the extract has a large medicinal value in controlling uterine contractions in women and in constricting blood vessels to aid in the control of hemorrhage.

In addition to the parasites, there are many saprophytic Ascomycetes of common occurrence. The *cup fungi* that we so often see growing on rotting logs in the forest also fall into this group. The "cup" itself is an elaborate reproductive branch put up by the mycelium, and the brightly colored lining of the cup is composed of thousands of asci standing compactly side by side (Fig. 63). Though the majority of edible fungi are members of the Basidiomycetes, the Ascomycetes furnish two edible forms that are usually regarded as rare delicacies. In the *morel* (Fig. 64) the saprophytic mycelium, growing on decaying vegetation at or near the soil surface, puts up an elaborate reproductive branch in which the pits of the honeycombed surface are lined with a compact stand of finger-shaped asci. In the *truffle* the reproductive branches remain so nearly buried in the litter of grass and dead leaves that the French have been obliged to employ trained pigs and dogs to scout out their location.

Yeast is a saprophytic plant that is commonly classified among Ascomycetes by virtue of its occasional production of an ascus-like sac of spores. The classification is rather questionable, particularly since this form lacks the mycelium that is characteristic of fungi in general. The body of the yeast organism consists of a single (usually oval) cell, with the qualification that the cell, under the conditions most favorable

Fig. 62.—Ergot. Sketch of one "head" of an infected rye plant, showing replacement of several of the grains by the hard, compact, dark-pigmented mycelium of the fungus.

to growth, develops into short chainlike colonies by the unique process of *budding*. In ordinary cell division the two resulting daughter cells are of essentially the same size, and the individualities of the two are delimited with comparative suddenness. In the budding of the yeast, the prospective daughter cell first appears as a tiny "blister," pushing out from the surface of the original cell, and gradually grows while still in intimate cytoplasmic connection with its parent. A parent may put out more than one such bud, and the buds themselves, even before they are full sized, may start to produce secondary buds. Thus there results a colony in the form of a simple or branched chain, but the colony readily breaks apart into its component cells (Fig. 65).

The economic importance of the yeasts arises from their remarkable capacity to conduct **fermentation.** Although most organisms can secure the energy from their food only with the assistance of oxygen in its free gaseous form, there are some—and most notably the yeasts— which can utilize their foods in the absence of free oxygen. Through this power of fermentation they can live, therefore, under conditions which would quickly suffocate most forms of plants and animals.

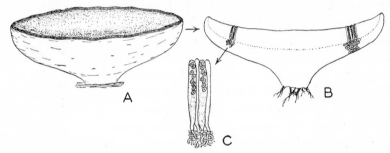

Fig. 63.—A cup fungus. *A*, as it might appear in nature; *B*, sectioned longitudinally to show relative position of the asci and the matted mycelium, which composes the bulk of the tissue of the cup; *C*, an enlargement of the asci, interspersed with erect, sterile filaments.

Yeast, in its fermentation, breaks down sugar into alcohol and carbon dioxide. In the commercial production of alcohol itself, yeast is put to work on some form of sugar solution. In "raising" bread it is the other product, the carbon dioxide gas, which does the work.

The Ascomycetes are comprised of over 25,000 species grouped into 4 subclasses and 15 orders. For this reason alone we would expect to find considerable variation in the morphological and physiological characteristics of the class. Because these variations do exist, the origin and relationships of the Ascomycetes are not easy to determine. One opinion is that the group evolved from the red algae. Similarities between the reproductive structures lead some botanists to believe this to be a very important factor in the relationship. Another opinion is that the Ascomycetes probably descended from the Phycomycetes. This view is based upon similarities in the development of asci and in the phycomycete zygote germination to form a sporangium. We also find that a few Ascomycetes have coenocytic hyphae typical of the Phycomycetes; furthermore, there is a similarity between the oögonial structure of both groups. The opinion that Ascomycetes have evolved from phycomycete-like ancestors is more generally accepted at present. Holders of this view regard the reproductive resemblances between Ascomycetes and red algae as parallel lines of evolution, rather than believing that one group has been derived from another.

Basidiomycetes. To most people the word "fungus" brings to mind mushrooms and toadstools. Although not all mushrooms are in this class, most of them are Basidiomycetes, or *club fungi,* and therefore most of the conspicuous fungi are in this group. We do not mean to be misleading by using the terms "mushrooms" and "toadstools" because, again, people seem to think that all mushrooms are edible and all toadstools poisonous. Actually it is far better to think of mushrooms as edible, inedible, and poisonous. The inedible ones are simply too tough or unpalatable but not poisonous. The term "toadstool" was possibly borrowed from the many fairy stories appearing in children's books. A mycologist, however, does not use the term. A fungus is not placed with the Basidiomycetes on the basis of whether or not

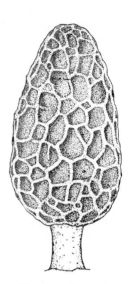

Fig. 64.—A morel

it looks like a mushroom. It must give rise, at some time in its life history, to a tiny club-shaped structure called the *basidium.* Just as the Ascomycetes are characterized by the ascus, the Basidiomycetes are characterized by the basidium. This structure occupies the same place and plays the same role in the life cycle as the ascus. Sex acts, often even more obscure than those of the Ascomycetes, are indirectly responsible for the basidia, and the early development of the individual basidium runs parallel with that of the ascus. But the final result is different, for the mature basidium commonly produces only four spores, and these are carried at the ends of little stalks. From this we recognize that the wheat rust fungus is a basidiomycete and that the little mycelium which emerges from one of its spores is a basidium.

The most conspicuous categories of pathogenic (disease-producing) Basidiomycetes are the smuts, the rusts, and the wood destroyers.

The various **smuts** occur not only on cereals but on onions and some other garden vegetables as well. Extensive compact masses of black spores form, to erupt later in an unsightly mess (Fig. 66). In one smut, which is commonly known as "bunt," or "stinking smut" of wheat, the spore mass yields an unbelievably bad odor (the odor of trimethylamine). The spores referred to are the important ones in distributing the species but are not the product of the basidium, which occurs at another point in the life cycle.

The story of the world of fungi would never be complete without an account of the **rusts.** Not only are these parasites of tremendous eco-

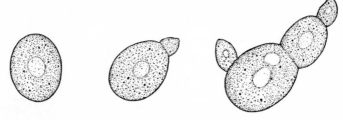

FIG. 65.—Yeast cells, highly magnified, showing the process of "budding," a form of "vegetative multiplication."

nomic importance, in a detrimental way, but they also illustrate the remarkable biological phenomenon of exploiting two or even more hosts. There are exceptions, of course, but most of them produce different types of spores from the mycelia which grow within their hosts. Man commonly attempts to combat the rust by exterminating whichever host is the less valuable. When they are both of nearly equal value, the problem becomes more difficult. Although there are a number of rusts which we could use as an example of such parasites, the one attacking wheat is probably of greatest importance. The complete life history of the wheat rust fungus, as it is understood today, includes quite an array of fantastic features. But it will serve our purpose to keep the terminology at a minimum and to give a simplified account.

During early summer in a wheat field of many thousand acres a single plant may be harboring a parasitic fungus which is pushing its main mycelium between the cells of its host and consuming a good many of them through the action of its small absorptive branches. The time arrives when parts of the mycelial body commence a development which is to culminate in the production of spores. A clumping of mycelial threads occurs which forms a tiny mat of fungus tissue just below the skin layer of the wheat plant. From this there arise thousands of microscopic stalks, lying compactly side by side and together pushing up the skin of the wheat into a blister of pinhead proportions. Each stalk cuts off at its end a single one-celled spore. Continued upward pressure of the fungus mass at last bursts the blister and exposes this tiny patch of spores. The individual spore, seen under the microscope, has a relatively faint pigmentation, but the mass of spores which breaks through the surface of the wheat plant appears to the naked eye as a distinctly rust-colored spore, hence the name of the disease. At this time the disease is also called the "red stem stage." In the course of a few days, thousands of these tiny rusty patches may crop out on our infected wheat plant (Fig. 67).

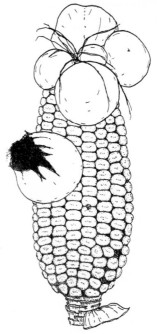

Fig. 66.—Eruption of "smut" pustules on ear of corn.

We will refer to these spores as "summer spores," naming them for the season of the year in which they are produced and in which they act. Their action is just what we might expect. Loosened from their stalks and carried by the wind, some of them reach neighboring wheat plants. There they produce a new generation of mycelia, which enter the breathing pores of the new hosts and establish themselves as internal parasites, similar in every respect to the parent mycelium.

This cycle may repeat itself frequently. The growing season of the wheat provides time for quite a series of crops of these summer spores, and each crop has ready accessibility to new hosts. Our single infected wheat plant of the early season may thus prove the source of an epidemic which spreads to millions of wheat plants before the time of harvest. The wheat crop may be impaired in quality or quantity, or even destroyed completely so far as its commercial value goes.

Two individual organisms with identical hereditary qualities may differ greatly in their expressed qualities if they have developed in significantly different environments. The same individual may change radically if exposed to a change of environmental conditions, particularly if this environmental change occurs during or before some period of active growth in the life of the organism. For most organisms the environment is the light and the air and the soil and all those things that we usually think of as making up the world about us. For an internal parasite the environment is provided by the tissues of the host. It follows that any significant change in the character of the host is likely to be followed by a change in the character of its internal parasite.

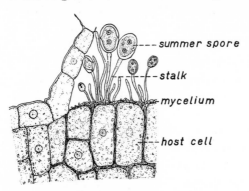

FIG. 67.—Section through the edge of a "blister" produced by eruption, through the skin layer of the wheat plant, of a mass of "summer spores." These are the distributing agents of the wheat rust fungus.

Toward the end of the growing season there is a waning of those conditions which have been favoring active food manufacture and growth in the wheat plant. The tissues of the wheat plant are now old, their life activities slowing down. The world in which the fungus has been living starts to change its character, and in response the fungus, too, behaves differently. The same mycelium that produced summer spores before now produces what we will call "winter spores," naming them not for the season in which they are produced (late summer or early fall) but for the season in which they exercise a highly significant function.

Just like the summer spores, the winter spores are produced singly on little stalks and emerge in small patches through the skin of the wheat, appearing on the stubble (stems) as well as on such leaves as may remain. These patches are black to the naked eye, and consequently the infection at this time is called "black stem stage." These individual winter spores show a heavy brown wall under the microscope. Unique among the spores that we have encountered, this spore is two-celled, but, as we shall see, the two cells are destined to act independently of each other in the production of new mycelia (Fig. 68).

The extremely heavy wall on the winter spore betrays to us the fact that this is the resting stage of the fungus. Attached to the stubble, the winter spore protects its two dormant cells until the coming of spring.

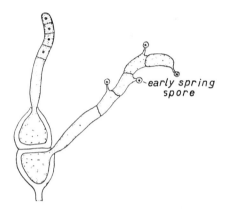

early spring spore

FIG. 68.—The two-celled winter spore of the wheat rust fungus. (The dark brown pigmentation of the heavy wall is not shown in this figure.)

FIG. 69.—Winter spore of the wheat rust fungus, producing the tiny mycelia, which in turn produce the early spring spores.

In early spring each of the two cells puts forth a mycelium which takes no nourishment, either parasitically or saprophytically, from its environment but subsists merely upon such food as has been stored within the spore itself. Under such a limitation it follows that this mycelium, at the stage of full development, is a dwarf by comparison with most other mycelia. At its free end it becomes divided into four cells, and each of the four puts forth a single stalk, bearing a single tiny spore (Fig. 69). These spores we will call the "early spring spores." This tiny mycelium, with its four cells, is the **basidium,** and the early spring spores are the **basidiospores.** Their action proved quite amazing to the botanists who first discovered it, and it continues to be amazing to modern botanists even though they know of many other similar cases.

As usual, chance alone determines where the early spring spore will be blown, but of all the types of plants on which it might be lodged there is only one that it can exploit, and that is *not* the wheat plant. Only when the spore reaches the common barberry bush will it establish an internal parasitic mycelium, for this barberry is the alternate host on which this fungus is just as dependent during one part of the year as it is dependent on the wheat during another. After falling on the common barberry leaf, the basidiospores form hyphae which pene-

Fig. 70.—Slightly enlarged sketch of an infected barberry leaf, showing four groups of "cluster cups."

trate the tissues of the host and develop into a many-branched mycelium. This mycelium forms small flask-shaped structures which emerge from the upper surface of the leaf. Very tiny spores called **spermatia** are produced by constriction from specialized hyphae in the structure. When these spores germinate, they in turn produce hyphae. There is a slight change with the type of spores and mycelia produced, both here and with the production of the basidiospores. The basidiospores may be of both + and − strains. They in turn produce hyphae and spermatia of + and − strains. When hyphae formed from + spermatia contact hyphae from − spermatia, a mycelium is produced, which for all practical purposes constitutes a union of gametes. No zygote is produced in the union, but there is a fusion of physiologically different kinds of protoplasm.

In the course of time this mycelium, too, produces its characteristic spores, "spring spores" in this case. In spore production the mycelium now formed within the barberry leaf develops a mass of stalks growing compactly together and pushing through the epidermis on the lower surface of the leaf. The general program resembles that which was followed in the production of summer spores and winter spores, but the final result is more picturesque. Instead of a single spore from each stalk, there is a linear series of spores, cut off successively and clinging together in regular formation. The entire "blister" is usually a perfect circle in this case, commonly known as a "cluster cup," of which many usually appear on the same leaf of the infected plant (Figs. 70, 71).

Once again spores are released; once again chance determines their distribution; and once again there is only one host that they can exploit. Such spring spores as chance to light on young wheat plants will produce an internally parasitic mycelium like that with which we started. The cycle is at last complete. In running its course, it has perpetuated the protoplasm of this fungus through five distinct types of mycelia and five types of spores. How this particular fungus, as well as many of its close relatives, ever evolved this strange method of exploiting alternate hosts is a question on which there has been much speculation and little elucidation.

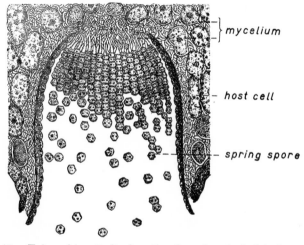

FIG. 71.—Enlarged longitudinal section through a single "cluster cup"

Although the most promising method of controlling wheat rust is the breeding of disease-resistant varieties of wheat, there is another line of attack on which the United States government has already spent millions of dollars, with moderately successful results. Taking a cue from the dependence of the fungus upon the alternate hosts, the government launched a campaign for the eradication of the common barberry from wheat-growing districts. In most regions the eradiction has been fairly thorough, and beneficial results have been observed.

It is doubtful, however, that the disease can ever be completely eradicated, because the summer spores overwinter in Mexico and southern United States; and then, as they are blown northward in spring, they infect field after field of growing wheat without going through the detailed cycle we have described.

Basidiomycetes of the wood-destroying type usually penetrate through a wound in the tree and may persist for decades within the host, until at last the weakened stem crashes in a windstorm. For reproduction the internal mycelium puts out the well-known "bracket," which carries millions of basidia with their spores (Fig. 72). These fungi are usually called **bracket** or **shelf fungi,** and the damage they cause runs into millions of dollars annually.

The most important Basidiomycetes, from an economic standpoint, are the parasitic forms, but the fleshy fungi, already referred to as

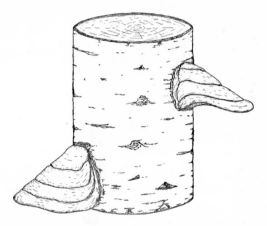

Fig. 72.—Two "brackets" emerging from the trunk of a host plant, within which the mycelium of the wood-destroying fungus has probably been present for many years. The tiny pores which cover the under surfaces of the brackets are the openings of cylindrical chambers which are lined with basidia.

mushrooms and toadstools, do occupy a conspicuous part of our saprophytic flora.

In the mushroom group the mycelium, ranging through the decaying vegetation at or near the soil surface, or through the tissues of a dead log or stump, puts forth reproductive branches which are enormous as compared with the vegetative mycelium itself. These branches are really very complex spore-bearing stalks, their "fleshy" substance being composed of a fairly compact arrangement of thousands of mycelial threads. In general contour they show variations on two conventional patterns, the "bracket" which extrudes from a log or stump, and the "umbrella" of the edible mushroom which arises from the ground. The fertile tissue of the reproductive branch is in the form of an extensive single layer of basidia, each of which yields the four (occasionally only two) spores. In the common edible mushroom and in many others this fertile layer coats the "gills" which hang in radial arrangement from the lower surface of the umbrella (Figs. 73, 74). In many forms the corresponding surface is flat, pierced by a vast number of tiny pores, the external openings of tiny cylindrical chambers which are lined by the layers of the basidia. The shape of the reproductive branches of some types is responsible for their name of **coral fungi;** here a good part of the outer surface is coated by the basidium layer. This is also true of the **spine fungi,** where the spore branch splits up rather irregularly and yields innumerable pendent spines (Fig. 75). The startlingly white color of the young spine fungus makes it an object of rare beauty, suggesting a winter scene from some Lilliputian forest.

Fig. 73.—Mushroom. The mycelium ("spawn") ranges through the decaying material at or near the soil surface and at last gives rise to the umbrella-like reproductive branches. The "button" shown at the right is the immature stage of the reproductive branch.

Scattered here and there through the mushroom group there are a few forms—fortunately fewer than is popularly believed—which produce poisonous alkaloids. These substances are of no apparent value to the organism themselves but are merely the inevitable by-products of their life processes. There is no sure criterion by means of which these poisonous forms may be distinguished in all cases, and therefore one must use extreme caution in collecting mushrooms for food.

In the mushroom group of the fleshy fungi the layers of basidia are carried on exposed surfaces, so that the spores are in contact with the external medium while they are ripening. In the **puffball** group the spores develop within a general enclosure from which they are released only when they are fully ripe. The common puffball itself is the simplest expression of this device. Here the entire reproductive branch constitutes the enclosure within which basidia are carried on a net-work of mycelial threads (Fig. 76). The size of the individual puffball varies greatly (probably hinging on the conditions surrounding its development), some being known to reach several feet in diameter. If one were to canvass the entire plant and animal kingdoms for the organisms with the highest potential reproductive ratio, he would have to award first place to some of the puffballs, for in some of the largest forms the number of spores produced by a single individual must exceed 1,000,000,000,000.

The **earthstar** (Fig. 77) is a puffball with a peculiar outer coat which peels back in the form of a star to expose the puffball proper

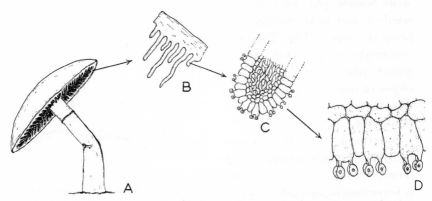

Fig. 74.—Spore production in the mushroom. *A*, the entire reproductive branch; *B*, longitudinal section through a few of the pendent gills; *C* and *D*, successive enlargements to show basidia and spores.

within. In the **bird's nest fungi,** shown in Figure 77 also, the pattern of the reproductive branches has to be seen to be believed. A surprisingly regular and trim nest of tissue contains a group of "eggs," each of which is actually a tiny puffball. Another interesting member of the group is popularly referred to by the inelegant title of **stinkhorn.** Here a mushroom-like stalk is surmounted by an enlargement which at maturity exposes a honeycombed surface covered with innumerable black spores (Fig. 78). The spore mass exudes the odor of carrion, which acts as a lure to the carrion flies. The flies lay their eggs on the sticky surface of the stinkhorn and also in the pores of many other forms. The spores forming in the fungus adhere to the bodies of the flies and are effectively distributed in this way. The fly eggs, on the other hand, hatch out into maggots, which then gain sustenance from the mushroom tissue and ultimately pupate into adult flies.

Deuteromycetes. Proper classification of any fungus—or of any plant, for that matter—demands a knowledge of its complete life cycle. If, for example, an ascus is present, the form will be put among the Ascomycetes; and then, on the basis of the detail of those structures which produce and surround the asci, as well as on the basis of the various spores and other features that may appear elsewhere in the life cycle, the form will be placed in the proper order, family, genus, and species of the ascomycete group.

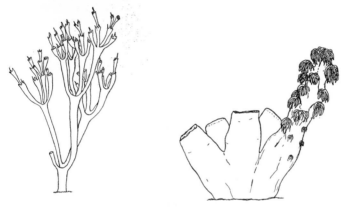

FIG. 75.—"Coral fungus," *left*, and "spine fungus," *right*

There remain many fungi, however, in which as yet man knows only a part of the life cycle, a part which includes no ascus or basidium but only spore types which are less definitive. This is not surprising in view of the microscopic proportions of fungi and the obscure quarters in which they sometimes live. Yet botanists are obliged to provide some classification for these imperfectly known forms, if for no other reason, because they include many that are of great economic importance. He meets the situation by assigning them to a great group known as *fungi imperfecti*. This he regards as a purely tentative assignment; for, as time passes, the missing stages of some of the life cycles are revealed, so that steadily the members of the **imperfect fungi** are transferred to the other groups, usually, as it turns out, to the Ascomycetes.

Many of the imperfect fungi are parasitic species; others are saprophytes. One of the best known imperfects is *Penicillium*. It is often classified with the Ascomycetes because of its vegetative habit and the type of spores it produces, but the perfect stage has never been observed, so we therefore classify *Penicillium* with the Deuteromycetes. Not only is *Penicillium* the fungus that produces the antibiotic penicillin from one of its species, but it has another species that grows in Roquefort cheese which gives this food its characteristic odor, color, and flavor. Occasionally we also see a blue mold growing on oranges or

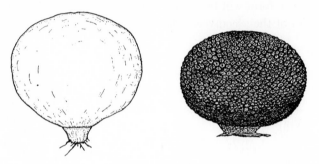

Fig. 76.—Puffballs

Fig. 77.—"Earthstar" on the left and "bird's nests" on the right

lemons; this is another species of *Penicillium* which ultimately causes complete decay of the fruit.

SYMBIOTIC ORGANISMS

Lichens. Many people, upon studying the dependent organisms and their various devices for exploiting living things, become genuinely depressed. To them it appears—particularly during their less vigorous and courageous moments—that a world in which success is built, in large part, upon a "ruthless" appropriation of the goods and destruction of the lives of other individuals is indeed an unhappy place in which to live. Since our universe is one in which matter and energy are never created but only transformed, the building-up process could not continue (for long) save at the expense of tearing down something else. So destruction of a sort will have to be accepted as a "law of life." To call it "ruthless" is to attribute to other organisms the concept of mercy, which is peculiarly human.

Some comfort, however, may be derived from the realization that destruction is by no means the only law of life. The needs of two organisms are often satisfied by a co-operation in which each is benefited and neither is damaged. A group of forms in which this is strikingly illustrated is the **lichens.**

A lichen is a compound of an alga and a fungus. The alga, surrounded and kept more or less moist by several layers of fungus mycelium, can utilize the sunlight that falls upon spots that would be far too dry to support the alga alone (Fig. 79). The fungus also benefits by this partnership through sharing the food that the alga has manufactured and does so without killing—and usually without even penetrating the cells of—its partner (Fig. 80). Both can thus live in regions that could support neither alone, and commonly in regions that can support no other form of life.

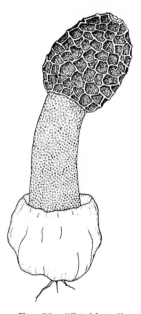

Fig. 78—"Stinkhorn"

The algal component can be removed from the lichen and can be kept alive independently. In some cases this has also been possible with the fungus component by providing a suitable nutritive medium. Some lichens have been synthesized artificially by bringing together algae and fungi that had not previously been thus associated in nature. In natural lichens the alga component is most commonly a unicellular blue-green or green alga, and the fungus component is almost always an Ascomycete.

The alga, imprisoned as it is within the surrounding fungus, has no opportunity to distribute itself by itself. The fungus may produce spores superficially and scatter them, but the resulting mycelia must come to naught save in those extremely rare instances when they might encounter a new algal partner. Effective reproduction of the lichen is accomplished by little budlike structures which include both alga and fungus elements, and which may be distributed by insects and other animals.

Some of the lichens are "professional pioneers." Repeatedly in the past, movements of the earth's crust have exposed great stretches of bare rock surface, thus creating dry, "sterile" areas, hopelessly in-

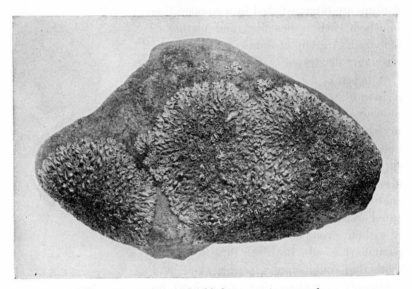

FIG. 79.—Photograph of lichens growing on rock

capable of supporting the ordinary forms of plant and animal life. But on these sterile rocky surfaces the lichens may make a start. Here they can eke out a living, for they have remarkable powers of resistance and dormancy to tide them over the long dry spells; and when rain comes they can soak it up like so much blotting paper and retain it to support a more "active" life for quite a period.

In the course of time, acids, which are by-products of the lichen's life processes, may gradually crumble the rock surface; and the lichen itself, dying and disintegrating, may add a bit of organic matter. In this way a tiny, shallow patch of soil is brought into existence, enough to provide a foothold for small hardy plants of other types. These, in turn, disintegrate the rock surface still more extensively and contribute their own dead bodies to the accumulation of material at the surface. More soil is thus produced; larger plants can come in; and there is thus launched a "plant succession" which culminates thousands of years later in a mighty forest, rooted in the several feet of soil which now cover the rock. Had it not been for the original lichen, this part of the earth's surface would have remained quite unavailable to man and beast.

Mycorrhizae. A relationship somewhat similar to that found in the lichens is that between certain soil fungi and the roots of higher plants. The term *mycorrhiza* is used to describe the combination of a fungus and a root. In some cases, such as with the roots of pine and related conifers, the fungi penetrate the root tissue and cause a hypertrophied growth similar to the bacterial nodules on legumes. These fungi are mostly of the **endotrophic** type, while those which remain on the outside of the root but in close association with it are of the **ectotrophic** type.

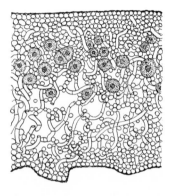

FIG. 80.—Microscopic view of longitudinal section through the body of a lichen, showing scattered cells of the alga component enmeshed in the mycelia threads of the fungus.

The biological significance of mycorrhizae is still conjectural, but they are not parasites in the true sense of the word. Soil parasites do exist in the world of fungi, and often they cause serious damage to crop plants, but mycorrhizae seem to have a very beneficial effect. In fact, some plants commonly associated with mycorrhizae do not do well when started as seedlings in soil lacking these fungi.

Herbaceous plants as well as broad-leaved trees almost always have numerous ectotrophic fungi associated with their roots, but few of them show the morphological changes associated with the mycorrhizae of the gymnosperms. The beneficial effect of these fungi is to aid in the decomposition of both organic and inorganic substances in the soil, helping to make available to the higher plants substances which would otherwise not readily go into solution. In a highly alkaline soil the additional carbon dioxide liberated by the fungi forms a greater amount of carbonic acid, which helps to lower the alkalinity and make available nutrients normally precipitated by a high pH. The immediate area around a root is known as the *rhizosphere.* Often this is only a few millimeters in diameter, including the root itself, but it is the area from which the root must absorb all of its water and nutrients. In this tiny environment the root finds itself associated with bacteria, fungi, algae, protozoans, and other microscopic forms, all of which live together far more satisfactorily than any could live alone.

XII. *The Invasion of the Land*

In present-day classification the botanist divides the plant kingdom into two subkingdoms, the THALLOPHYTA and the EMBRYOPHYTA. We have already seen that the former is a very heterogeneous group of organisms and is divided into nine phyla, while the latter is divided into only two. Certain outstanding differences are apparent between the two subkingdoms. The *thallophytes* are essentially aquatic plants; their reproductive bodies, if present, are unicellular and without multicellular protective walls; the zygote, when produced, is usually released soon after fertilization to fend for itself; and upon germination it produces zoospores or a new plant directly. With the appearance of the *embryophytes* we have plants which live primarily on land, although a few have gone back to water or moist soil, to which they are better adapted. Furthermore, we find that in the embryophytes the sex organs are multicellular. The egg is always surrounded by at least one layer of protective cells, and sperm have a similar protective jacket. The zygote in this group is retained within the female sex organ for some time, during which it divides to form a mass of cells which differentiate into the *embryo.* This characteristic is similar to that in the higher animals, where the embryo develops in the body of the female parent and secures its nutrition until it is capable of independent existence. The appearance of the embryo in the plant kingdom is correlated with the terrestrial habit. How this took place is largely conjectural, but possible explanations are certainly worthy of consideration.

At one time the thallophytes must have been exclusively water plants. The algae apparently made a start in fresh water, for today we find practically all the members of the most primitive group (blue-greens) living in that medium. Later on, a few lines of descent evidently invaded the oceans; today we find that with very few exceptions the members of the more specialized groups (brown and red algae) live their lives in salt water. The green algae, which represent a more heterogeneous group than any of the algae, probably arose in fresh water, and most of them stayed there, although a few found the sea more suitable. In all probability the fungi also made a start in water. This is suggested by the fact that there are today many water-inhabiting types among the primitive (alga-like) classes of fungi.

Hence one pictures the ancient earth as devoid of any vegetation on the exposed land surfaces—a barren, lifeless land, for if there were no land plants there could hardly have been land animals. At the same time, many of the fresh-water streams and ponds and the oceans themselves may have been teeming with life. Countless billions of simple alga plants, endowed with chlorophyll, were busily converting some of the simple materials which bathed them into food and protoplasm. Primitive animals, which may well have put in their appearance by this time, were doubtless preying upon the food-containing algae. And preying upon both algae and animals were water-inhabiting fungi and countless tiny bacteria.

This state of affairs may have continued for millions of years, with few significant changes in the picture. And all this time there lay at the very doorstep the great domain of the land surface, a treasure land for living things, with its vast wealth of unexploited energy and its tremendous variety of prospective habitats.

Inevitably a few of the water organisms were cast out onto the land by waves, stranded by falling tides or by the seasonally receding waters of fresh-water ponds and streams. In practically all cases the result was death. Protoplasm had been adapted to a water medium; it was fundamentally of such a nature that its activity and continued existence depended absolutely upon the presence of water. Stranded on land, the alga would be bathed in air, so that its protoplasm would dry out and die.

Some few of these early adventurers, however, may have managed to maintain themselves on land and there eke out a precarious existence. Today one encounters a very few types of green algae (e.g., *Protococcus*) and a few more of the blue-greens that live not actually submerged in water but in places that are moist, or usually moist.

Perhaps these few types have been successful (where most of their associates failed) through some quality of their walls or sheaths which resisted somewhat the drying influence of the air. Perhaps it was because they had perfected the trick of dormancy, putting their protoplasm to sleep on very low water rations during times that were dry and reawakening it when rain, dew, or moist air returned. In any event, these diminutive early invasions led very little further. They suggest the early Viking colonies in North America. Thoroughgoing conquest was to come much later and was to be initiated along other lines.

Fungi (and bacteria) are today fairly successful land-living forms. Only a moment's consideration, however, tells us that the invasion of the land by fungi was an event (or better, a series of events) that occurred comparatively late in the history of life on earth. Fungi are dependent forms, parasites and saprophytes. The parasites could not have invaded the land until host plants and host animals were already established there. The saprophytes could have taken the step only after there had been enough living organisms on land to leave a litter of organic debris.

It is quite conceivable, however, that the lichens effected an early invasion of the land surface that was successful along limited lines. We have no evidence to tell us when this might have occurred. In any event, it is clear that lichens have not given rise to descendant forms that are significantly higher than themselves. The conquest of the land surface that was to lead to our higher plants was initiated by still another group of invaders.

Of the two remaining phyla, which we have not described—the **Bryophyta** and **Tracheophyta**—the former have species which offer a possible explanation for land invasion. The exact origin of the bryophytes is still one of the unsolved problems of plant evolution, but there is considerable agreement that they may have been derived from green algae of aquatic habit. One of the reasons it is so difficult to place the bryophytes in a position of much greater antiquity than the tracheophytes is that we cannot find fossil remains of them, with any certainty, beyond that of the earliest tracheophytes. Still, their simplicity is such that they must have had very humble ancestors, and they have the characteristics of plants that are not long removed from the aquatic habit.

The Bryophyta are divided into three major classes: Class Hepaticae (liverworts), Class Anthocerotae (hornworts), and Class Musci
(mosses). The order in which they are given here is not necessarily
their correct phylogenetic sequence; for this group, as it is now interpreted, has several distinct lines of evolution, all of which seem to have
developed in a parallel manner. It would be to our advantage to consider first the general nature of that portion of the plant body which
first managed to survive on land.

The thallus which we find among the simplest of liverworts today
suggests the type of structure which first emerged from the water.
Clearly the ancestor of plants with such a body was a green alga, and
in all probability it was a type of green alga that possessed a platelike
body. True, most green algae possess single-celled or filamentous
bodies, and this was doubtless as true in the past as it is today, for such
bodies are well adapted to a water medium. By the same token, however, such bodies are poorly constructed for life in the air. The single-
celled type would have its entire cell surface exposed to the drying
influence of the atmosphere, and in a filament, whether it was
branched or unbranched, the bulk of the surface of every cell would be
exposed. But if the body were a plate of cells (one layer of cells in
thickness), all the cells save those at the very edges would be pretty
well protected by contact with their neighbors and would be exposed
only on the upper and lower surfaces. Presumably such an alga,
stranded on the bank of a pond, would stand a better chance of surviving than would most of its relatives.

Of the first countless millions of green algae with platelike bodies
that were left out on muddy banks, perhaps all but one wilted and perished. This one may have survived in the new habitat for any of a
number of reasons—most likely because it chanced to be better
adapted to life in the new medium, because it happened to possess
some feature which better enabled it to resist the drying influence of
the atmosphere. What this particular feature was is a matter of conjec-
ture. About all that we can be confident of is that three significant features were connected with the invasion of the land, for even the simplest of the surviving liverworts possess these three features.

One feature—probably the first one—was a **compact body,** i.e.,
a body several layers of cells thick. In such a body all the cells save
those in the superficial layers are insulated against the evaporating

influence of the air, so that the total surface area of the plant is reduced in proportion to its volume, and the "average exposure per cell" is considerably less than in a body one layer in thickness.

A second adaptive feature was the **prostrate habit.** Those plate-like green algae which we find today either float free or are, at best, attached to their substratum by one "corner" only. This might be expected where it is to the advantage of the organism to expose a maximum of surface to the surrounding medium. Of necessity, however, the early land invaders must have adopted a different habit. The ribbon-like bodies of liverworts lie flat in the mud and are attached to it all along their lower surfaces. This reduces the exposed surface by practically half and maintains effective contact with the only available source of water (Fig. 81).

The third primary adaptation was the introduction of the first real **tissue,** one of vital significance to all land-living descendants, as is the corresponding tissue to all land animals. This tissue was the **epidermis.** In plants, "epidermis" refers to the one superficial cell layer which surrounds the entire body.

Fig. 81.—Sketch of the prostrate, ribbon-like body of the liverwort *Marchantia.*

The cells of the epidermis are packed closely together, leaving no interstices between; in regions where the body surface is exposed to the air, the cell walls (particularly the outer cell walls) are thickened and impregnated with a waterproofing material. Thus the land plant is provided with a natural "raincoat," but the value of this coat is in preventing the exit of water rather than its entrance.

Any innovation, valuable as it may be in moderation and in serving pressing current needs, usually proves dangerous if carried to an extreme. An epidermis is of value in keeping a land plant from drying out, but a perfect and complete epidermis would kill the plant just as surely, by starvation as well as suffocation. The process of food manufacture by green plants requires light as a source of energy and water and carbon dioxide as the raw materials. Algae, submerged in fairly shallow water, get their sunlight from above and readily take in from the surrounding medium not only water itself but carbon dioxide, which is dissolved in the water. For a land plant, such as our pioneer liverwort, the situation is different. Sunlight readily penetrates the transparent epidermis to the chloroplast-containing cells beneath. Water is soaked up (diffuses) from the mud beneath and passes to the chloroplasts. For a land plant, however, the small amount of carbon dioxide that might be dissolved in the soil water would provide an inadequate supply for the purposes of food manufacture. Instead, the carbon dioxide of the atmosphere must enter in the form of gas. It is for this reason that a complete epidermis would prove fatal. The epidermis is impermeable to gases as well as to water vapor.

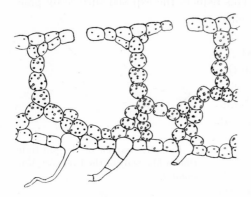

FIG. 82.—Longitudinal section through a very primitive liverwort body, showing simple breathing pores in the upper epidermis opening into simple air chambers.

One finds, therefore, that the epidermis of every land plant is punctured by many microscopic pores which open into air chambers. In the simpler liverworts the pores are little more than irregular clefts in the epidermis (Fig. 82). Among some of the more specialized liverworts, however, the **breathing pore** is a fairly elaborate device surrounded by a "chimney" arrangement of tiny epidermal cells and leading into a rather symmetrically designed air chamber beneath (Fig. 83). Plants of still higher phyla possess a fairly well standardized type of pore, in which the opening itself is surrounded by a pair of sausage-shaped cells, which you will remember is called a *stomate* (see Fig. 4).

A biological principle that is illustrated by countless examples in the plant kingdom, and by even more striking examples in the animal kingdom, is as follows: *Organisms which are usually surrounded on all sides by the same conditions have homogeneous bodies; organisms which usually encounter different sets of conditions on different sides are organized into different body regions, each region being adjusted to the conditions which it meets.*

Among the highest types of plants and animals this specialization of body regions is quite complex and adapts the organism remarkably well to the general enterprise of "getting the most that is possible out of the environment." But these niceties of adjustment have not been worked out overnight. They are the end-products of an incredibly long series of evolutionary changes which are continuing even today.

An illustration of the earlier and simpler stages in the differentiation of body regions is provided by the **liverworts.** Here the body shape

Fig. 83.—Longitudinal section through the body of the liverwort *Marchantia*, showing one of the chimney-like breathing pores opening into an air chamber. The filamentous extension into the air chamber of those cells which are best equipped with chloroplasts makes for a rapid supply of carbon dioxide to those cells that are using it most.

and orientation is such as to create two distinct surfaces, upper and lower, which continuously encounter different sets of environmental conditions. The upper surface is coated with a protective and transparent epidermis, save for the tiny breathing pores which permit the entrance of gaseous carbon dioxide in the interests of food manufacture. Beneath the breathing pores the first few layers of cells are in a spongy rather than compact organization; i.e., a system of connected air channels permits the carbon dioxide to reach the surfaces of all the chloroplast-containing cells.

But the cells in the lowest layers of the body are poorly situated for food manufacture. They are virtually "in the shade," for the cells above have caught the sunlight first, permitting only a tiny remnant of the energy-giving rays to filter through. One finds the cells of the lower layers in fairly compact arrangement. Their job is not food manufacture but water intake. The lowest layer of all is, technically, an "epidermis." On this part of the epidermis, however, cell walls are thin and are *not* impregnated with waterproofing material. It is to the advantage of the plant that water should pass easily through this surface.

The intake of water through the lower surface of a liverwort is proportional to the area of that surface. Here one encounters another biological principle that comes into play in many and various situations in the plant and animal kingdoms. *Where the amount of the function depends upon the area of some exposed surface (and where it is to the advantage of the organism to increase the amount of that function), there will be a change, in the course of evolution, from a smooth to an irregular surface.* The absorbing area on the lower surface of a liverwort is greatly increased by extending some of the cells in **rhizoids,** long, hairlike processes that penetrate the soil (see Fig. 83).

Here, then, one sees the beginnings of a differentiation into upper and lower body regions. The sharpness and the elaborateness of this differentiation are less among some (presumably the more primitive) than among other (presumably the more advanced) liverworts, and in no liverwort is the differentiation carried as far as among plants of still higher groups.

The adaptations we have discussed thus far, namely, compact body, prostrate habit, and epidermis, are by no means the only changes that have taken place. Nor do we mean to imply that these changes evolved together and simultaneously. Actually these adaptations must have been evolved gradually, probably one before the other; or first one progressed a bit and then another. But they were all headed in the same direction, and that was to make this plant better suited for life on land. Again it must be made clear that this did not involve "thought" on the part of the plant. It did not try an epidermis and then say to itself, "I like this tissue; I seem to be able to live longer out of water with it. Now I'll try a more compact body and see what that does." What happened was that these structures simply occurred through the millennia because of changes in the chromosomes which brought about desirable characteristics in the plant, and these characteristics survived and were inherited from generation to generation. Gradually other innovations appeared, and finally many of these were brought together in new individuals. Such plants were able to survive, and did; others were unable to meet the stresses as did their more successful brothers, and perished.

XIII. *Life among Liverworts and Mosses*

Subkingdom EMBRYOPHYTA
    Phylum BRYOPHYTA
        Class Hepaticae—liverworts
        Class Anthocerotae—hornworts
        Class Musci—mosses

Hepaticae. Members of this class are somewhat more varied in form than those of the other two classes. Most of the liverworts have ribbon-like bodies that are quite simple in external outlines but usually thicker than those of the other groups. Exceptions to the thick thallus, described in the preceding chapter, do exist, and these are generally referred to as *leafy liverworts.* They often have tiny leaflike lobes sprouting off a main axis; this gives them a "mossy" appearance.

We have discussed some of the innovations which occurred in the vegetative body in the transition of plants from water to land. It would be surprising indeed if the land habit did not also bring innovations in reproductive methods. For the most part we have used a liverwort as an example of this transitional land plant. One of the best known of the liverworts is the genus *Marchantia*, which we will use to describe changes that took place in reproduction. In *Marchantia* one finds three methods of reproduction, two asexual and one sexual. Not all liverworts have the same asexual methods, but basically the sexual organs are the same, fertilization occurs in the same way, and the embryo develops similarly with some modifications.

At one end of the ribbon-like body of *Marchantia* one always finds a characteristic notch. It is a small group of actively dividing cells right around this notch that is primarily responsible for growth of the body.

The notch is the *growing point,* and it moves forward as it lays down new cells behind it. Occasionally the growing point divides itself into two co-ordinate growing points, each of which continues with the process of laying down new cells. This results in a forking of the ribbon-like body into two small ribbons of equal magnitude (see Fig. 81). Later each of these branches may fork again, and so on, without any apparent limit. Under this system of growth the youngest parts of the body are always at the front, nearest the notch, the oldest parts behind. Hence death "from old age," or as some call it, "death from behind," occurs first in the rearmost portion of the ribbon and moves forward from that point. When death reaches a fork, it effectively divides the plant in two, for the two branches, no longer connected by living tissue, continue to carry out independent existences. Here, then, is about the simplest conceivable method of *vegetative multiplication* or *fragmentation,* corresponding to what we encountered in the bread mold and to what occurs in innumerable other plants.

A second method of reproduction that occurs in *Marchantia* and in some of the other liverworts is apparently a more refined and specialized method of vegetative multiplication. Here and there on the upper surface of the body appear dainty *cupules* about one-eighth of an inch in diameter. Within each of these little cups there develop a score or so of tiny disk-shaped bodies, each at the upper end of a very short stalk. These bodies, single-celled at the outset, are at maturity many-celled affairs a little smaller than the smallest pinhead. Each disk bears a pair of notches on opposite sides, so that the whole disk suggests an attached pair of "twin" parts; hence the name *gemma* has been applied to the disk (Fig. 84). Breaking from their stalks, the gemmae are sometimes distributed by becoming attached temporarily to the bodies of birds, insects, or other small animals. If a gemma reaches moist soil, it will proceed to grow, for each of its notches contains a growing point. Theoretically it should develop into a double-ended *Marchantia* plant. Actually, one of the growing points almost always gains ascendancy over the other, so that the resulting *Marchantia* plant develops in only one direction.

The third type of life cycle that appears in *Marchantia* is much more elaborate. At certain seasons, some of the growing points cease adding to the length of the body and produce instead vertical stalks surmounted by horizontal disks. Prior to this, all *Marchantia* plants have looked alike, but now it becomes evident that there are really two types of plants with respect to their potentialities. On some of the plants the stalked disks are comparatively flat and almost perfectly rounded, with only a series of slight indentations along their borders; but on other plants the corresponding indentations are much greater, so that the edges of the disks are broken up into a series of pendulous promontories called *rays.* As we shall see, the former plants are male, the stalks they yield being *male gametophores* and the disks *antheridial disks;* the latter plants are female, their stalks being *female gametophores* and their disks *archegonial disks.*

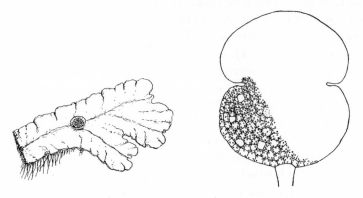

Fig. 84.—*On the left,* a "cupule" on the upper surface of the body of *Marchantia,* as one might see it under a hand lens. *On the right,* a microscopic view of a single "gemma," together with a portion of the stalk which carried it.

A vertical section through an antheridial disk (Fig. 85) reveals several cavities within. In each cavity, and almost filling the cavity, is an *antheridium,* or male sex organ. This is a many-celled affair composed of a short sterile stalk and an enlarged upper portion. The outermost layer of this upper portion is merely a protective epidermis. Within is a solid mass of packed cubical cells, each of which, at maturity, produces two tiny, ciliated *sperm.* With the maturing of the sperm, the wall of the antheridium breaks, and a small passageway between the antheridial chamber and the upper surface of the disk opens. A drop of rain or a film of dew provides a medium through which the sperm can swim out into the open.

Meanwhile *archegonia,* the female sex organs, have been developing on the archegonial disks. In this case the sex organs are not buried

in cavities but hang down from the lower surface of the disk (Fig. 86).
The archegonium is also a many-celled structure, shaped like an old-
fashioned wine flask, with long, thin neck and swollen base. The base
is attached to the archegonial disk and consists of a protective layer
(usually becoming more than one cell in thickness as the archegonium
matures) and one large, passive *egg* within. The long, pendulous neck
is perfectly sterile. In a young archegonium this neck is solid tissue,
but, by the time the egg is mature, a passageway opens up through the
core of the neck, leading from the free end of the neck up to the egg
itself.

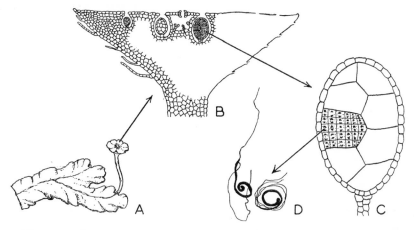

Fig. 85.—The sperm-producing structures in *Marchantia*. *A*, horizontal body of
male plant with erect male gametophore surmounted by antheridial disk; *B*, longitudinal section through antheridial disk, showing antheridia carried in chambers
near the upper surface; *C*, enlargement of a single antheridium, with stalk, epidermis, and mass of sperm-producing cells; *D*, mature sperm, greatly enlarged.

Since the sperm requires a medium of water for its movement, the
transfer of the sperm from the point of its origin to its functional destination becomes a serious problem in *Marchantia*, where the sex organs are produced upon different plants. As among many algae, the
egg exudes a chemical which directs the sperm in their movements, but
only a very rare set of conditions would make it possible for this chemical to diffuse through a continuous medium of water to the antheridial
disks. Actually, fertilization fails very often in this genus. The conditions favoring fertilization are a dense growth of mixed male and female plants (so that the two types of gametophores form a thick

miniature forest) and a drenching rain. At such a time some sperm may indeed find a continuous water passage to the eggs, but probably still more of them reach their destination by being splashed over from antheridial to archegonial disk.

The resulting zygote germinates immediately. Its product is not another plant of the type on which it was produced but a plant of the **alternate generation.** In liverworts, and in all higher plants, sexual reproduction is consistently tied up with a life cycle that is character-

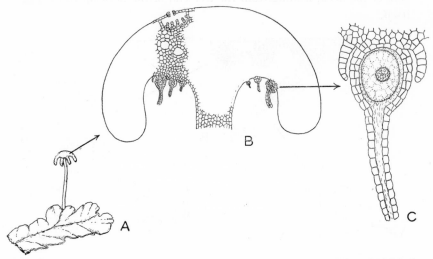

Fig. 86.—The egg-producing structures in *Marchantia*. *A*, horizontal body of female plant with erect female gametophore surmounted by archegonial disk; *B*, longitudinal section through archeogonial disk, showing archegonia hanging from the lower surface; *C*, enlargement of the flask-shaped archegonium containing its single egg.

ized by this alternation of generations. The main body of the plant (i.e., male and female plants), which has already been described, con- stitutes the **gametophyte** (gamete-producing plant). The gameto- phyte generation produces gametes, which fuse to form a zygote. This zygote develops into the **sporophyte** (spore-producing plant).

In *Marchantia* the gametophyte is the green, independent genera- tion of the two. The sporophyte, practically devoid of chlorophyll, de- velops parasitically at the expense of the gametophyte. The first cell of the sporophyte generation is the zygote itself. The zygote, remain- ing within the swollen base of the pendent archegonium, divides repeatedly to form a mass of cells. These cells soon become organized into three body regions: (1) a *foot,* which pushes its way back into the tissues of the archegonial disk, anchors the developing sporophyte, and secures food for it from its host; (2) a *stalk* just below the foot, short at first but elongating just before the maturity of the sporophyte; and (3) at the lower end, a *capsule,* which becomes a spheroidal body consisting of an inclosing epidermis and a mass of spores, together with a few specialized sterile cells, within (Fig. 87).

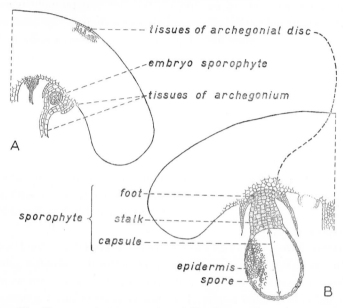

tissues of archegonial disc

embryo sporophyte

tissues of archegonium

A

sporophyte { foot

stalk

capsule

epidermis

spore

B

Fig. 87.—The sporophyte generation of *Marchantia. A,* young embryo sporophyte retained within the swollen base of the old archegonium; *B,* mature sporophyte which has burst through the old archegonium and is now anchored by its foot in the tissues of the archegonial disk.

During its early stages of development the sporophyte is retained in the swollen base of the old archegonium, which for a time enlarges to keep pace with the growth of the embryo plant within. Sooner or later, of course, the archegonium wall is ruptured, and shortly thereafter the epidermis of the capsule breaks, releasing a shower of ripe spores. (The same archegonial disk commonly carries quite a number of sporophytes in various stages of development.)

As in the air-living fungi, these spores, instead of being naked and ciliated, are covered with walls that resist desiccation. Clearly they are adapted for distribution by currents of air, and the average extent of their distribution will depend on the height from which they are dropped. In this connection one notes an unusually awkward form of adaptation in *Marchantia*. To facilitate distribution of spores, *Marchantia* elongates its gametophores. In a way this effects the desired result, but at the expense of putting the sex organs in such a position as to make fertilization difficult. Living organisms are, in general, remarkably efficient bits of machinery, but not uncommonly one encounters adjustments that are seemingly quite clumsy. One must conclude that the capacities for adaptation by living organisms in the course of their evolution are by no means infinite but are actually restricted within rather narrow limits that are set by the structural peculiarities of their ancestors.

Reaching moist ground, the spore germinates to produce the gametophyte generation. Though all spores are quite alike in appearance and in the apparent characteristics of their immediate products, some of the young gametophytes develop into males and the others into females. When spores of the same plant are similar in appearance, the plants are said to be **homosporous;** when they are different, the plant is **heterosporous.** All members of the Phylum Bryophyta are homosporous.

Anthocerotae. Although often included as an order in the Hepaticae, the Anthocerotae constitute a natural series that shows a general relationship to other members of the phylum, but it does not seem to be immediately related to any. The class consists of but 5 genera and about 320 species. *Anthoceros* is the most commonly studied **hornwort,** and it would serve our purpose well to give a brief description of its growth habits.

In *Anthoceros* the gametophyte generation is quite simple in both form and structure. In fact, bryologists often consider the gametophyte of *Anthoceros* to be the simplest in the bryophytes. The sex organs, instead of being borne up on elaborate gametophores, are simply produced in little grooves on the upper side of the gametophyte. Both antheridium and archegonium are similar in structure to those of *Marchantia*, but the latter has its neck pointing up rather than down. After fertilization—a much simpler matter than in *Marchantia*—the zygote immediately develops into the sporophyte. Necessarily this sporophyte grows upward from the gametophyte rather than downward from the archegonial disk. A recognizable foot pushes back into the gametophyte tissue, but the rest of the sporophyte, instead of being differentiated into stalk and capsule, consists merely of a cylinder of tissue, about the size of a small grass blade, which rises vertically into the air (Fig. 88).

In cross-section, the sporophyte of *Anthoceros* reveals a series of tissues, arranged concentrically: on the outside, an epidermis; next, a zone of sterile cells, several cell layers in thickness, usually containing chloroplasts; next, a zone of **sporogenous** (spore-producing) cells; and on the inside, a core of tiny, sterile cells (Fig. 89). The sporogenous cells at the upper end are the first to yield mature spores, and this ripening process occurs progressively from the top to the bottom of the sporophyte. As fast as the spores are ripe, the sterile regions outside release them by splitting and peeling back, somewhat as one might peel a banana. Thus the spores are distributed over quite a period of time.

FIG. 88.—*Anthoceros*. Three sporophytes arising from the horizontal gametophyte. In each case the sporophyte foot is invisible, being bedded in the tissues of the gametophyte. The little "collar" around the base of each sporophyte consists of gametophytic tissue.

Perhaps the most significant feature of the *Anthoceros* sporophyte, however, is connected with the sterile zone which lies just inside the epidermis. Each cell in this zone contains a large chloroplast. Thus the *Anthoceros* sporophyte is green and photosynthesizes food. The epidermis contains a number of stomates which facilitate the exchange of gases for photosynthesis and respiration. Through the instrumentality of its foot, the sporophyte still depends on the gametophyte for water and soil salts, but it has taken the most significant step in shaking off its dependency and becoming a self-sufficient generation. As we shall see later, the significant progress of plants of the higher groups was based upon the attainment of an independent sporophyte generation. Of all bryophytes known, *Anthoceros* most strongly suggests the condition of the ancestor from which the higher groups descended.

In the Bryophyta we have introduced an alternation of generations in which one phase, known as the gametophyte generation, is completely independent. By "independent" we mean that the plant possesses chlorophyll and is able to carry on all its life processes without the aid of any other parts. The gametophyte generation begins with the spore and has the haploid or reduced number of chromosomes. Alternating with the gametophyte generation is the sporophyte. In all EMBRYOPHYTA the sporophyte generation begins with the zygote, and, because it is the result of the union of a haploid egg and a haploid sperm, it becomes a diploid zygote. All tissues derived from the zygote are diploid until reduction division occurs; it is accomplished by the division of the spore mother cells in the sporangia to form spores.

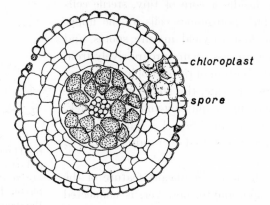

FIG. 89.—Enlarged cross-section of the green sporophyte of *Anthoceros*

Steps involved in such a life cycle are represented in the summarized diagram of *Marchantia* (Fig. 90). In the Bryophyta the sporophytic generation is parasitic on the gametophyte. In other words, all or most of its sustenance must come from the gametophyte. Later we shall see that both generations may be independent in some higher plants, and in still higher ones the gametophyte becomes parasitic on the sporophyte.

Musci. There are about 650 genera and approximately 13,500 species of mosses. They are world-wide in their distribution and occupy as diverse a group of habitats as any of the terrestrial plants. Nevertheless, they remain a fairly inconspicuous part of our flora. They have not achieved what we might call an "area of dominance." That is, they have never been the dominant plant in any large area. They have always remained marginal plants. We do find that the mosses are less restricted than the Hepaticae and Anthocerotae, but even so, the area Musci cover is usually limited to a few square feet. A few of the mosses are aquatic, and some live under very desiccating conditions, but the majority live in densely wooded areas, growing on soil, rocks, logs, and the bark of living trees.

The term **moss** is often misused in the identification of different plants. The green scum floating on a quiet pond is often called "moss"

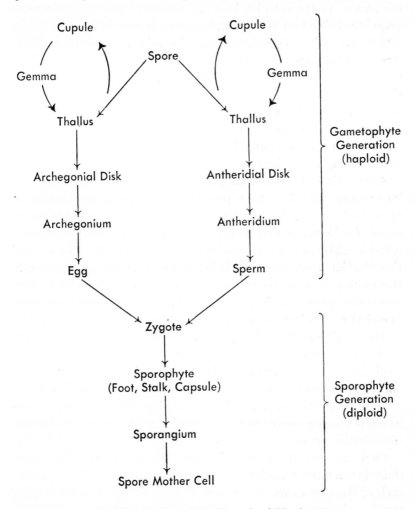

Fig. 90.—Outline of the life cycle of *Marchantia*

when actually it is an alga; an edible red alga is called "Irish moss"; a genus of lichens used for food by caribou has been given the common name of "reindeer moss"; among the tracheophytes is a group of small plants related to the ferns and called "club mosses"; finally there is a small epiphyte related to the pineapple which grows on trees and other supporting structures in our southern states and is known as "Spanish moss." With this free use of the term, it is no wonder that we are often confused in trying to identify, with any certainty, many of our plants. To the botanist, however, a moss plant is a very definite organism. It is a very tiny plant, but so gregarious in its habit that it usually grows in a very dense mat. The primary moss body which emerges from a spore is nothing more pretentious than a branching, green filament, resembling the body of a green alga, which helps to show a possible origin from an algal ancestor. This body grows horizontally on the surface of moist soil, soaking up water and carrying on the manufacture of food by means of its chloroplasts. Altogether this structure, the *protonema,* is so small that it usually escapes the notice of the casual observer.

After a time the protonema produces tiny "buds" which open up into vertical branches. Each protonema may produce a number of these vertical branches, or "leafy shoots," as they are frequently called. The branch is much larger than the primary body, being many-celled in caliber, and it is covered throughout its length with a series of tiny, leaflike structures. (Technically these are not "true leaves," though they resemble the true leaves of higher plants not only in their superficial appearance but in their function.) It is this erect leafy branch that constitutes the moss plant of popular experience (Fig. 91).

The growing point at the upper end continues to add to the length of the erect branch and to give off more and more "leaves" until the total size has been attained that is characteristic of the species. (This may be anywhere from a fraction of an inch to a few inches in height.) At this stage the growing point, instead of adding further to the length of the vegetative body, devotes itself to the construction of the reproductive organs.

From the very tip of the axis there will arise several tiny, club-shaped structures. Examination under the microscope will reveal that each of these structures is a many-celled affair. The basal portion is merely a short stalk composed of several *sterile cells,* i.e., cells which are not destined later to yield reproductive cells. This short stalk is surmounted by a swollen and roughly cigar-shaped region, which consists of a single, sterile, epidermal layer on the outside and a mass of cubical *spermatogenous* cells on the inside. As the name implies, the spermatogenous cells are destined to produce the sperm, each cell producing two minute, ciliated male gametes. When the sperm are fully developed, the sterile epidermal wall breaks, so that the sperm can escape and swim about in any water that may be present at the tip of the leafy branch.

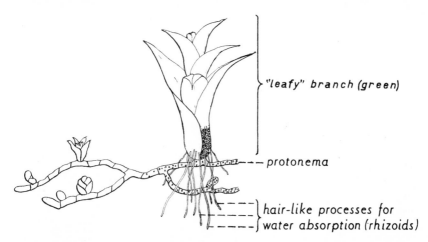

"leafy" branch (green)

protonema

hair-like processes for water absorption (rhizoids)

Fig. 91.—Diagram to show the relationship of the primary filamentous body of a moss and the "leafy" branch which arises from it. The filamentous body is seldom noticed by the casual observer, for it is relatively even smaller than the diagram indicates and is stretched out horizontally on the soil surface, where it is often pretty well concealed by the soil particles.

The sperm-producing structures are, of course, antheridia, and as in all Bryophyta they are many-celled structures (Fig. 92). With but few exceptions, the sex organs of thallophytes are single-celled, so that we have here one of the best of distinctions between the two great groups. The significance of the distinction is really connected with the land habit of the bryophytes, for the many-celled condition is due (in large part) to the protective epidermal layer around the gamete-producing cells.

Female sex organs are also produced at the upper ends of the leafy branches. In some species of moss the two kinds of sex organs grow mixed together at the end of the same leafy branch, while in other species male and female organs are produced on separate plants. The terms commonly given these situations are **monoecious** and **dioecious**. When only female or male sex organs are produced in a single leafy branch, the plant is dioecious; when both female and male sex organs appear together in a leafy branch, the plant is monoecious. The female sex organ is also many-celled. The base (at maturity) consists of one large passive egg surrounded, as in all archegonia, by one or more layers of sterile epidermal cells (Fig. 93). When the egg is ready to be

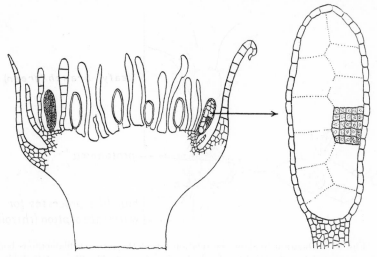

Fig. 92.—The male reproductive structures of the moss: *at the left,* a longitudinal section through the tip of a "leafy" branch, showing male sex organs interspersed with sterile hairs; *at the right,* an enlargement of a single male sex organ, showing the sterile stalk and epidermis and the fertile "spermatogenous" cells within.

fertilized, the neck canal cells disintegrate, and sperm are attached to this passageway by a chemical exuded from the egg.

The zygote that results from fertilization starts at once to produce the next generation. This new generation, however, is very different from the one which preceded it, for the life cycle of the moss is characterized by an alternation of generations similar to that in *Marchantia,* although the individual parts are morphologically quite different.

The young sporophyte of the moss, in the earliest increment of its growth, pushes a bulbous foot down into the tissues of the leafy branch, thus providing anchorage and a means of absorbing food for the mature sporophyte that is to come. With these basal connections well established, the developing sporophyte next enters into a period of rapid elongation, producing an upright "stalk" that is usually a little longer than the leafy branch that carries it (Fig. 94). As the stalk elongates, its tip region begins to swell, culminating at last in the production of the **capsule.** This is the most complex structure that is to

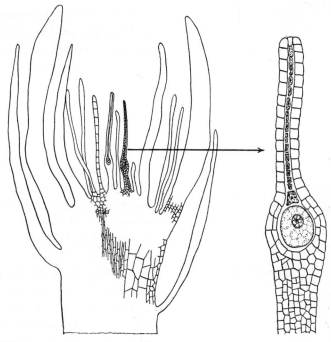

FIG. 93.—The female reproductive structures of the moss: *at the left,* a longitudinal section through the tip of a "leafy" branch, showing female sex organs interspersed with sterile hairs; *at the right,* an enlargement of a single female sex organ, carrying its single egg.

be found among bryophytes, and yet it ends with this group. Its complexities appear to be devoted to the production of thousands of tiny spores and to the release of these spores into the air when they are ripe. The few fortunate spores which reach moist soil develop into the green, branching filaments, the protonemata, of the next gametophyte generation. Thus sexual (gametophyte) and sexless (sporophyte) generations regularly alternate in the life cycle of the moss.

Among the many subgroups of the mosses there is one that deserves special mention. This is the group of **bog mosses.** Though these forms possess certain structural peculiarities, it is not difficult to recognize the correspondence between their structures and those of the other mosses. It is not their structure, however, that here commends them to our attention, but rather their habitat and their interesting action on that habitat.

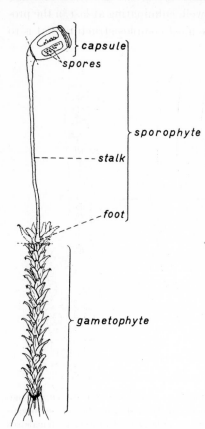

FIG. 94.—Diagram of the parasitic sporophyte of the moss, imbedded in the leafy branch of the gametophyte.

Geological events, notably the action of glaciers, have left many northern regions spotted with small ponds and lakes. It is along the shores of such small, quiet bodies of water that the bog mosses take up an abode. Starting at the very water line, these little plants, by copious branching and vegetative multiplication, produce an ever widening mat of vegetation which steadily pushes inward over the surface of the pond. In time the pond is completely roofed over by a fairly thick layer of the material and is thus converted into a "quaking bog." If one walks out onto such a surface, it gives under his feet in a disquieting way, and the vibration spreads in all directions, since the surface layer is cushioned on water.

At a still later stage the pond is practically eliminated, being filled up completely by debris dropped from the bog moss and by the older moss bodies themselves, which are constantly forced downward as new branches are added at the upper surface. This action paves the way for a succession of larger plants, whose root action and dying bodies gradually convert what was once a body of water into an area of rich soil. Our bog mosses have thus been the pioneers in a "plant succession" which culminates in the production of a forest of lofty trees.

The bog mosses have but a single genus, *Sphagnum;* yet from an economic standpoint they are of greater importance than all other members of the phylum. The "leaves" of *Sphagnum* are very absorptive structures; during Civil War days wads of *Sphagnum* were used to dress the open wounds of men from both armies; it has also been used in stuffing furniture and as humus in soil to increase water retention capacity; and today its most important use is fuel. Many square miles of peat lands have been built up through years of *Sphagnum* growth. It has proved to be a cheap but valuable fuel in many of our northern countries.

The question frequently asked in connection with the Bryophyta is, Why are mosses so small? Why didn't they go on to evolve bigger and better mosses and bigger and better liverworts? Why didn't they become dominant land plants? Here is a group of organisms that has been on the earth for millions of years but appears today much the same as the fossil remains of those found in the Carboniferous rocks.

The bryophytes which we have today may be regarded as remnants of a group of plants which made an attempt to leave the water and live on land but never succeeded fully. Why they failed may not be an easy question to answer; but certainly they needed a number of morphological modifications which simply never evolved for them, and they retained ancestral structures which impeded progress. They have always lived the life of a frog—partially out of the water but so dependent on it that they have to be kept moist all the time lest they immediately dry up and die.

For a submerged plant, the ciliated sperm represents a device that is comparatively efficient in effecting fertilization. For the land-living bryophytes, however, it would have been more useful to have sperm that could move entirely through the air from the point of production to the normal destination. But bryophytes still have the ciliated sperm of their algal ancestors. Hence fertilization is a possibility only when a continuous film of water is present through which the sperm may swim from the male sex organ to the egg.

Another structure of doubtful value is the long neck of the archegonium. Protection for the developing egg is amply fulfilled by the layers of sterile cells immediately around the egg. There appears to be no value whatsoever in the long neck, which obviously makes it more difficult for the sperm to reach the egg than if a simple aperture had been provided.

There are many other reasons often given for the failure of the Bryophyta. Among them is the failure to develop a vascular system which would make possible the conduction of water and minerals to a much greater height. And, like all aquatic plants, liverworts and mosses failed to develop adequate water-retaining tissues and surfaces which would have allowed them a wide range of habitat. So, too, mechanical tissue is almost nonexistent in this phylum—which again is typical of the THALLOPHYTA.

Possibly as important as any of the points mentioned is the continued emphasis on the gametophyte. In their several classes the bryophytes worked out quite a number of variations on this underlying motif of independent gametophyte and dependent sporophyte. Some advances were made, but apparently the characteristic limitations always prevailed and they were not able to take the big step. We must concede that they almost did it once. When *Anthoceros* came along, the bryophytes came up with a sporophyte that contained enough chloroplasts to be self-supporting. But this was not enough. Even this sporophyte was still bedded by means of its foot in the tissues of the gametophyte. If it could have taken the additional step of rooting itself directly in the soil, this sporophyte would have been inpendent—but *Anthoceros* never made it. The bryophytes failed to capitalize on their big opportunity.

XIV. *The Vascular Plant and the Independent Sporophyte*

In human history the center of the stage has been occupied not by one race or nation continuously but by a succession of different races and nations. One group of men, after some critical maneuver, occupies a strategic position and may then strengthen that position over a period of time until it comes to dominate some region of the earth's surface. But this dominance does not persist; a different group supersedes the first. The new group, when we first catch sight of it, is usually more primitive than its predecessor, judged in terms of its entire culture or degree of civilization. Yet the newcomer possesses a certain "freshness" or "energy of youth" that enables it to build a new and somewhat different civilization. More often than not, the new civilization at last surpasses the old, so that over a long period of time, progress inevitably results.

In the history of the plant and animal kingdoms, a corresponding phenomenon is manifest. Though underlying causes may be somewhat different in the two situations, the effects are strikingly similar. One group of living organisms, after some critical evolutionary change, passes into a period of variation and conquest, based upon its ability to compete successfully with its neighbors or to enter new territory as a pioneer. This period culminates in the production of a considerable array of related types, the group as a whole having attained a greater complexity of structure and behavior than had ever been attained before. The new group is thus the dominant group of the times.

In the course of time a still newer group pushes itself into the center of the stage. The newer group is more primitive than its predecessor. Yet it possesses a capacity for evolution along certain new lines. By exercising this capacity, it becomes dominant, with related types which establish a new high point in complexity of structure and behavior.

In short, the history of life on earth, like the far briefer history of man himself, contains several major acts or chapters, in each of which the same characteristic sequence of events is repeated. Repeatedly, the relatively simple and primitive evolves into the more complex and advanced. Repeatedly, a comparatively humble and distant relative of the earlier dominant group develops into the dominant group of the moment. Repeatedly, a somewhat new form supersedes and usually transcends an older form. Hence at any moment the direct ancestors of those that are to dominate in the future are likely to be found not in high places but in much less conspicuous and less impressive positions.

In the history of the plant kingdom the bryophytes, while by no means exterminated, were superseded by another great group which came to dominate the earth's surface to a degree that had never been attained before. Just how these plants made the transition from algal ancestors to important terrestrial plants is purely speculative, but considerable support can be obtained for such an event.

One suggestion is that the algal ancestor was a form similar to *Fucus*, but green, and that it had a dichotomously branched thallus. Probably it lived as a marginal plant, much as *Fucus* does today in the intertidal zone. Gradually a portion of the thallus penetrated the ground and became transformed into a root system; another portion became erect and formed the main axis, or stem, while other branches from this main axis flattened out and became leaves. It is unlikely that any one plant developed all three structures—roots, stems, and leaves —all at once. But from a similar beginning some forms may have developed stems, while other related forms evolved roots, and still others, leaves. Gradually—through the processes of cross-fertilization, hybridization, and mutation—these important organs were brought together in the same plant. It is likely that this evolutionary process took place many times rather than but once, for we have considerable variation among even the most primitive of land species. Furthermore, there may have been a number of ancestral types which gave rise to land plants of the vascular group.

Whatever the origin of land plants, however, the emphasis had to be on the sporophyte. At first, no doubt, these independent sporophytes were puny affairs, and they probably remained a very inconspicuous part of the plant population for millions of years. Step by step, however, they made evolutionary progress, steadily increasing the efficiency and the size of their sporophyte generation. Thus there emerged a new great phylum, the **Tracheophyta.** As time went on, these newly evolved tracheophytes branched out into numerous lines of descent, getting larger all the time, until at last many of them took the form of trees which towered over their bryophyte contemporaries and formed by far the most conspicuous part of the land vegetation.

The large-sized sporophyte, which rose to a considerable height from the soil surface, was made possible by a new type of body organization, together with the introduction of certain new tissues. The body as a whole was organized into the three general body regions of root, stem, and leaf. The roots provided for anchorage and the intake of water and soil salts; the stem provided the main axis on which the leaves were displayed in the sunlight; and the leaves conducted food manufacture for the benefit of the plant as a whole.

This in itself was not enough. More than ever before, provision had to be made to retain the water that was already in the plant, to secure a copious and fairly continuous supply of new water, and to transport this new water fairly rapidly to the uppermost parts of the plant. Retention of water was improved by the perfection of an epidermis which, while not differing in its general character, was somewhat more efficient than that of the bryophytes. The increased supply of water was made possible by a large root system which, through its many ramifications, presented a tremendous absorbing surface and penetrated the soil to a greater depth than had any of the absorbing organs of other terrestrial plants. Rapid transport of water to the upper regions of the sporophyte body was made possible by a new tissue which consisted of elongated, tubular cells, the tracheids of the xylem, joined end to end. By introducing these new specialized cells, tracheophytes became the first of the vascular plants. And vascular plants have been the only plants that have ever raised their bodies to any substantial height from the surface of the ground. This vascular tissue, xylem, provides the highly significant conducting tubes familiar to us as **wood.** It is interesting that a tissue which has meant so much in plant history has also played a tremendous part in human history.

By virtue of the new body organization and the new conducting tissue, the majority of vascular plants far outstripped the bryophytes in the matter of size, and became the dominating land vegetation. Landscapes came to bear a gross resemblance to those of modern times, but the individual species were still different. The vast forest which sprang up was composed of tree ferns and their allies. These plants were partly responsible for the immense coal deposits then laid down. The bodies of many of these early vascular plants, instead of disintegrating when they died, were preserved in swamps, gradually incorporated into the sedimentary rocks that were in the process of formation, and transformed at last into the coal deposits which man, millions of years later, learned to put to his own uses.

In those early days fern and lycopod forests stretched over a wide range of latitude. Today such species as survive are limited strictly to the tropics and subtropics, where tree ferns, stretching forty feet or more in the air, are not an uncommon sight. But the herbaceous ferns of temperate regions have been rather thoroughly superseded by a still more modern group, and the few that are left are indeed puny remnants of what was once a mighty array of plants.

XV. *The Early Land Plants*

Subkingdom EMBRYOPHYTA
  Phylum TRACHEOPHYTA—vascular plants
    Subphylum Psilopsida
      Class Psilophytineae
        Order Psilophytales
        Order Psilotales
    Subphylum Lycopsida
      Class Lycopodineae
        Order Lycopodiales—club mosses
        Order Selaginellales—small club mosses
        Order Lepidodendrales—giant club mosses
        Order Pleuromeiales
        Order Isoetales—quillworts
    Subphylum Sphenopsida
      Class Equisetineae
        Order Hyeniales
        Order Sphenophyllales
        Order Equisetales—horsetails

In total number of species the Tracheophyta far exceed any of the other phyla. There are about 210,000 living species of tracheophytes and the fossil remains of hundreds more which occupied the earth millions of years ago. One of the earliest was a little plant given the name of *Rhynia*, a name based on the locality in which its fossil remains were found. *Rhynia* had a simple body consisting of a slender, creeping rhizome, from which arose dichotomously branched stems.

At the tips of some of the branches small sporangia developed, in which homosporous spores were formed.

Rhynia had neither roots nor leaves. Rhizoids developed from the rhizomes for absorption; chloroplasts, in the outer cortical layers of the stem, provided for the manufacture of food. Internally the stem was composed of a central xylem made up of trachids. The xylem was surrounded by a simple phloem which in turn was incased by a thick cortex and an epidermal layer. This arrangement of the vascular tissue is the simplest in the plant kingdom and is known as a **protostele.** *Rhynia* usually grew only from about ten to twelve inches in height, although one species is described as twenty inches tall. Taking everything into consideration, this is indeed a primitive vascular plant; but it is vascular, and we are now on our way to a successful land plant.

Psilopsida. There have been quite a few fossil species assigned to this subphylum, including *Rhynia*, but of all those that once occupied the earth only two genera with three species now survive. One living genus is *Tmesipteris;* the other, *Psilotum*, is a small plant of the tropics and subtropics which looks very much like *Rhynia*. It has the same erect, dichotomously branched stem arising from a horizontal rhizome; roots are absent, and the only leaves are tiny scalelike emergences arising at the nodes. The biggest difference between the two genera is the sporangium, which in *Psilotum* is lateral and is found in the axil of the scalelike leaves (rather than terminal, as in *Rhynia*).

The vegetative body of members in this subphylum seems to offer evidence that the root evolved from a portion of the main axis. The underground portions of the stem became adapted to the functions of the absorption of water and soil salts and remained as this type of organ throughout the phylum. There is also evidence that these plants may have given rise to leaves in two different ways. In some plants they developed as tiny emergences or scale leaves; in others, leaves were formed by a flattening of branches from the main axis. Superficially, both leaf types are still found in the Tracheophyta.

Lycopsida. The subphylum **Lycopsida** is comprised of 4 living genera and about 900 species. It is a group whose ancestors can be traced back to the Silurian rocks, where our evidence of the first land plants can be found. Actually, fossil members of the Lycopsida have been found in more ancient rocks than those of the Psilopsida—which might indicate that the latter arose from the lycopods. Most botanists, however, are of the opinion today that the Psilopsida arose from algal ancestors and that the former in turn gave rise to the remaining subphyla.

At one time there were lycopods over one hundred feet tall, but they declined sharply after the Carboniferous, until today the four remaining genera are insignificant remnants of a once great floral landscape. (See Geologic Time Chart, pp. 216–17, for probable antiquity of all groups.)

Of these four genera—*Phylloglossum, Isoetes, Lycopodium,* and *Selaginella*—we will give some space to the last two, with particular reference to *Selaginella,* because with this genus we have the introduction of heterospory. Some of the large fossil forms of the group were also heterosporous, but *Selaginella* is the only living genus in the Lycopsida with this characteristic today.

Lycopodium (Fig. 95), which has larger sporophyte bodies than *Selaginella,* is often encountered in the woods of the northern United States. It prefers acid soils and bogs, while *Selaginella* may be found in alkaline situations. The main stems of *Lycopodium* commonly sprawl prostrate along the surface of the ground, sending up erect branches to the height of a foot or more. Because all the stem parts are copiously coated with small, sharp-pointed leaves, it is often called "ground pine"; and, since its small leaves resemble superficially those of moss, it is called "moss." Then, since it produces spores in a very compactly organized group of spore-bearing structures, which resemble a tiny club, it is called "club moss." Furthermore, because members of this genus are larger than those of *Selaginella,* they are the "giant club mosses."

Some species of *Lycopodium,* apparently more primitive than the rest, lack definitely organized strobili. Instead, spore production occurs at many points along the erect branches. Though all the leaves are superficially alike, some of them are spore-bearing. A spore-bearing leaf is technically known as a **sporophyll,** and a cluster of sporophylls is a **strobilus.** The sporophylls carry on their upper surfaces kidney-shaped sporangia which in turn contain the spores. In the majority of species all leaves on the main stem and the lower regions of the erect branches are strictly vegetative, and the sporophylls are closely organized into strobili at the upper tips of the branches. In all species the leaflike character of the sporophyll is quite plain.

GEOLOGIC TIME CHART OF THE DOMINANT ORGANISMS AND PROBABLE CLIMATIC CONDITIONS UNDER WHICH THEY LIVED*

Eras and Approximate Number of Million Years Ago	Periods	Approximate Number of Years Ago and Duration of Each Period or Epoch	Dominant Organisms	Advances in Plant Life	Advances in Animal Life	Climate; Geologic Events
Cenozoic 60,000,000	Quaternary	Recent	Age of herbs and man	Dominance of herbs	Rise of civilization and agriculture	Modern seasons
		Pleistocene 0–1,000,000		Extinction of many trees; increase in number of herbs	Extinction of great mammals	Periodic glaciation
	Late Tertiary	Pliocene 1,000,000–12,000,000		Increasing restriction of plant distribution and of forests; rise of herbs	Appearance of man	Continued cooling of climate with temperate zones appearing; Cascades, Coast Ranges
		Miocene 12,000,000–28,000,000	Age of angiosperms, mammals, and birds	Restriction of distribution of plants; retreat of polar floras; forest reduction	Mammals abundant; carnivores at peak	Climate greatly changed, cool and semiarid; Himalayas, Alps
	Early Tertiary	Oligocene 28,000,000–40,000,000		World-wide distribution of tropical forests	Rise of higher mammals and birds	Climate warm, humid; Pyrenees
		Eocene and Paleocene 40,000,000–60,000,000		Modernization of flowering plants; luxuriant forests of angiosperms even in Arctic regions	First primates appear; modern birds and marine mammals appear	Climate cool, semiarid, then warm, humid; mountain glaciers
Mesozoic 185,000,000	Late Mesozoic 60,000,000–130,000,000	Upper Cretaceous		Angiosperms dominant; gymnosperms dwindling	Rise of primitive mammals	Climate fluctuating; Rocky Mountains and Andes
		Middle Cretaceous		Rapid development of angiosperms	Extinction of great reptiles	Climate fluctuating
		Lower Cretaceous	Age of higher gymnosperms and reptiles	Rise of angiosperms; conifers and cycads still dominant		Climate very warm
	Early Mesozoic	Jurassic 130,000,000–155,000,000		First known angiosperms; conifers and cycads dominant; cordaites disappear	Primitive birds, flying reptiles, and dinosaurs abundant	Climate warm; Sierras, great continental seas in western North America
		Triassic 155,000,000–185,000,000		Floras not luxuriant; higher gymnosperms increase, including cycads, conifers, and ginkgoes	First mammals; rise of giant reptiles (dinosaurs)	Climate warm, semiarid, mostly temperate

* Estimates of time based on the U.S. Geological Survey Chart of 1956; descriptive data after Fuller and Tippo, *General Botany* (Henry Holt & Co., 1954).

GEOLOGIC TIME CHART—*Continued*

Eras and Approximate Number of Million Years Ago	Periods and Approximate Number of Years Ago and Duration of Each Period or Epoch	Dominant Organisms	Advances in Plant Life	Advances in Animal Life	Climate; Geologic Events
Paleozoic 520,000,000	Late Paleozoic — Permian 185,000,000–210,000,000		Dwindling of ancient groups; first cycads and conifers	Rise of land vertebrates	Climate dry with periodic glaciation; Appalachians, Urals, drainage of seas from continents
	Pennsylvanian (Upper Carboniferous) 210,000,000–235,000,000	Age of lycopods, seed ferns, and amphibians	Dominant calamites, lepidodendrons, ferns, seed ferns, cordaites; extensive coal formation		Period of crustal unrest; alternation of marine and terrestrial conditions
	Mississippian (Lower Carboniferous) 235,000,000–265,000,000		Dominant lycopods, horsetails, and seed ferns; early coal deposits	Rise of primitive reptiles and insects	Widespread shallow seas on North American continent; Acadian Mountains
	Middle Paleozoic — Devonian 265,000,000–320,000,000	Age of early land plants and fishes	Early land plants; Psilopsida, *Rhynia*, etc., primitive Lycopsida, Sphenopsida, horsetails, ferns, and seed ferns; first forests		
	Silurian 320,000,000–360,000,000		First known land plants; algae dominant; *Rhynia*	Lung fishes and scorpions (air-breathing animals)	
	Early Paleozoic — Ordovician 360,000,000–440,000,000	Age of algae and higher invertebrates	Possible rise of land plants; marine algae dominant	Corals, starfishes, pelecopods, etc.; first vertebrates; armored fishes	
	Cambrian 440,000,000–520,000,000		Algae, especially marine forms	Many groups of invertebrates; dominance of trilobites	Narrow seas within the borders of North America; climate warm, uniform over earth
Proterozoic 2,100,000,000	520,000,000–2,100,000,000	Age of primitive marine invertebrates	Bacteria and algae	Worms, crustaceans, brachiopods	Grand Canyon, younger Laurentian rocks, chiefly sedimentary; glaciation
Archeozoic 3,250,000,000		Age of unicellular life	No fossils found; all organisms probably unicellular or very simple		Older Laurentian rocks, mostly igneous or metamorphosed; few sedimentary

All spores of *Lycopodium* are of the same type. In size the spores are among the most constant of biological objects, and it is for this reason that the early microscopists often mounted a few *Lycopodium* spores on the same slide with other objects which they wished to measure.

Lycopodium also produces only the one type of gametophyte. Very

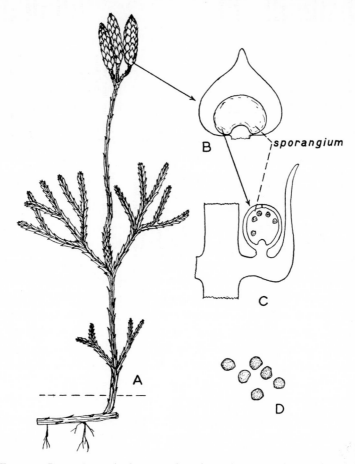

Fig. 95.—*Lycopodium*. *A*, the sporophyte body, bearing a cluster of strobili at the upper end. *B*, upper view of single sporophyll. *C*, longitudinal section to show side view of single sporophyll and its relation to the axis of the strobilus. *D*, spores.

few collections of botanical material contain *Lycopodium* gameto- phytes, for they are extremely difficult to find. In many species the gametophyte, after it has been produced from the spore, works its way down into the ground. Thereafter it maintains a subterranean, saprophytic existence. The thallus is a tiny, irregular, tuberous affair usually less than three-quarters of an inch long. In other species the gametophyte, though subterranean in the main, is near enough to the surface to push some of its tissue into the air and conduct photosynthesis. In a few species the gametophyte is entirely aerial.

Antheridia and archegonia are imbedded in the upper surface, and the biflagellated sperm still require water to effect fertilization by swimming to the eggs in the archegonia. As the embryo develops, following the initial divisions of the zygote, it produces a young leafy sporophyte which for a time is parasitic on the gametophyte. In fact, similar to the sporophyte of the Bryophyta, a special absorptive organ, the "foot," is produced by the embryo and serves for a brief period until the root is formed. Eventually the gametophytic tissue decays, leaving the independent sporophyte to carry on alone.

The genus *Selaginella* is represented by over 400 species in the tropics, and, although not abundant in the temperate regions, it is found in limited quantity in many areas. In our own Southwest over 15 species grow, from habitats of extreme dryness to the tops of the Rocky Mountains, where moisture is seldom a problem. One species, which grows on very rocky terrain, in the deserts of southern Arizona, New Mexico, and southwestern Texas, is commonly called the "resurrection plant." When dry, its stems and leaves roll inward, forming a ball, but when moisture is supplied, the plant unfolds; and in a few hours it is green and once again back in the business of carrying on photosynthesis. This plant may survive for years, but it is active only during the rainy season, which is seldom more than a few weeks each year.

Species of *Selaginella* are commonly called the "small club mosses" because they are consistently smaller and more delicate in texture than those of *Lycopodium*. In general appearance, however, the sporophyte bodies are much like those of *Lycopodium*. At maturity there appear at the tips of the branches rather compact strobili composed of distinctly leaflike sporophylls, each with a single sporangium on its upper surface, as in *Lycopodium*.

At this point, however, the resemblance ceases, for it is in *Selaginella* that we encounter for the first time in living forms the phenomenon of **heterospory**. Heterospory, or the production of two different types of spores, was a feature of the life cycle that meant a great deal to the evolution of the plant kingdom. Introduced some hundreds of millions of years ago among a few of the early vascular plants, it opened the way for the subsequent introduction of the seed, that culminating reproductive achievement of the entire plant kingdom which appears only in the members of the highest group. Apparently heterospory arose a number of times in plants of parallel evolutionary series. Even in the Lycopsida it appeared in different contemporary plants but did not enable most of them to survive. Today we see that heterospory is rare among the surviving club mosses and fernlike plants, most of which retain the more primitive homosporous condition. Nevertheless, heterospory is in part responsible for the seed habit, and in the highest and most successful terrestrial plants it is the only type of spore condition found. The heterospory of *Selaginella* is so beautifully diagrammatic that this genus is commonly used to illustrate this type of reproduction and to show its possible influence in the development of the seed.

The two types of spores in *Selaginella* (Fig. 96) are referred to as **megaspores** (large spores) and **microspores** (small spores). A megaspore has almost ten times the diameter (and a thousand times the volume) of a microspore. Both are produced in the same strobilus, but within different sporangia and on different sporophylls. Accordingly, we say that the strobilus is made up of **megasporophylls** and **microsporophylls.** Actually there is no difference whatsoever in the sterile or "leaf" portion of the two sporophylls, but the one carries on its upper surface a single **megasporangium,** the other a single **microsporangium.** The cream-colored megasporangium carries only four gigantic megaspores, far larger than any spores hitherto encountered. The reddish microsporangium carries a few thousand of the much smaller microspores. The megasporophylls usually (but by no means always) are carried lower in the strobilus and the microsporophylls nearer to the tip (Fig. 97).

A further *Selaginella* feature that is prophetic of the condition found in seed plants lies in the fact that the gametophytes are retained within (or practically within) the walls of the spores that produce them. Since this prevents exposure to sunlight, the gametophytes are necessarily dependent, their only supply of food being that which was stored within the spores. Thus the gametophyte, the dominant generation among bryophytes, has dwindled in magnitude until at last it has lost its independence completely and become a rather inconspicuous part of the life cycle.

While still retained within the microsporangium, a microspore produces a tiny male gametophyte, which consists of no more than a single vegetative cell plus a single, small but many-celled male sex organ, the entire gametophyte being completely contained within the

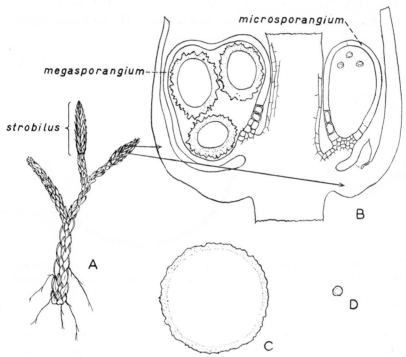

Fɪɢ. 96.—*Selaginella. A,* the sporophyte body. *B,* longitudinal section of portion of strobilus, including one megasporophyll and one microsporophyll. *C* and *D,* megaspore and microspore, drawn to the same scale.

microspore wall. While still retained within the megasporangium, a megaspore produces a female gametophyte, small by comparison with the gametophytes that we have seen in other forms but vastly larger than the male gametophyte. The female gametophyte is not quite contained within the megaspore wall but protrudes slightly at one point where the spore wall becomes ruptured. The bulk of this gametophyte is made up of many vegetative cells, well stocked with a food supply for the benefit of the embryo sporophyte that is to come. The protruding portion of the gametophyte carries a few female sex organs (see Fig. 97).

Once again, fertilization depends upon the swimming of a ciliated sperm through a film of water, but this no longer occurs in the customary setting of the soil surface. The sporophylls, which up to this time had been held rather tightly in the compact strobilus, unfold somewhat, like the petals of an opening flower, so that the sporangia on their upper surfaces are now well exposed. The megasporangium

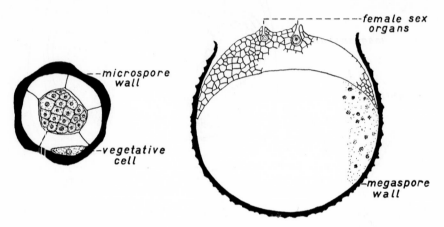

FIG. 97.—The gametophytes of *Selaginella. On the left,* the tiny male gametophyte with its single sex organ, consisting of a surrounding layer of sterile cells and a packed mass of spermatogenous cells within. *On the right,* the much larger female gametophyte.

walls crack open but still retain the megaspores, like eggs in a nest. Microsporangium walls rupture and release showers of microspores, some of which lodge among the megaspores of sporophylls which were lower in the same strobilus. It is at this stage that the microspore wall ruptures, as does also the wall of the male sex organ. The sperm, now released, swim through a film of water to the exposed female sex organs nearby. Thus, within the strobilus itself, there appear many embryo sporophytes, each growing parasitically at the expense of the female gametophyte, which is still largely buried within the old megaspore wall. A little later, whether megaspores fall singly from the withering strobilus, or whether the strobilus as a whole drops to the ground, some of the young sporophytes will be able to get primary roots into the soil, green leaves into the air, and thus become established for an independent existence. Outlines of the life cycles of *Lycopodium* and *Selaginella* are given in Figure 98.

Throughout the plant kingdom, wherever a structure can be identified exclusively with one sex or the other, the prefixes "micro" and

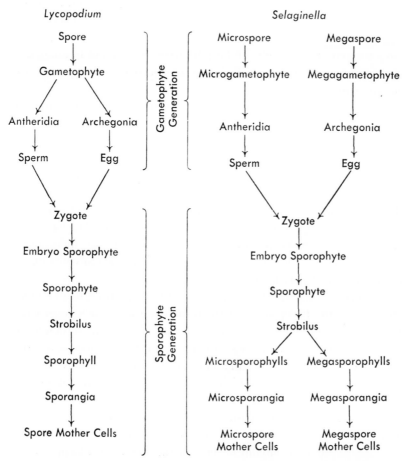

FIG. 98.—Outlines of the life cycles of *Lycopodium* and *Selaginella*

"mega" are used. A miscospore gives rise to the male gametophyte, which is the **microgametophyte.** This in turn gives rise to antheridia, and the antheridia produce the sperm. Similarly, we find that the microspore is produced by reduction division from the microspore mother cell, which is contained in the microsporangium and carried on the microsporophyll. When both male and female parts are carried in or on a single structure, it has no special sexual designation. Thus the strobilus, which in *Selaginella* carries both microsporophylls and megasporophylls, is given no specific sexual term, although when we study a pine tree we will see that there it is.

In *Lycopodium*, as in many other plants, the gametophyte carries both archegonia and antheridia, but in *Selaginella* the antheridia and archegonia are on a separate microgametophyte and a separate megagametophyte, respectively. In keeping with this type of terminology, the sperm in plants are called **microgametes,** and the eggs are **megagametes.**

In the life cycles of all plants there is always the same order of parts. Simpler plants have fewer parts, and the more advanced ones have more parts, but we retain the same order. The zygote is always the first stage of the sporophyte, and the sporophyte gives rise to the spore, but there may be a number of stages in between. The spore is always the first stage of the gametophyte, and the latter always produces the gametes. In the lower plants we have seen that the emphasis has been on the gametophyte. Now we find that in the Tracheophyta the emphasis is on the sporophyte; consequently, there are more stages of development in the sporophyte generation, and the individual parts are for the most part larger.

Phylogenetically the Lycopsida probably arose from one or more members of the Psilopsida; yet the former is a line which never gave rise to any of modern-day groups of plants which came to dominate the earth. They were very successful during the Carboniferous, but the competition of more successful and newer forms—or possibly changes in climatic conditions to which they could not become adapted—meant their demise. The lycopods, nevertheless, attained a fairly advanced status. Features arising in this group are true roots, true leaves, sporophylls united into a strobilus, heterospory, secondary tissues arising from a cambium in some of the larger fossil forms, and a gametophyte formed and retained within the spore wall.

Sphenopsida. This is another subphylum which arose at the same time as the Lycopsida. Members of this group had about the same history as those before. They were also quite variable in appearance; some were herbaceous, others vinelike, and some reached the size of trees. Two simple genera, *Hyenia* and *Calamophyton*, apparently arose from simple psilopods, which they very closely resembled. *Calamophyton* seems a logical ancestral type to a group of plants in this subphylum, which is now extinct. *Hyenia* was probably the progenitor of a much larger group of plants which we call the **horsetails.**

The horsetails are today represented by only the single genus *Equisetum*, comprised of about twenty-five species. All are characterized by the same unique sporophyte body, with several features which distinguish it sharply from the bodies of other vascular plants. The main stem is horizontal and subterranean, like that of most modern ferns. Unlike the fern, however, the horsetail sends up aerial branch stems of a striking type.

The fossil record tells us that many of the ancient horsetails developed sizable leaves. In living forms, however, the leaves are mere scalelike vestiges, quite inadequate to supply food for the entire body. Instead, food manufacture is conducted in the aerial branches themselves, which carry chloroplasts in a zone slightly below the epidermis. In these branches we encounter a conspicuous, jointed effect, roughly suggestive of the bamboo. This is due to a sharp differentiation of the branch into alternate nodes and internodes. The capacity to produce lateral members is restricted to the very short nodes. Thus, a single "whorl" or "cycle" of tiny leaves is produced at each node, while the long internodes in between are entirely devoid of leaves. By pulling, one can rather easily separate these aerial branches into sections, the breaks occurring at the nodes (Fig. 99).

In popular parlance the horsetails are often referred to as "scouring rushes." A handful of the aerial branches provides an abrasive which is quite effective for scouring pots and pans, for these branches instead of being perfect cylinders are fluted in contour, and their epidermal layers are impregnated with a deposit of silica.

In some species there is but one type of aerial branch, which takes care of both food manufacture and spore production. In others, these two functions are allotted to separate types of aerial branches, which are produced at different times in the season. In such cases the subterranean main stem will put up only the green, vegetative branches during the summer. In these the surface for food manufacture is increased by the production of subordinate branches (smaller replicas of the primary branches) which come off at the nodes in the axils of the diminutive leaves (i.e., in the angles between the leaves and the main axis),

The vegetative branches die away in the fall, but much of the food that they have produced has been stored in the underground stem. On the basis of this food supply the stem in some species throws up fertile branches the next spring. These are not self-supporting, being unbranched and provided with relatively little chlorophyll. At the tip of each fertile branch is a strobilus in which the spores are produced (see Fig. 99).

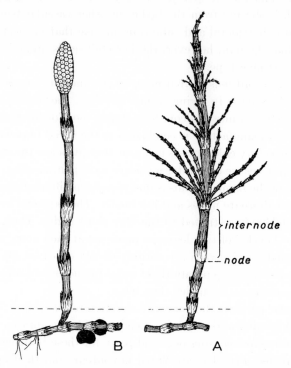

FIG. 99.—The sporophyte of *Equisetum*. *A*, portion of the underground main stem, giving rise to the aerial "vegetative" branch, which, in turn, is giving off numerous subordinate branches from its upper nodes. *B*, a "fertile" branch, surmounted by its strobilus.

In some plants, like *Selaginella*, the leaflike character of the sporophylls is apparent. In others, the sporophylls have become so highly specialized for spore production as to bear little resemblance to an ordinary leaf. This last is conspicuously true of the sporophylls of *Equisetum*. Here the sporophylls consist of simple cylindrical stalks which come off at right angles from the axis of the strobilus and terminate in expanded shieldlike structures. The outer surface of an immature strobilus is composed of hundreds of these hexagonal "shields" with their edges fitted together perfectly. From the inner surface of each shield there extend five to ten finger-shaped sporangia (spore cases), arranged in a ring around the stalk of the sporophyll (see Fig. 100, *A*). At the stage of maturity the shields pull apart at their edges, slits appear in the sporangia, and the spores are thus released into the air.

The spores of the horsetail were objects of fascination for the early microscopists. In addition to the surrounding wall, present in most spores, those of the horsetail possess an outer wall which acts in an

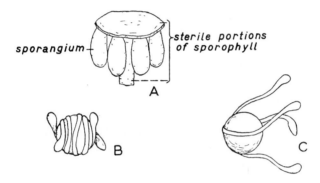

FIG. 100.—*A*, single sporophyll of *Equisetum*. *B* and *C*, single spores, showing the peculiar attached strips, coiled and uncoiled.

amazing way. At the time of spore-shedding this outer wall cracks in a very regular pattern into two ribbon-like strips, arranged spirally around the spore. Each strip remains attached, in its central region, to one pole of the spore, but elsewhere it becomes loosened from the spore surface. At shedding, therefore, each spore, like a Maypole, carries these four radiating streamers (see Fig. 100, *B*, *C*). The streamers are **hygroscopic**, coiling and uncoiling in response to slight changes in the humidity of the atmosphere. The net result of it all is that *Equisetum* spores become tangled with each other and fall in clumps rather than singly. Perhaps this peculiar feature has adaptive value. Certainly it increases the likelihood that several gametophytes will grow in close proximity; and this, in turn, favors fertilization, for the gametophytes of this form are differentiated into male and female individuals.

Though all the spores are of the same size, half of them produce male gametophytes and the other half produce female gametophytes. Both gametophytes are flat, green bodies, roughly suggesting those of the fern. Apparently, however, these gametophytes follow a very disorderly program of development, branching wildly and having at maturity a highly irregular contour. Male and female gametophytes are alike in general appearance, but the female is several times as large as the male. This feature doubtless bears a functional relation to the higher nutritive content of the female gamete and to the fact that the young sporophyte develops for a time at the expense of the female gametophyte.

The remainder of the life cycle of *Equisetum*, though peculiar in some of its details, is in the main like that of the club mosses. Large, ciliated sperm, released from the male sex organs of the male gametophyte, swim through films of water to reach the female sex organs of the female gametophyte. The zygote yields a sporophyte, which pushes a small foot back into the tissues of the female gametophyte, thereby extracting the nutrition needed to carry it through its early stages of development. After a root has established adequate soil relations and green branches have been pushed up into the sunlight, the sporophyte embarks upon an independent existence.

XVI. *The Ferns*

Subkingdom EMBRYOPHYTA
  Phylum TRACHEOPHYTA
    Subphylum Pteropsida
      Class Filicineae
        Order Coenopteridales
        Order Ophioglossales
        Order Marattiales
        Order Filicales

The subphylum *Pteropsida* is the largest of the four major groups
of vascular plants. Included in it are three classes: (1) Filicineae, or
ferns; (2) Gymnospermae, the conifers and their allies; and (3) Angiospermae, the flowering plants.

Filicineae. Today there are some 175 living genera of ferns with
about 8,000 living species, and although they are still widely distributed throughout the earth, the most successful survivors are
limited to the tropics, where tree ferns, stretching forty feet or more
in the air, are not an uncommon sight. Most of the ferns of temperate
regions have been rather thoroughly superseded by a still more modern group, the seed plants, and the few ferns that are left are indeed
insignificant remnants of what was once a mighty array of plants. In
the past, ferns and their allies, the club mosses and horsetails, formed
the dominant vegetation in the *Carboniferous,* a period often called
the "Age of Ferns."

The typical fern of temperate regions has an underground stem, a
rhizome, which in some ferns is in a stubby, compact arrangement
and in others stretches out horizontally to a considerable length. Nu-

229

merous small roots stretch downward from this underground stem. The only parts which extend above ground are the leaves. In ferns this organ is quite distinctive and is called a *frond*. It is characteristically large and compound, being divided (and often further subdivided several times) into many leaflets or *pinnae.* The compoundness of the frond, by itself, is not a very serviceable identification, for there are quite a number of higher plants which also possess compound leaves. There are, however, two characteristics of fern leaves that are fairly distinctive: (1) When the young fern leaf, put forth by the underground stem, first emerges from the soil, it is coiled up at the tip into a crozier-like formation. As development proceeds, the leaf gradually uncoils until it has straightened out completely. This unusual manner of growth and development is termed *circinate vernation.* (2) The smaller veins in a fern leaf exhibit a forked branching; i.e., the vein of larger magnitude splits into two equal veins of the next smaller magnitude. This is usually called *dichotomous venation,* and it contrasts sharply with the venation of higher plants, where the vein of larger magnitude gives off along its length a whole series of veins of the next smaller magnitude.

Roots, stems, and leaves together constitute the sporophyte generation of the fern (Fig. 101). Just as in all tracheophytes, this is clearly an independent generation, capable of manufacturing its own food and procuring its own water and soil salts. As a reproductive unit the sporophyte must, of course, yield spores. These are produced in a specialized sporangium and in a manner that is unique with ferns.

Even after the fern leaf (sporophyll) has attained its maximum size, it shows, for a time, no traces of the spores but devotes its tissues completely to the manufacture of food. Oncoming age, the season, and environmental conditions, however, apparently stimulate the under surface of the leaf to burst forth rather suddenly with a large crop of spore-producing structures. Doubtless the reader himself has noticed these numerous, small, brown and black patches scattered over the lower surfaces of the older fern leaves. These patches, called *sori,* are so small as to reveal very little to the naked eye (Fig. 102, *A*). The microscope, however, or even a good hand lens, will show that each sorus contains a score or more sporangia. The sporangia are carried on long, thin stalks which radiate outward from a central area of attachment. In the earlier stages of development the patch of young

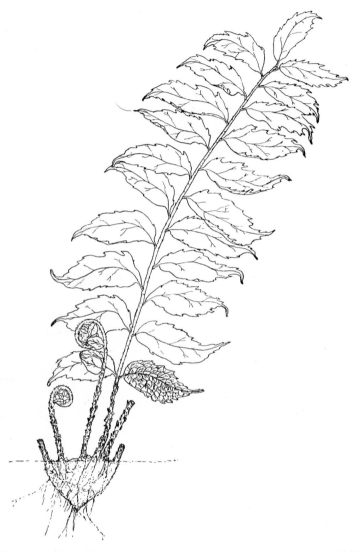

Fig. 101.—The sporophyte generation of the fern, with its underground stem and roots and its compound, aerial leaves.

spore cases is covered by a protective flap of sterile tissue, which in some ferns resembles a shallow pocket and in others an inverted umbrella (Fig. 102, *B*). This structure is the **indusium**. It is of considerable taxonomic significance in the identification of ferns because of the variety of shapes and forms it may have in the different species. As the sporangia enlarge and ripen, the indusium is pushed out and eventually sloughed off.

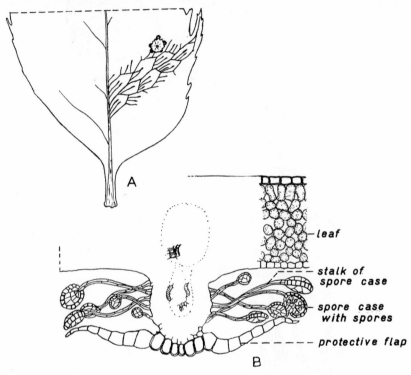

Fig. 102.—*A*, enlarged portion of lower surface of fern leaflet, as one might see it with a hand lens, showing one of the patches of spore cases covered by its umbrella-like (or shieldlike) flap. *B*, longitudinal section cut through the leaflet at the point where one of these patches of spore cases is carried.

Within a single layer of sterile epidermal cells each spore case carries a group of spores, usually sixty-four in number. Mature spores are liberated not by a simple rupture of the epidermal covering but by an active movement of a specialized band of cells, the **annulus,** which forms a ring almost completely around the sporangium. The individual cells of the annulus have three thick inner walls and an outer thin wall; as moisture conditions change and the spores mature, it begins to operate on the principle of a catapult (Fig. 103). At certain times it bends back, then suddenly flips forward, hurling the spores out with considerable force, to provide its own dispersal mechanism.

Since a single sporangium may contain sixty-four or more spores, since there are scores of sporangia in a single sorus, and since there

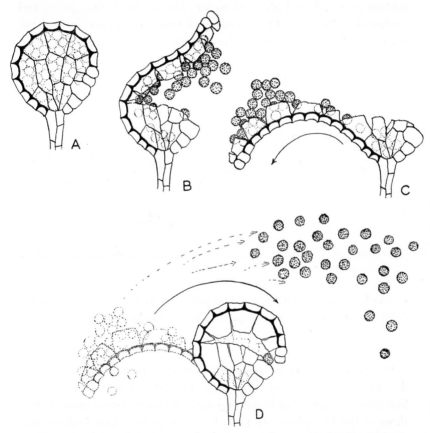

Fig. 103.—Series of diagrams to show sequence of events involved in the forceful discharge of spores by the spore case of a typical fern. A single line of heavy-walled epidermal cells stretches almost completely around the spore case, forming a springlike structure. In response to the drying influence of the atmosphere, this "spring" is slowly bent backward and then very suddenly snaps forward again into its original position of rest.

are hundreds of sori on the under surface of a large fern leaf and a number of leaves to a plant, the total annual output of spores from a single sporophyte may run into the millions. Here, then, is another example of a tremendously high potential reproductive ratio coupled with a high mortality, for it is only the tiniest fraction of the number of spores that reach conditions suitable for their developing any further.

The gametophyte that develops from the fern spore is quite small, seldom over half an inch in diameter. The thallus is flat, green, and anchored to the ground by a number of tiny, hairlike protrusions, the rhizoids. The thallus develops through the activity of a growing point

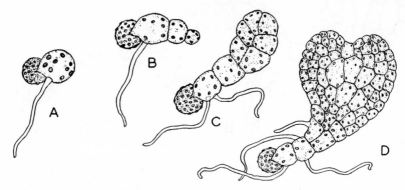

Fig. 104.—Series of early stages in the development of the fern gametophyte from the spore.

in the base of a notch. Since forward growth does not continue indefinitely, the mature fern gametophyte lacks the ribbon shape of the liverwort but culminates its existence with a heart-shaped contour (Fig. 104).

On the under surface of the gametophyte, next to the moist soil, develop the two types of sex organs (Fig. 105). These are essentially like those of earlier tracheophytes and, of course, much smaller than those of the Bryophyta. In most ferns the mature gametophyte carries the antheridia near the pointed (posterior) and the archegonia near the notched (anterior) end.

When the very young gametophyte emerges from the spore, it has the shape of a short filament. Very soon, however, the growing point establishes itself at the base of a notch, as in liverworts. Thereafter, the growth of the gametophyte is based upon the activities of this growing point, which keeps giving off new cells—by cell division— that enlarge to increase both the length and the width of the gameto- phyte. In this process the notch is continuously carried forward, and the heart-shaped contour of the gametophyte is maintained as the gametophyte enlarges.

When the gametophyte is still comparatively young, it produces a few score antheridia. These male sex organs are spherical in shape and are mounted on very short stalks. Each antheridium (Fig. 106, *A*) contains only a few ciliated sperm, but they are about as large and elaborate as any sperm in the plant kingdom (Fig. 106, *B*). As the

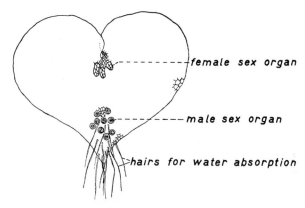

female sex organ

male sex organ

hairs for water absorption

FIG. 105.—Diagram of undersurface of mature fern gametophyte

gametophyte continues to grow, the notch leaves the antheridia be- hind. Later, when the gametophyte is approaching its full size, a half- dozen or so archegonia are developed in the region which is at the time just behind the notch. The less numerous archegonia are similar to those of the other groups (i.e., containing a single large egg in an en- larged base with a sterile neck), but they are much smaller than those of the bryophytes. In ferns the base (venter) is imbedded into the tissues of the thallus and the neck is bent backward, away from the notch of the gametophyte (Fig. 106, *C*).

This difference in the time of production of the two types of sex organs is probably correlated with the nutritive capital of the gameto- phytes at the time of their production. Sperm, which are relatively small, may be produced on the basis of the nutritive capital of a young gametophyte. Eggs, which are large and packed with nourishment, can be produced only by a gametophyte which has had time to lay up a comparatively large nutritive capital.

One might be tempted to account for the backward bending of the necks of the female sex organs as an adaptation to facilitate the entrance of sperm released by the male sex organs of the same gametophyte. But self-fertilization is the exception rather than the rule in ferns. The male sex organs of a given gametophyte have usually dis-

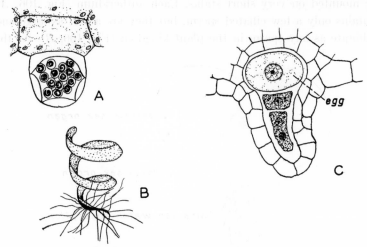

Fig. 106.—*A*, longitudinal section of an antheridium of fern. *B*, single sperm, enlarged. *C*, longitudinal section of slightly immature archegonium of fern. The mature female sex organ will probably have its neck bent even more, and the cells now forming the core of the neck will have disintegrated, thus clearing a continuous passageway through which the sperm may enter.

charged their sperm before the female sex organs of the same gametophyte are ripe to receive sperm. The eggs of the latter can be fertilized, therefore, only by the sperm of other, younger gametophytes in the neighborhood.

The backward bending of the neck is probably no more than the inevitable result of obvious mechanical forces. The neck of a young female sex organ protrudes straight down and imbeds itself among the soil particles. Since the gametophyte is still elongating, and since a part of this elongation involves the cells around this particular sex organ, the latter is "dragged forward," and the imbedded tip of its still elongating neck is "left behind."

With the breaking of the antheridial wall, the sperm find themselves in the thin film of water that is commonly present on the soil surface. As is so common in both plants and animals, the sperm are influenced by a chemical exuded through this film of water from an egg in the neighborhood. These chemicals, which are known in a few cases to be organic acids, differ in different types of plants, the sperm of a given species being responsive to only one type of chemical (or perhaps to a limited number of types). If the sperm of a moss and of a fern are thoroughly mixed together in a small container of water, they may be separated by introducing at one point in the container the tip of a small pipette containing the chemical that is characteristic of either

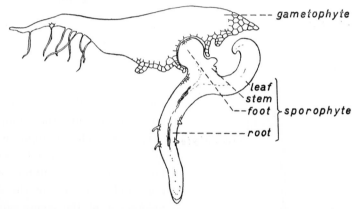

Fig. 107.—Longitudinal section through young fern sporophyte while it is still completely dependent on the gametophyte.

moss or fern eggs. This will attract only the sperm of one type and thus segregate them out of the mixture.

As usual, the first sperm to arrive fertilizes the egg, the outer membrane of which is thereby altered so as to exclude sperm that may arrive subsequently. Fertilization has been accomplished, the zygote is now formed, and we have the first cell of the sporophyte generation.

As in all members of the EMBRYOPHYTA, the fern zygote initiates at once the long series of cell divisions that is to culminate in the production of the mature sporophyte. A young developing organism, more than any other, needs a supply of energy and materials. In the life of the fern sporophyte one may recognize three somewhat overlapping stages with respect to the sources of energy and materials.

As among the bryophytes, the thing that is emphasized in the first stages of growth is the foot. By pushing this foot well up into the overlying tissues, the young sporophyte establishes a parasitic relationship with the gametophyte. It cannot truly be said, therefore, that the sporophyte of the fern is a completely independent plant, for there is always this temporary stage of dependency on the gametophyte. During this stage there is a rapid development of those sporophyte structures which will be needed to put the plant on an independent basis, for, again, the supply of nutrition provided by the tiny gametophyte is rapidly exhausted (Fig. 107).

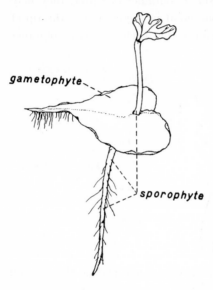

FIG. 108.—Sketch of stage slightly later than that in Figure 107. The first leaf of the sporophyte has now found its way into the sunlight.

A primary root is pushed down into the soil, and a first leaf—absurdly small as compared with the leaves of the adult fern—coils around through the notch of the gametophyte and emerges into the sunlight (Fig. 108). The sporophyte is now "on its own." Food manufactured by the leaf supplies energy and materials for the development of the stem, which has been neglected up to this time. No longer of service, the foot withers away, as does the parent gametophyte in most cases. Steadily the stem increases in size, the roots, in both size and number. Larger and larger leaves are put out, and the sporophyte is well launched on its way toward the adult condition.

In summary, the life history of a fern such as *Polypodium* is given in Figure 109.

Although we have described the growth of a "typical" fern, it is obvious that, in a class comprised of 4 orders and over 8,000 living species, there must be considerable variation in the organs of the different members. In a genus such as *Cheilanthes* we find many species adapted to arid and semiarid situations; those like *Pteridium* or *Polypodium* have a body better suited to the temperate climates and higher rainfall; *Marsilea* and *Salvinia* live directly in water. The former lives attached to the substrata, and the latter is free floating.

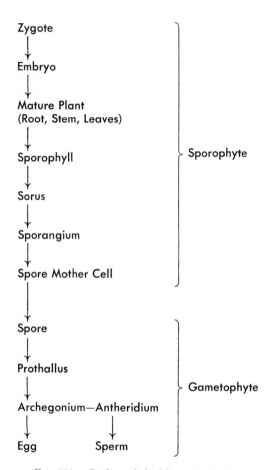

Zygote

Embryo

Mature Plant
(Root, Stem, Leaves)

Sporophyll

Sorus — Sporophyte

Sporangium

Spore Mother Cell

Spore

Prothallus

Archegonium—Antheridium — Gametophyte

Egg   Sperm

Fig. 109.—Outline of the life cycle of a fern

In the Filicinae the rhizome may have any of several different types of vascular arrangement. The simplest is the **protostele,** which has been described. In addition we have the **siphonosteles,** in which the vascular tissues surround a central pith. One is the **amphiphloic siphonostele.** It has a layer of phloem inside the xylem as well as outside. An *ectophloic siphonostele* has the phloem only on the outside of the xylem, and a *dictyostele* has the xylem and phloem in the form of discrete vascular bundles.

In phylogenetic development the different vascular systems apparently arose at different times and independently of each other. As we move into the seed plants, we will see that the protostele has been retained as the major vascular arrangement in roots and that the ectophloic siphonostele is the type used in nearly all stems.

Although most members of the Filicinae are homosporous, a few are heterosporous. This is typical of the Lycopsida, where both types are found. Formerly, greater emphasis was given to heterospory, but it is now recognized that the attainment of heterospory is not necessarily indicative of phylogenetic relationships; actually it arose several times in unrelated groups and had, in effect, a history of parallel evolution.

ECONOMIC IMPORTANCE

Compared to the seed plants, there is very little we can say, from a dollars-and-cents viewpoint, about the ferns. Yet ferns have been used for centuries for their decorative and beautiful foliage. Floral shops use the fronds in countless floral arrangements, and potted ferns are found in millions of homes and business establishments. Where tropical landscaping is possible, ferns are freely used. In temperate climates they are often a major portion of the vegetation in rock gardens. A few species are reportedly eaten, and medicinal qualities are ascribed to some. Thousands of tons of ferns also contributed to coal formation during the Carboniferous. Economically, we could do without them, but from a biological standpoint they had a very important role in evolution which they performed admirably.

XVII. *The Primitive Seed Plants and Cone-Bearers*

Subkingdom EMBRYOPHYTA
   Phylum TRACHEOPHYTA
      Subphylum Pteropsida
         Class Gymnospermae
            Subclass Cycadophytae
               Order Cycadofilicales
               Order Bennettitales
               Order Cycadales
            Subclass Coniferophytae
               Order Cordaitales
               Order Ginkgoales
               Order Coniferales
               Order Gnetales

Gymnospermae. An earlier system of classification, which divided the plant kingdom into four divisions, designated the fourth as the spermatophytes or seed plants. This system completely separated the ferns and their allies from the remaining vascular plants. Certainly there are a number of differences between the Filicinae and seed plants, but we are now of the opinion that undue emphasis has been placed on the **seed habit.**

Actually, the seed habit evolved from the condition of **heterospory,** which developed independently several times in the lower vascular plants. The important feature in the evolution of the seed has been the partial development of the young sporophyte (embryo) within the tissues of the mother sporophyte. This, accompanied by an increase in quantity of stored food and of protective tissue around the embryo, has produced a structure much better able to survive under adverse conditions and also more capable than a reproductive spore of producing a new plant.

Among seed plants the botanist recognizes the two co-ordinate classes which we may describe roughly as *cone-bearers* and *flowering plants.* The fossil record tells us that the cone-bearers are much the more primitive. Apparently they were derived from very early fernlike ancestors during the Carboniferous or before. The earliest of the seed plants are in the order *Cycadofilicales,* now extinct. The name implies that these early plants were much like ferns but produced seeds. In fact, they are usually called *seed ferns.* The seeds were carried exposed on modified leaves but not in cones, as in the later groups. The reason all of these are called "gymnosperms" is that the seeds are naked; i.e., the seeds are freely exposed, on the sporophyll, whatever its form.

As to the exact group of early tracheophytes that gave rise to Gymnospermae, there is a difference of opinion. The Cycadofilicales, which were so plentiful during the Paleozoic era, provide a beautiful transition between the ferns and the cycads. It is not easy, however, to visualize how the Cycadofilicales, either directly or indirectly through the cycads, may have given rise to all other types of seed plants. It is highly probable that the great assemblage of forms which today possess seeds had a polyphyletic rather than a monophyletic origin; in other words, some seed plants may have been derived from one subdivision of the early tracheophytes, while other seed plants had independent origins in other subdivisions of tracheophytes. Such an idea embodies the assumption that the seed itself was evolved not merely once but on several occasions. The fossil record makes it clear that heterospory was evolved independently in several vascular groups, and heterospory is clearly a step toward the production of the seed.

In addition to the Cycadofilicales, there are two other orders of gymnosperms that are now entirely extinct. One of these, *Bennettitales,* is found in large numbers, as fossils, in many places in the world and especially in the Black Hills of South Dakota, where we have many of these specimens protected in the Fossil Cycad National Monument. Members of this group probably arose from the Cycadofilicales. Here the megasporophylls and microsporophylls lost their foliage-like character and formed loosely organized cones. Some theories on the origin of the flower trace its beginnings back to this group, but our view today is that the flower-like reproductive organ of the Bennettitales is another case of parallel evolution with no definite evidence that they gave rise to the angiosperms.

The **Cordaitales,** also known only as fossils, resembled cycads only to a small degree. For the most part they were large trees with a much greater similarity to the conifers. They may have had a common origin with the Cycadofilicales, but before they became extinct it is believed that they gave rise to the Coniferales and the Ginkgoales.

Among living gymnosperms, four orders are usually recognized: The order **Gnetales** is a strange little group whose past history is practically unknown. Apparently this represents a short evolutionary sideline, rather modern in origin as gymnosperms go, which has become adapted to life in the arid districts of the tropics and subtropics. It has but three widely scattered genera; *Ephedra* (Fig. 110) is probably of greatest interest to us since it has about ten different species inhabiting the southwestern United States. The Gnetales are largely low-growing plants, but a few of the species of *Ephedra* are shrubs reaching a height of six to eight feet.

Still smaller but much more ancient is the order **Ginkgoales.** With a fossil record that reaches back into the Paleozoic and an extensive display of forms in the Mesozoic, the order is today represented by only a single species, *Ginkgo biloba,* the "maidenhair tree" (Fig. 111). Clearly this is an archaic type. In fact, it has been suggested that the group would have become extinct ere this had it not been carefully cultivated in the temple gardens of China and Japan.

The order **Cycadales,** though not so ancient in itself, has a rather clear line of ancestry, through a series of fossil forms, back to the Cycadofilicales of the Paleozoic. Today the cycads are represented by nine genera and about a hundred species, all of which are tropical or subtropical (Fig. 112). *Zamia* is the only genus in this order native to the United States. It occurs rather abundantly in Florida, where it grows in well-drained coral soils along with slash pine and other subtropical plants. Many of the other cycads have been brought into gardens in Florida, California, and other southern states, where they have been growing for years and doing quite well.

In contrast to the cycads, the members of the order **Coniferales** are for the most part restricted to the north and south temperate zones. This is by far the most conspicuous order of living gymnosperms in terms of numbers of species (about 540), size of individuals (many of which are the giants of the plant world, including trees over

Fig. 110.—Photograph of *Ephedra*, one of the few living representatives of the Order Gnetales.

300 feet in height, e.g., giant sequoia and redwood), and economic significance (providing the "softwood" trees of the lumbering industry). With few exceptions the conifer is an **evergreen,** retaining its leaves through the winter season. Though a few conifers have broad-bladed leaves, more characteristic of the group is the narrow, "needle"

FIG. 111.—Photograph of the "maidenhair tree" (*Ginkgo biloba*) growing on the University of Chicago campus. (The leaves of this form exhibit the forked veining that is otherwise restricted to the fern group.)

type of leaf. The more familiar conifers of this part of the world are the pine, spruce, fir, hemlock, cedar, juniper, Douglas fir, and giant sequoia.

The life cycle of the pine is the life cycle of conifers in general, and it is fairly representative of the entire gymnosperm group. Like all seed plants, and like *Selaginella*, the pine is heterosporous. Unlike

Fig. 112.—Photograph of a cycad, growing in the University of Chicago greenhouses.

Selaginella, but like all conifers and most gymnosperms, the pine produces two types of strobili.

The one type of strobilus, the male "cone," is composed of microsporophylls only. The individual microsporophyll is small (about $\frac{1}{8}$ inch in length) and delicate in texture. Its lower surface is completely occupied by a pair of elongated microsporangia, each packed with thousands of microspores. Prior to the release of the microspores, the sporophylls are arranged with perfect compactness in the strobilus, which is about $\frac{1}{4}$ inch in diameter and 1 inch in length. The strobili are pro-

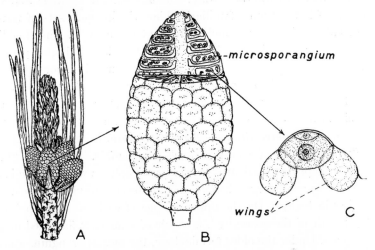

Fig. 113.—*A*, cluster of small (staminate) cones carried on a twig of the pine. *B*, a single cone, shown in partial section to reveal the nature of the microsporophylls. *C*, an enlargement of one of the winged pollen grains, showing the young male gametophyte within the old microspore wall.

duced on the tree in clusters of about a dozen each, and the entire tree may bear thousands of these clusters. Hence the total output of microspores by a single pine tree is prodigiously large. During a brief period of a few days' duration in each season most of these tiny yellowish spores are released, producing an effect that has often been referred to as "showers of sulfur." Each microspore is equipped with a pair of passive "wings," by virtue of which it may be sustained in the air for a considerable time before it lodges somewhere (Fig. 113).

Since seed plants are in general our largest and most conspicuous plants, it is not surprising that the earliest botanists gave most of their attention to this group. For the various reproductive structures which they encountered they coined names which of course in no way reflected the relationship between seed plants and ferns or the correspondence ("homology") between the successive stages in the two life cycles. It was later, after the ferns and club mosses had been studied intensively, that botanists produced those more enlightened terms which refer to the various structures that occur in connection with heterospory. It is these more modern terms that we have employed in our descriptions thus far. The older terms were used so long, however, as to intrench themselves firmly. The unfortunate result is that the student of botany must familiarize himself with both sets of terms, since botanical literature makes frequent use of both. The strobilus of our modern terminology is the *cone* of the older and more popular usage. Our microsporophyll is a *stamen;* our microsporangium, a *pollen sac;* and the microspores themselves, as we shall see, develop into the *pollen* or *pollen grains.* Since there are the two types of strobili in the pine, the one we have been discussing is distinguished as a *staminate strobilus* or *staminate cone,* in modern usage.

The other type of cone is a much larger affair. This is the "pine cone" of popular experience. The megasporophylls which make it up are not only much larger than are the microsphorophylls but are much tougher in texture. On the upper surface of each, near the point of attachment of the sporophyll, is a pair of somewhat flattened megasporangia. Under the older terminology, the megasporangium was an *ovule.* Here the ignorance of the older terminology is revealed clearly, for ovule means "little egg" (taken from the ovum or egg of animals). The pine does, indeed, contain eggs, but they should not be confused with the much larger megasporangia. The megasporophyll is also called a *carpel,* while the entire cone is a *carpellate cone* or an *ovulate cone* or an *ovulate strobilus* (Fig. 114).

It is the megasporangium that is destined to become the seed, but not until quite a program of events is properly enacted. The megasporangium (or ovule) of seed plants has a wall many layers of cells thick. Bedded down in the center of this tissue is a single megaspore mother cell. This cell undergoes two divisions, one of which is a reduction division, to produce four megaspores. Three of these abort, and the remaining one undergoes free nuclear division to produce the female gametophyte (megagametophyte). This is even smaller than in *Selaginella* and is retained completely within the megaspore wall. At one end the female gametophyte produces a very few imbedded archegonia, each with its large, passive egg (Fig. 115).

The microspore, even before it has been shed from the microsporangium, has commenced to produce internally a diminutive male gametophyte which consists of only a very few cells (the exact number of cells being a variable among gymnosperms). The pollen grains, therefore, at the time they are being showered down from the staminate cones, are not simple microspores but objects which consist of microscopic male gametophytes within microspore walls.

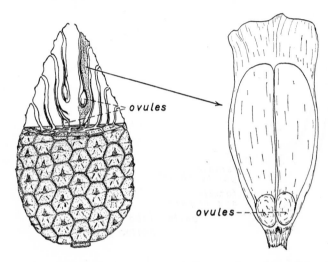

Fig. 114.—*At the left,* the ovulate cone of the pine, shown in partial section. *At the right,* an enlargement of a single megasporophyll, seen from the upper side.

Pollination, or the transfer of pollen from the place of its production to the place where it may function, is in the pine about as wasteful a process as occurs anywhere in plant or animal kingdoms. At the time of pollen-shedding, the ovulate cones of most of the pine trees in the vicinity are prepared to receive pollen. The megasporophylls have pulled apart at their outer edges, leaving a series of rifts into which pollen grains might be carried. There is nothing, however, to direct the pollen grains. They are at the mercy of currents of air, and the ovulate cones are tiny targets in the entire field through which the pollen grains travel. It is for this reason that the production of pollen grains must be prodigious to insure that even a few of them will lodge in the ovulate cones.

Those grains that do enter the ovulate cones will slip down the upward-slanted megasporophylls and come to rest in the angle where the sporophyll attaches to the axis of the strobilus. This brings them

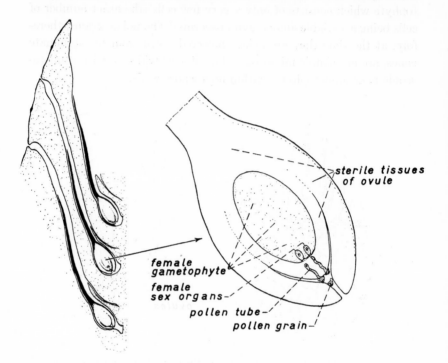

FIG. 115.—*At the left,* longitudinal section of a portion of the ovulate cone. *At the right,* enlargement of a single ovule, shown in the same orientation. Pollen grains, having slipped down and come to rest in the angle where the megasporophyll is attached to the axis of the strobilus, are drawn into the little opening at the end of the ovule by an interesting process. Through this opening the tissues of the ovule first secrete a gummy substance to which the pollen grains adhere. Later this gummy substance is resorbed by the tissues of the ovule, and the pollen grains are drawn back along with it through the opening.

in contact with the lower ends of the ovules, at a point where the ovule walls are thinner than elsewhere. At this stage, therefore, male gametophytes within pollen grains are separated by only a few layers of cells from a female gametophyte that is imbedded within the ovule.

The male gametophyte now pushes through the wall of the pollen grain and develops into what is known as the ***pollen tube.*** This pollen tube resembles a tiny parasitic fungus, for it grows by digesting its way through those cell layers of the megasporangium wall which are covering the female gametophyte at this point. At this same period the male gametophyte matures by producing two sperm. These are not produced within any retaining structure which can be recognized as a male sex organ but are merely two free cells that are carried along within the advancing tip of the pollen tube. The pollen tube reaches the female gametophyte at the point where it carries the several imbedded archegonia. Here the tip of the pollen tube bursts, releasing the two (non-ciliated) sperm, one of which usually succeeds in fertilizing an egg (see Fig. 115).

Since several pollen tubes may be present and several archegonia regularly are present, it is quite possible for more than one zygote to be produced within the same female gametophyte. Almost invariably, however, the embryo sporophyte which results from one of the zygotes will outgrow and crowd out the sister embryos which may have started to develop at its side. The final result is a single embryo sporophyte developing within the old female gametophyte, which is surrounded, in turn, by the simple cell wall of the old megaspore and the many-layered wall of the megasporangium or ovule. The whole structure is still being carried on the upper surface of a megasporophyll, which is merely one of the units in an ovulate strobilus.

Following fertilization, because of the stimulating effect of hormones, certain changes are brought about in the cells and tissues associated with the egg. Changes which occur in the uterus of the human and other animals following pregnancy are quite similar to those which take place in the megasporangium wall of plants. In this region, which was up to this time a soft tissue, cell changes occur which gradually transform a part of the megasporangium wall into a tough coat, completely surrounding the female gametophyte. The embryo sporophyte develops parasitically at the expense of the female gametophyte only so long as it receives a supply of water from conducting tissues which are feeding into the outer regions of the megasporangium. As the hard coat on the outside completes itself, it cuts off this water supply and hermetically seals off the female gametophyte and its contained embryo. As a result, the embryo is thrown into a state of dormancy. The first chapter of its development is at an end, and it may now lie for months or even for many years in a state of arrested development, well protected within the surrounding structures.

What was once the ovule or megasporangium is now the seed. For gymnosperms, then, we may define a seed as a transformed megasporangium which now consists of a tough seed coat containing the remnants of an old female gametophyte and a young embryo sporophyte.

In the pine, as in many other conifers, a long flap of the megasporangium wall, which has been stretched outward along the upper surface of the megasporophyll, becomes a single "wing" for the seed.

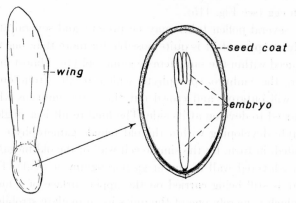

FIG. 116.—*At the left*, the winged seed of the pine, surface view. *At the right*, a longitudinal section through the pine seed, wing omitted.

When the old ovulate cone gradually opens out and sheds the seeds, these "wings," like those of the pollen grains, increase greatly the chances that seeds will be carried to some distance by the wind. Biologically this is of large importance, for the seed is the only agent of distribution in an organism of this type. If pine seeds dropped to the ground like plummets from the points where they were produced, we would doubtless today find groves of pines in only a few restricted localities. By virtue of the winged seed (Fig. 116), however, a slow but effective distribution of pines has occurred through the past, so that today we find them present over extensive areas.

We have stated that gymnosperms are usually evergreens. This feature, however, will not distinguish the group sharply from angiosperms, for actually there are a few gymnosperms that are ***deciduous*** (i.e., shed their leaves every winter) and a few angiosperms that are evergreen. We have stated that gymnosperms are cone-bearers. This feature, too, fails to be quite distinctive, for there are some of the more primitive angiosperms which bear reproductive structures that are virtually cones or strobili rather than true flowers. The real distinction

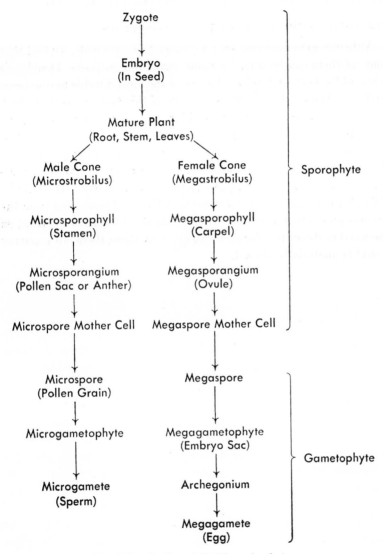

FIG. 117.—Outline of the life cycle of pine

between the two groups is referred to by their titles. Gymnosperm means "naked seed." The seeds, as we have seen, are produced on the exposed surface of the megasporophyll. Angiosperm, on the other hand, means "incased seed," for in the latter group, as we shall see, the seeds are produced within an inclosing case of tissue. In summary, the life history of pine would be as represented in Figure 117.

ECONOMIC IMPORTANCE OF GYMNOSPERMS

Although gymnosperms are all classified as softwoods, we find that some of them can be used for many structural purposes. Douglas fir is one of the best, and redwood is one of the most durable in resistance to decay. Among the various uses made of this type of wood are fuel, posts, heavy timber, shingles, excelsior, pulp and paper, rayon, plastics, distillation products of wood and resins, Christmas trees, furniture, amber (a hard resinous product from a now extinct species of pine), and the turpentines, which are basic to the naval-stores industry, one of the oldest and largest of the forest industries. It would be difficult to estimate the total value in dollars and cents, but from the various products it is obvious that hundreds of industries depend on the wood of these trees for their existence. Without them our economy would be materially altered.

XVIII. *The Flower and Higher Seed Plants*

Subkingdom EMBRYOPHYTA
   Phylum TRACHEOPHYTA
      Subphylum Pteropsida
         Class Angiospermae
            Subclass Dicotyledoneae
               Archichlamydeae
               Metachlamydeae
            Subclass Monocotyledoneae

Angiospermae. The culminating attainments in the evolution of the plant kingdom appear among the angiosperms. Although there is tremendous variation as to body form in this vast assemblage of over 195,000 species, there is surprising uniformity with respect to the main features of the reproductive program. This uniformity suggests that the reproductive features involved are of great biological value, that they have been at least somewhat responsible for the obvious success of the great group in which they occur.

In general, the angiosperms are flowering plants. This feature, however, does not provide a sharp or true distinction between this group and the cone-bearing gymnosperms, for actually there are quite a number of the relatively more primitive members of the angiosperm group which bear reproductive structures that are more like cones than flowers. The true distinguishing feature for the angiosperms is described in the name itself: *angiosperm* means *incased seed.* As we shall see, all angiosperms produce their seeds within an inclosing case. This is true of none of the **gymnosperms,** which uniformly produce **naked seeds.**

The angiosperm group is sufficiently large to show great variation with respect to such relatively unimportant features of the flower as the number, size, and shape of the various floral parts. Without pausing to concern ourselves with this variation, we propose to describe the life cycle of the angiosperm in terms of an "ideal" flower, i.e., one

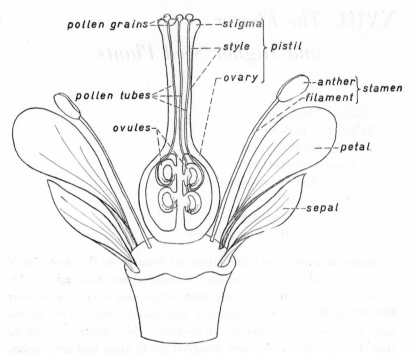

Fig. 118.—Diagram of an ideal flower, shown in longitudinal section. (The pollen grains and pollen tubes are disproportionately large, as is the free space shown within the ovary cavity.)

which stands for a rough "average" condition for flowers in general (Fig. 118).

In such an average or typical flower we would find four sets of floral parts, arranged concentrically. The outermost whorl is composed of parts known individually as **sepals** (referred to collectively as the **calyx**). These are usually leaflike in both color and structure, though commonly smaller in size than the purely vegetative leaves that are produced elsewhere on the sporophyte body. In its early developmental stages the flower is arranged in the form of a "bud," with the sepals folded together on the outside, inclosing and protecting the more delicate structures within. Here, then, we encounter one more example of tissues which incase and protect certain critical structures of the organism while they are passing through the tender stages of early development, and later unfold and expose those structures when they are mature and prepared to function in the medium of air.

With the sepals unfolded, we would encounter just within them a whorl of **petals** (referred to collectively as the **corolla**). These are commonly larger than the sepals (when the flower is mature), more delicate in texture, and endowed with a bright coloration. To the majority of people, the flower is nothing more than an object of aesthetic value, and this value is contained largely in the petals, which, in most cases, are by far the most conspicuous part of the flower. But nature had evolved the petals of flowers long before she had evolved human beings, and their evolution was directed into channels of value to the plants that produced them. The value of petals lies in their power of attracting insects, which, in the majority of angiosperms, are necessary agents for the completion of the life cycle.

Inside the petals there is a cyclic arrangement of **stamens,** each one consisting of a long, thin *filament* surmounted by a club-shaped **anther.** The appearance of the stamen is suggestive of a spore case on a stalk; and the appearance is not deceptive, for the anther of the stamen is indeed a spore case, containing numerous tiny spores, and the filament is a stalk which so elevates the anther as to put the spores in a favorable position for distribution when the proper time comes. As we have indicated in the previous chapter, the stamen is a microsporophyll, and the anther is comprised of four microsporangia which, when mature, coalesce to form either two or in some cases just one large spore case (Fig. 119).

At the center of the flower lies the **pistil.** This is the most critical part of the flower, for it is here that the seed (or seeds) will be produced. Three parts are usually recognizable in the pistil: at the bottom is a swollen **ovary;** extending upward from the middle of the ovary is a stalklike **style;** and at the top of the style is a small platform of tissue known as the **stigma.** As we shall see, each of these three parts has a distinct function in connection with those events which lead to fertilization and the production of the seed and fruit. A pistil may be composed of one or more **carpels** (megasporophylls). Since the major portion of the pistil is the ovary, we usually speak of the number of carpels which make up the ovary, rather than pistil, particularly because it is the ovary that ripens into the fruit.

In earlier chapters we saw how the life cycles of moss and fern pursued a regular and similar course in which the following stages were encountered successively: zygote, embryo, mature plant, spore, gametophyte, gametes, zygote. Every complete generation for the organism contains a great many generations for the individual cells, for it is a long series of cell divisions that carries the organism from zygote

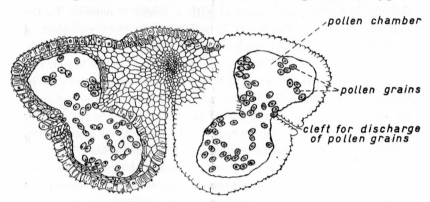

FIG. 119.—Cross-section of a mature anther

around to zygote again. One might think of a toy train moving steadily around its circular track, save for just one stage which this analogy would fail to depict. Throughout most of the cycle the heritage of the species is moving along a single track, but at the stage of the gametes it is moving for a very short time along double tracks which meet again in the zygote. In the case of the seed plant, double tracks occupy a greater portion of the entire cycle, for the separation occurs at the stage of the spore and continues until the zygote is reached. So we may expect to encounter two types of spores, followed by two types of gametophytes and two types of gametes.

Let us first give our attention to the **microspores.** When the microsporangia are maturing in the anther, there are a number of microspore mother cells undergoing reduction division and forming microspores. When the stamen is mature, the anther at its upper end contains two chambers full of microspores, or **pollen grains,** as they are commonly called (see Fig. 119). At first each spore is organized as a single cell; within each spore coat there is just the single nucleus surrounded by cytoplasm. Even before the time of pollen-shedding, however, the contents of each spore have divided up into three diminutive cells. This three-celled body, contained entirely within the spore wall, is actually a **gametophyte.** Far smaller than any other gametophyte in the plant kingdom, it produces no recognizable sex organs. Instead, two of its three cells become organized as sperm, and the third is the tube nucleus which ultimately will initiate the formation of a pollen tube. Hence we know the content of a microspore to be a male gametophyte, or microgametophyte, since it produces gametes of only this one sex. It is noteworthy that the sperm are not ciliated. At last, as in the gymnosperms, the plant kingdom has evolved a method of getting the sperm to the eggs which does not depend upon the presence of a film of water. Note also that the "pollen grain" at the time of shedding is something more than a simple spore. The spore wall is there, but inside it is a diminutive male gametophyte.

The **megaspores** are produced within the ovary at the base of the pistil, buried within structures to which we must give some attention. When the early botanists cut into the ovary, they found a cavity that was almost filled with small, ovoid objects, projecting into the ovary cavity from their points of attachment on the ovary wall or axis. These objects bore some superficial resemblance to animal eggs. So the older botanists called them "little eggs" or "ovules," and it was for this reason that their container was called the ovary. Now the ovule of any seed plant is an exceedingly significant structure, for it is the structure which, following certain transformations, is to become the seed. But the ovule is far from being what it was first thought to be, a "little egg." Instead it is actually a spore case, but one which differs in several important respects from the spore cases that we have encountered hitherto.

1. The wall of the spore case of thallophytes was nothing but a cell wall, within which an internal division of the protoplasm occurred to produce the spores. The spore case of the fern was a many-celled structure, but its wall consisted of no more than a single layer of epidermal cells. In the ovule of the seed plant, however, we have a spore case that is comparatively thick walled, the wall being composed of

several layers of sterile cells, as seen in longitudinal section in Figure 120.

2. All previous spore cases contained numerous spores. The ovule of the seed plant is peculiar in maturing just one.

3. But the most significant of all the peculiarities of the ovule lies in its failure to shed the spore. All spore cases that we have seen to date except those of gymnosperms have broken and released the contained spores at the time that they were ripe for shedding. The ovule, however, retains its single spore indefinitely, and it is this feature that makes it possible for the ovule and its contents to become the *seed*.

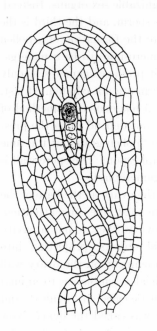

As compared with the gametophytes of lower plant groups, the female gametophyte of angiosperms is markedly reduced in size. As compared with the male gametophyte of angiosperms themselves, it is large, corresponding to the greater size of the spore which contains it. At first the megaspore contains only the one nucleus, together with a large supply of cytoplasm. In its subsequent development the spore passes through a series of three nuclear divisions, so that the mature female gametophyte contains a total of eight nuclei. One of these nuclei becomes the egg. It is located at the *micropylar* end of the megagametophyte, and usually closely associated with it are two of the other nuclei, the *synergids*. The latter are probably vestiges of the archegonium, which made its last appearance in the gymnosperms. Three of the remaining nuclei, the *antipodals*, are near the end of the megagametophyte opposite the micropyle, and the last two, the *polar nuclei*, are found in the central area. Whereas the tiny microgametophyte contains two sperm, the decidedly larger megagametophyte has a total output of only one egg (Fig. 121).

Fig. 120.—Longitudinal section of a young ovule (of *Erigeron*). Four potential spores have been formed, but three are being aborted and only one is developing further.

The stage is now set for fertilization, but the bringing of the sperm to the egg is a much more complicated process in the angiosperm than in the lower plants that we have examined. There are two distinct chapters or stages in the process, the first being pollination and the second being the growth of the pollen tube.

By **pollination** we refer to the transfer of pollen from the anther, where it is produced, to the stigma at the upper end of the pistil. In

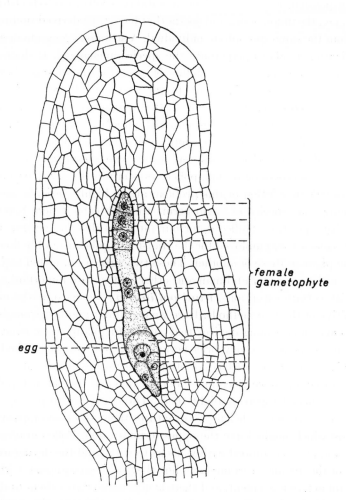

Fig. 121.—Longitudinal section of an older ovule (of *Erigeron*), containing a mature female gametophyte.

some species *self-pollination* is the rule, i.e., transfer of pollen to the stigma of the same flower. Here the problem is comparatively simple. By the action of gravity the pollen may merely fall from the anther to the stigma, which is carried at a slightly lower level in such cases. In other cases the anthers grow compactly together, forming a tube; when pollen is ripe the style elongates, forcing the stigma up through this tube, where it collects pollen by direct contact.

Self-pollination, as we shall see, inevitably results in *self-fertiliza-tion,* i.e., the union of egg and sperm that have been derived (indirect-ly) from the same sporophyte individual. A sustained program of self-fertilization tends to perpetuate the species unchanged. It does not absolutely preclude the possibility of evolutionary change, but it makes for a slower evolutionary progress than might result if occasional *cross-fertilization* occurred. It is not surprising, therefore, to find that the majority of angiosperms exhibit at least a certain amount of cross-fertilization. This is accomplished, of course, by devices which favor, and in some cases absolutely insure, *cross-pollination.*

In cases of cross-pollination, pollen transfer presents a real problem. The details of solution of this problem are so highly variable among the numerous species of angiosperms that we cannot here hope to cover the question. Suffice it for our purposes that, in general, two great agencies are employed for the transfer of pollen from the flowers of one plant to those of another. These two agencies are wind and insects, although water and man and other animals are important.

With certain exceptions, *wind pollinating* seems to be the more primitive of the two methods. Here we encounter another example of the remarkable timing devices that successful plants have evolved. During the comparatively brief period when pollen is being shed by one plant, the stigma surfaces of other plants in the vicinity are exuding a sticky liquid which equips them to catch and to hold such pollen grains as may happen to alight there. Though this feature may impress us as to the "efficiency" of nature, there is an accompanying feature which might leave the opposite impression. Pollen grains are light and are so equipped with walls as to withstand the drying influence of the air for a certain time, but they have no equipment whatever for active movement, and there is nothing to direct them to their proper destination. They are absolutely dependent on air currents, which may carry them anywhere in a field in which the stigmas of flowers of the same species present targets that are both tiny and few. The successful plants have met this problem by producing a tremendous quantity of pollen, the vast bulk of which comes to naught. This may seem wasteful, but it is not a meaningless, prodigal wastefulness, for it is necessary to insure a reasonable amount of effective pollination under this obviously inefficient program of wind pollination.

Two incidental points are worth noting. Wind pollination charges the air with a profusion of microscopic pollen grains. Reaching the eyes and the noses of certain people, these produce the well-known effects of *hay fever,* an example of the non-beneficial interaction of different organisms. The other point to be noted is that wind-pollinated flowers have petals that are usually small and not brightly colored, or they may be lacking completely. We assume that when, in the course of evolution, individuals of these species varied in the direction of inconspicuous flowers and it did not lessen their chances of reproducing, such varieties survived alongside their showy relatives. The new trait probably became dominant when the same strains developed other variations which happened to have real selective value along with the petal changes, which did not matter.

The other main agency for pollination is *insects.* Here we have a much more "efficient" device which moves pollen with surprising directness and accuracy from source to destination, and a smaller output of pollen is needed than in the case of the wind-pollinated species. Insect pollination is the most conspicuous and the best known of the many existing examples of interaction between living organisms of different types to the advantage of each. The value of the insect to the flower is efficient cross-pollination (sometimes self-pollination). The value of the flower to the insect is a food value. Usually the food is in the form of *nectar,* a sugar solution secreted by certain glandular cells in the flower, though in some cases the insects devour a part of the pollen supply itself. The brightly colored petals and the odors which some flowers exude have an important indirect value in advertising the presence of the flowers to the insects.

Here we encounter an even more striking example of "timing" in nature. Within the same brief period, pollen is ripe for shedding, petals are at their largest and brightest, odors are most intense, nectar is being secreted, and stigmas of other flowers are in proper condition for reception of pollen. In the process of pollination the insect thrusts all or part of its hairy body down into the tube of the flower in quest of the nectar, which is produced by certain cells at the bottom. The physical characteristics of flower and insect are such that this movement inevitably rubs portions of the insect body past the shedding anthers. On its visit to the next flower these pollen-smeared portions of the insect brush past the sticky stigma, and thus the pollen arrives at its proper destination.

The foregoing statement reveals the main principles involved in insect pollination but fails miserably to do justice to the tremendous diversity of fine adjustments to this process that have been evolved in the bodies of the many pollinating insects and in the many flowers which they pollinate. Not only are the size, shape, and general physical equipment of a particular insect remarkably adapted to the physical peculiarities of the (one or a few) types of flowers that it pollinates, but its instincts direct it in making exactly the appropriate movements. The fossil record tells us that primitive insects were first evolved toward the end of the Paleozoic era and that the number of insect types was increasing rather slowly in the subsequent time periods. During the latter part of the Mesozoic, however, the evolution and diversification of insect types took on new impetus. It has proceeded at such a great rate ever since that today the insect species far outnumber the total of all other groups in the animal kingdom. The new impetus to the evolution of insects was the appearance of flowering plants, and during this period when insects were evolving into myriad types, angiosperms were doing the same, so that today they, too, outnumber all other groups within their own kingdom.

The adaptive interrelationship of insects and flowers has been so perfected that the great Charles Darwin, about 1870, when presented with a new flower of rare dimensions, was able to predict correctly that a moth of corresponding dimensions would be discovered living in the same region.

After the pollen grains have arrived upon the sticky surface of the stigma, they behave in a manner reminiscent of the spores of parasitic fungi. The protoplasm within expands and pushes through the spore walls like the young mycelium of a fungus. The tiny filament that is initiated by the tube nucleus is known as the *pollen tube.* Very rapidly it burrows its way down through the stigmatic surface and into the tissues of the style. This pollen tube is the male gametophyte, which has escaped from the confines of the spore wall and has related itself to the tissues of the pistil very much as a fungus mycelium relates itself to the tissues of its host. Rapidly it progresses through the process of digesting its way, until it has completely traversed the style and has arrived at the ovary cavity. Directive forces that are influenced by the female, however, guide the growing pollen tube to the nearest ovule. The pollen tube enters the ovule through a tiny opening, the *micropyle,* which has been left by the megasporangium and its protective covering, the *integument.* Penetrating the ovule tissues (Fig. 122), the growing tube comes at last to lie in actual contact with the female gametophyte. Meanwhile, other pollen tubes, following much the same general course, are directed to pass farther and penetrate other ovules which have not been pre-empted (see Fig. 118).

Before the pollen tube has emerged very far from its confinement within the old spore wall, the two male gametes slip downward to take a position near the tip of the advancing tube. The sperm are not flagellated—angiosperms have no need of that—but are moved to their new position by streaming movements of the cytoplasm within the male gametophyte. Hence when the female gametophyte has been reached, there are two sperm in readiness at the tip of the tube (see Fig. 122). At this stage a rupture in the end of the tube is followed by extrusion of the two sperm, so that they are now free within the confines of the female gametophyte. One of the two sperm fertilizes the egg, and thus at last the zygote is produced. Now, however, something else has been added. The two polar nuclei fuse together in the center of the megagametophyte to form a diploid structure which we call the *fusion nucleus.* This fusion takes place sometime before the sperm enter the megagametophyte. The second sperm now unites with the fusion nucleus to form a triploid *primary endosperm nucleus.* Thus in angiosperms we have a *double fertilization,* a union of one sperm with the egg and a union of the second sperm with the fusion nucleus.

As in all EMBRYOPHYTA, the seed plant zygote immediately gets under way with the production of the young sporophyte. Very rapidly this developing embryo obliterates the old female gametophyte and comes to occupy the corresponding space within the ovule. The female gametophyte, or megagametophyte, is often referred to as the **embryo sac** since it is in this organ that the embryo is formed. After the embryo has undergone a certain amount of growth and differentiation, it stops growing and passes into a state of dormancy. In some plants, as we shall see, this period of dormancy may be for only a few days; in others it may last for years.

In earlier chapters we noted that living tissues were often thrown into a state of dormancy by a cutting-off of their water supply. This is exactly what happens to the embryo sporophyte. In some manner,

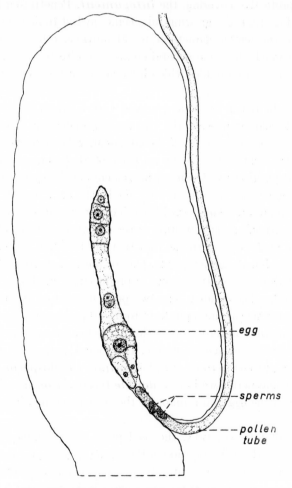

egg

sperms

pollen tube

FIG. 122.—Pollen tube entering the mature ovule

growth hormones stimulated either by fertilization itself or by some influence of the pollen tube provide a stimulus which initiates changes in the wall of the ovule. These wall tissues (integument and often megasporangium), which have hitherto been soft, start to undergo a transformation. This is occurring at the same time that the embryo sporophyte is developing within. Soft tissues are gradually transformed into a tough (and in some cases an exceedingly hard and thick) wall, which at last completely surrounds the embryo and throws it into dormancy by cutting off its water supply.

The resulting structure is the **seed.** Hence a seed may be defined as a transformed ovule, consisting now of a tough seed coat surround-

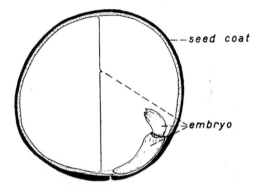

FIG. 123.—Section through a pea seed

ing an embryo sporophyte. These two components are always present in a seed, and sometimes there is also a third. For its future development the young embryo is going to need a good supply of food. In some seeds (e.g., bean and pea) this food supply is stored within certain parts of the embryo itself. Hence when we peel off the coat from a seed of this sort, we encounter nothing but a rather large embryo within (Fig. 123). In other seeds (e.g., corn and wheat) the food is stored not in but around the embryo. Within such a seed one finds a rather small embryo imbedded in a larger food storage tissue, the **endosperm** (Fig. 124). The latter is formed by many divisions of the primary endosperm nucleus, which grows in size within the embryo sac, just as the embryo itself does, but the endosperm cells undergo very little differentiation. However, whether the food is stored as endosperm or within the embryo itself, it is often exploited by man and devoted to his own nourishment. A summary of the life history of a flowering plant is given in Figure 125.

The release and distribution of seeds and the emergence of the young sporophyte are matters that we shall discuss in the next chapter. For the present, however, let us consider the biological value of the seed. Biological value it must have, for the seed is the structure that is largely responsible for the overwhelming success of the seed plants.

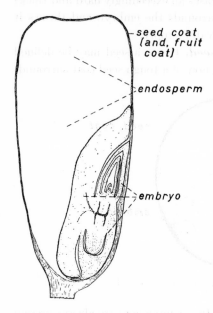

In an earlier chapter we called attention to a great evolutionary trend which appears in both animal and plant kingdoms. Among the more progressive lines of descent we find that both animals and plants have increasingly made provision for their young, so that the highest animals of today and the highest plants of today have perfected devices for giving their offspring a good start in life. The seed is such a device. The food stored in or around the embryo sporophyte will enable it, when the proper moment arrives, to make rapid growth and quickly to establish itself as a self-supporting plant. Even more significant, however, is the fact that the earliest and most sensitive

Fig. 124.—The longitudinal section through a corn grain. (The so-called grain is technically a "fruit" rather than merely a seed, for the coat of the seed proper is closely surrounded by a thin layer of tissue that was derived not from the ovule itself but from the ovary wall.)

stages of sporophyte development have occurred in a well-protected place, attached to the body of the parent. A third biological value of the seed is its value as an agent of distribution, and a fourth lies in its power to tide the species over a period of adverse conditions; these are matters that will be treated in chapter xix.

Before returning to a discussion of the seed and fruit, it might be well for us to consider again the flower. The origin of this organ still

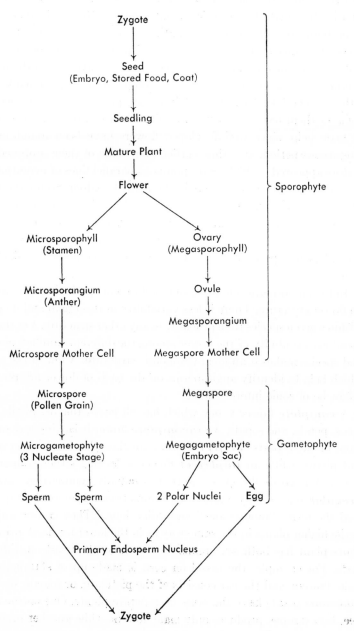

Fɪɢ. 125.—An outline of the life cycle of a flowering plant

remains a mystery, but it has essentially the same parts as a strobilus and is often described as originating from a flattened strobilus. This is probably too simple an explanation, and it is very likely that the flower has appeared several times from more than one source. Some botanists are of the opinion that the Gnetales gave rise to the angiosperms since they produce not only strobili but also a modified flower. Others suggest that the Bennettitales are possible ancestors because some of them have flower-like strobili. The fossil record, however, is of little help, since well-developed flowers have been found in the Cretaceous period, at a time earlier than some of their supposed ancestors appeared—which again points to parallel lines of evolution for this structure as well as others in the plant kingdom. So for the present our information leads us to believe that the flower originated from one of the gymnosperm groups; that group may have been the Cycadofilicales, which, as we have seen, is an order that is ancestral to several gymnosperm orders and now possibly the flowering plants as well.

In the angiosperms identification of different species is based largely on flower structure. There is less variability in this organ and its parts within a given species than probably in any other structure. Yet the tremendous variability of the flower among the different families, genera, and species makes it an ideal taxonomic structure. A few of the terms which help to identify angiosperms on the basis of flower morphology might be of some interest here.

A *complete* flower is one which has all parts, that is, pistils, stamens, petals, and sepals. An *incomplete* flower is lacking any one or more of these parts. *Perfect* flowers are those having both stamens and pistils, while an *imperfect* flower is lacking either stamens or pistils. A *regular* flower is one that is radially symmetrical, and an *irregular* one is only bilaterally symmetrical. Previously we have used the terms "monoecious" and "dioecious." They can be applied to the higher plants in the same way as in the lower forms. A *monoecious* plant has both sex organs on the same plant but on different parts. For example, the tassel on corn is made up of staminate, or male, flowers, and the ear consists of the pistillate, or female, flowers. *Dioecious* plants have the sexes on separate plants. One cottonwood tree, for example, produces only male flowers, while another produces only the female flowers.

It is not our purpose to take up all the variations occurring in flowers. Suffice it to say that they vary in numbers of any and all parts from zero to dozens of each; they may have all parts separate or united; some parts appear above and some parts below the others. Some flowers are borne singly; others are borne in variously shaped clusters. Color obviously is an important characteristic as well as odor, both of which are as variable as any factor in the plant world.

Since the angiosperms now dominate the plant kingdom both ecologically and phylogenetically, it would be prudent for us to include a few of the more prominent families. These families are selected on the basis of their biological interest and their economic importance to us.

As we have previously mentioned, the class of angiosperms is divided into two subclasses, the *dicotyledons* and the *monocotyledons*. The titles refer to the primary and most reliable distinction between the two groups—a distinction based upon the nature of their embryos. The major, root-stem axis of the embryo carries lateral members known as *cotyledons* ("seed leaves"). Among dicotyledonous seeds, two cotyledons are present; among monocotyledons, one. In addition to this primary distinction, there are other features which, with few exceptions, will serve to distinguish the two groups. Dicotyledons have their vascular bundles organized into a single great vascular cylinder (see Fig. 15), net-veined leaves (see Fig. 5), and floral parts most commonly in fours and fives; monocotyledons have scattered vascular bundles (see Fig. 20), parallel-veined leaves (see Fig. 5), and floral parts usually in threes or multiples of three. Phylogenetically we consider the monocotyledons as more advanced than the dicotyledons, although the two subclasses must have had, in part, parallel lines of evolution.

Dicotyledoneae. The dicotyledonous plants are divided into approximately fifty orders, far too numerous to list here, but for convenience the class is divided into two great groups: the Archichlamydeae, in which the petals are either quite separate from each other or are entirely lacking, and the Metachlamydeae, in which the petals are fused through part of their length into a tube which surrounds stamens and carpels. This state of the petals is merely one of the several differences which exist between the two groups. A few of the outstanding families of Archichlamydeae will be mentioned first.

Archichlamydeae.—Several small families of the lower Archichla-mydeae include our most common hardwood or deciduous trees. Simple, inconspicuous, wind-pollinated flowers are present, arranged in such characteristic conelike clusters (catkins) as those that we notice in early spring on the cottonwood trees. Besides the cotton-wood, other well-known forms are the elms, walnuts, hickories, oaks, chestnuts, willows, birches, beech, and poplars other than the cotton-wood itself.

The "buttercup family" (Ranunculaceae) includes herbaceous plants characterized by five sepals, usually five petals, and numerous distinct pistils and stamens. Clematis, anemone, hepatica, marsh marigold, peony, larkspur, and columbine are included here.

The "mustard family" (Cruciferae) includes herbaceous plants with a pungent taste, which is exaggerated in commercial mustard. The flowers have four sepals, four petals in one set, four long and two short stamens, and two carpels. Included here are stock, sweet alyssum, candytuft, wallflower, water cress, horse-radish, mustard, cabbage, turnip, and radish.

One of the most beautiful, and at the same time useful, of plant groups is the "rose family" (Rosaceae), in which the flower suggests that of the buttercup. The plant body may be in the form of herb, shrub, or tree. In addition to the many roses themselves, the family contributes a large portion of our commercial fruits, including straw-berries, raspberries, blackberries, peaches, apricots, plums, cherries, apples, pears, and quinces.

Largest of the Archichlamydeae families is that of the "legumes" (Leguminosae), characterized by its irregular flowers, highly adapted to insect pollination, and by the ripening of the ovary into the well-known "pod." The legumes are of widespread distribution, with a plant body that ranges from a small herb to a tree of large size. Its better-known representatives are sweet pea, wisteria, lupine, sensitive plant, black locust, honey locust, Kentucky coffee tree, clover, alfalfa, pea, numerous beans, and the peanut, also the acacias, rosewoods, and many other tropical trees.

One of the most advanced Archichlamydeae families but not very conspicuous is the Umbelliferae, characterized by an inferior ovary (which means that the sepals and petals arise at a point above the top of the ovary) and an organization of flowers into flat-topped clusters known as umbels. The umbellifers include parsnips, carrots, and celery.

Well-known Archichlamydeae that are not included in the families mentioned above are the tulip tree (yellow poplar), magnolia, linden (basswood), sycamore, maple, buckeye, box elder, sweet-gum, tupelo (black gum), violets, pinks, geraniums, nasturtiums, fuchsias, cotton, flax, hemp, currants, gooseberries, grapes, citrus fruits, tea, and the cacao tree (which yields chocolate).

Metachlamydeae.—The Metachlamydeae, with their tubular corollas, include the families of the highest rank among the dicotyledons, a few of which are mentioned below.

The "heath family" (Ericaceae) is characterized by two sets or cycles of five stamens each, so that the floral parts as a whole are arranged into five whorls. Woody shrubs for the most part, these plants grow most frequently in the cooler regions of the earth. Included are trailing arbutus, bearberry, heather, rhododendron, azalea, mountain laurel, wintergreen, huckleberries, blueberries, and cranberries.

The "mint family" (Lamiaceae) is characterized by a "two-lipped" corolla, square stems, opposite leaves, and an ovary conspicuously divided into four lobes. It includes basil, pennyroyal, lavender, mint, horehound, hyssop, savory, marjoram, thyme, balm, sage, rosemary, and catnip.

In the "nightshade family" (Solanaceae) one finds a conspicuous, regular, tubular corolla, with floral parts arranged in four cycles. Here we find the nightshade itself, red pepper, ground cherry, belladonna, jimson weed, potato (Irish potato), tomato, and tobacco.

Highest of all dicotyledon families is the Compositae, characterized by the organization of numerous small flowers into a head so compact as to resemble a single flower. Herbaceous plants, widely distributed and very numerous in temperate regions, the composites include dandelion, sunflower, goldenrod, thistle, beggar-ticks, blazing star, daisy, aster, everlasting, rosinwood (compass plant), ragweed, cocklebur, zinnia, dahlia, cosmos, marigold, chrysanthemum, sagebrush, burdock, and lettuce. It is interesting to note that this family is of little commercial value to man and actually supplies a large portion of those "weeds" that interfere with his cultivation of other plants.

Well-known Metachlamydeae that are not included in the families mentioned above are the coffee plant (which yields the coffee berry of commerce), cinchona (which yields quinine), sweet potato, olive, and the gourd fruits (watermelon, muskmelon, cucumber, pumpkin, squash).

Monocotyledoneae. The monocotyledonous plants are divided into twelve orders and about thirty-five families, but only four of the latter will be considered here. Of all families in the entire plant kingdom, the one that is of greatest economic importance to man is the "grass family" (Gramineae). Here the flowers are exceedingly simple, having neither sepals nor petals, being surrounded by tough, leaflike "bracts." The flowers are arranged in a loose or compact cluster. The sporophyte body as a whole ranges from that of the tiny lawn grasses with horizontal underground stems to that of the towering bamboo, whose thin, erect stem may be almost one hundred feet in height. Economically, the bamboo is of tremendous importance in the tropics, where man has come to depend upon it for structures of all types. The small grasses of temperate regions provide pasture and hay for our livestock, as well as lawns and golf courses for ourselves. Together with the sugar beet (a dicotyledon), another "monocot," sugar cane, provides the world with its sugar supply. Greatest in economic importance are those grasses that we speak of as the "cereals." From the time that agriculture was first started by prehistoric man, its largest emphasis has fallen upon the raising of cereal crops, and this single activity has been extremely influential in molding human history and human culture. For those of us who live in temperate regions, wheat is the most important cereal, but corn, oats, rye, and barley should not be overlooked. In the tropics, rice is the principal food of hundreds of millions of human beings.

Widespread in the tropics and of great utility to man is the "palm family" (Palmaceae). Here an enormous cluster of simple flowers develops within a single bract. The sporophyte body is most commonly a tree, with unbranched trunk surmounted by a dense crown of large leaves. The coconut palm, date palm, and others are put to innumerable uses by the natives of tropical regions.

Most typical and easily identified among monocotyledons are the members of the "lily family" (Liliaceae). Here the floral parts stand out conspicuously and symmetrically in threes or multiples of three, with the petals brightly colored and sometimes the sepals as well. The plant body is usually herbaceous and is usually provided with a bulb or some other form of underground stem which makes possible a rapid development of aerial parts at the opening of the season favorable to growth. Although this family gives us our asparagus and onion, it is better known for its beauty than for its usefulness. Most commonly encountered are the trilliums, the lily of the valley, various true lilies, tulips, the dogtooth violet, and the hyacinths.

Most advanced and specialized of all the monocotyledons is the "orchid family" (Orchidaceae). Surpassing the other monocotyledon families in number of species, the orchids are actually rather rare plants. Such plants as the grasses dominate huge stretches of the earth's surface with a dense mass of vegetation that includes countless billions of individual bodies. Orchids, on the other hand, are scattered here and there as isolated individuals, quite difficult for the collector to find in temperate regions but more plentiful in the moist tropics. The orchid flower is characterized by an inferior ovary and by a strange specialization of one of the petals. This one petal, known as the "lip," becomes quite unlike the others, assuming an expanded tubular or saclike shape, and is often spurred. Actually, the orchid flower includes several peculiar details which have apparently evolved as adaptations to insect relations. One could almost say that for every orchid species there exists in the same locality a species of insect that is equipped with the particular size, shape, and instincts that are required for the pollination of that orchid. The sporophyte body is herbaceous, moderate in size, and often epiphytic. Much prized for their beauty, the orchids are actually of little economic importance, save for one Mexican form which is our source of vanilla.

Not included in the four families that we have just sketched are two monocotyledons of considerable economic importance. The banana is a moderate-sized tropical tree with enormous leaves and a fruit that is a substantial part of the diet of millions of people. The pineapple, cultivated in the West Indies and Florida and Hawaii, is a low plant with stiff, sword-shaped leaves that produces the remarkable, large compound fruit of commerce and is also a source of fiber.

XIX. *Seeds and Fruits*

In the preceding chapter we left the seed, along with its companion
seeds, inclosed within the ovary of the pistil. To accomplish any useful purpose, these seeds must emerge and get distributed. How seeds
emerge and how they may be distributed depend, in large part, upon
the surrounding structures. If we examine these surrounding structures, we find that they, too, have undergone transformations. While
the seeds have been ripening, the structure that we call the fruit has
been ripening around them.

When the layman uses the term *fruit* he is referring to edibles of a
category that would be rather difficult to define. When the botanist
uses the term "fruit" he is referring to the part of the plant in which
the seeds are contained. In most cases this structure is nothing but
the ripened ovary. An orange, for example, is an ovary that has
ripened into a fleshy, juicy condition. This would be recognized as a
fruit by both the botanist and the layman. Botanically speaking, however, the tomato is likewise a *fleshy fruit,* though the layman would
be likely to exclude this from his classification on no better grounds
than that it was grown in a garden instead of an orchard (Fig. 126).
Botanically, a nut is a fruit, and so is the pod of a pea, for these are
also ripened ovaries containing seeds, though *dry fruits* of this sort
are rarely recognized as fruits by the layman (Fig. 127). In some cases
the fruit is more than a single ovary. A raspberry, for example, is an
aggregate fruit, in which each tiny lobe has been derived from the
ovary of a separate pistil; and a fruit like the pineapple is even more
elaborate, being the fused product of a great many flowers and including not only the transformed ovaries but other floral parts as
well (Fig. 128).

It should be realized that the fruit that we buy at a fruit stand is usually a very different thing from the fruit that was evolved by angiosperm plants growing in a state of nature. During the past few centuries man has directed the course of evolution along lines which catered to his own interests. Starting with the relatively puny fruits

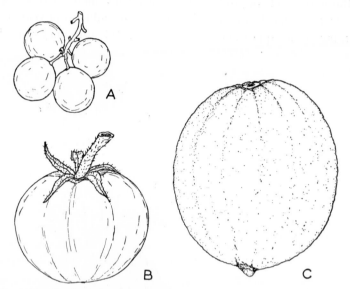

Fig. 126.—Simple fleshy fruits: *A*, grape; *B*, tomato; *C*, orange. In these cases the entire fruit is derived from the tissues which composed the wall of a single ovary.

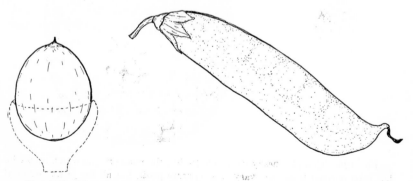

Fig. 127.—Dry fruits. *On the left*, a "nut" (the acorn of the oak in this case). *On the right*, the "pod" of the pea.

which nature provided, he has gradually led his cultivated plants to produce bigger, tenderer, juicier, and tastier fruits. We moderns, with our appetites adjusted to the charms of modern cultivated fruits, would in most cases turn up our noses if offered the fruit of the original, wild, ancestral types.

But nature did not produce the original fruits merely to nourish and delight mankind. Fruits were in existence for millions of years before man put in his appearance, and during all this time they must have

Fig. 128.—Complex fleshy fruits. *On the left*, the raspberry, in which each lobe has been derived from the ovary of a separate pistil, but all the pistils involved have been parts of the one flower. *On the right*, the pineapple, produced by the transformation and fusion of the tissues of a great many distinct flowers.

been serving a useful purpose for the species which produced them. The ripe fruit has one minor biological value in carrying on the function which was started by the young ovary, i.e., protecting the seeds until they are ripe to be released. In the case of some fruits, there may be some biological value in "manuring" the little spot of ground in which the young sporophyte is to take root, for a fallen fruit will disintegrate and enrich the soil at the very place where the contained seed will sprout into young plants. But undoubtedly the main biological value of the fruit is in providing just one of the many means of accomplishing seed distribution, as we shall see shortly.

DISTRIBUTION OF SEEDS

Among the three lower groups of the plant kingdom, the spore is prevailingly the agent of distribution for the species, and a rather effective one, too, owing to its small size and the ease with which it may be carried through air or water. With the revision of the life cycle that appears among seed plants, however, the spore can no longer play this role. The megaspores are never released, as such, and the microspores or pollen grains—if they are to function at all—must do their functioning at spots where the ovules are already located. With spores eliminated as a means of distribution and the plant body itself unable to migrate, there remains only the seed as an effective agent for spreading the species over an increasing territory. The widespread present distribution of seed plants is enough to tell us that seeds must have played this role very effectively during the past.

Seed distribution is accomplished by many different devices. To a very limited extent, gravity may effect distribution, as when nuts fall to the ground and roll down a slope. Much more important is water, as in the case of those seed plants which grow actually in the water, as well as those which we commonly encounter on the banks of streams and rivers. A few plants accomplish seed distribution on a small scale by devices of the fruit which make for a forceful ejection of seeds, as in the "touch-me-not" and the "squirting cucumber." But the major agencies for seed distribution are the animals and the wind.

Animals appropriate both dry and fleshy fruits as articles of diet. If animals were to digest the entire contents of every fruit which they picked off the plant, the net results would be adverse to the success of the plant species. Such, of course, is not the case, or fruits which so attract the animals would probably not have been evolved. A few animals, such as the squirrel, often actually plant seeds by burying nuts and failing to return for them. There are many more that eat the fruit and eschew the seeds, and many that eat the seeds at the same time but pass them unharmed through their alimentary tracts.

Edibility is not the only device for winning the co-operation of animals. Some plants form burs through barbed extensions of the seed coats or coats of the dry fruits which surround the seeds (Fig. 129).

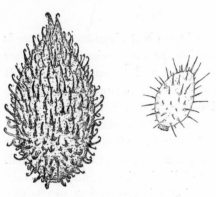

Furred animals may carry these burs for great distances before dropping them. The small seeds of a good many plants, coming to rest on the muddy banks of streams and ponds, may be carried tremendous distances through adhering to the feet of migratory birds. And we must not forget that, among the animals, man himself, voluntarily and involuntarily, has effected a great deal of seed distribution in the course of his migrations.

Fig. 129.—Burs: cocklebur, *left;* grass bur, *right.*

Wind is employed even more extensively as an agent of seed distribution. Some seeds (e.g., grasses) are tiny, flat, and light, and can be readily borne on the wind. Others, somewhat larger and heavier, make use of the glider or parachute principle (Fig. 130). In the pine, and in many other gymnosperms, an extension of the seed coat itself forms a passive wing, while in maple, ash, and elm, wings are formed by extensions of the dry fruit. In milkweed, in the cottonwood, and in the cotton plant itself, the seed coat is covered with many fine, hairlike outgrowths which provide such great air resistance as to keep the seeds aloft for a long time through the action of chance air currents. The dandelion fruit is provided with a beautiful little parachute which has been derived from certain outer regions of the flower. In the tumbleweed the entire plant goes bouncing along in the wind, dropping seeds as it goes.

GERMINATION

In order for a seed to germinate after it has settled into or on the soil, several environmental conditions must prevail. (1) An adequate amount of *water* must be present for the seed coats to imbibe and become softened enough for the embryo to break through. It also acts as a solvent for the foods in the seed to move from the cotyledons or endosperm to the growing tips of the embryo. Water also activates the protoplasm and enables it to carry on the processes of digestion, respiration, assimilation, and growth. (2) **Oxygen** is also necessary but in varying amounts for different seeds. When a seed begins to ger-

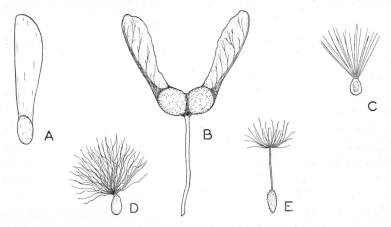

Fig. 130.—Wind-borne seeds and fruits: *A*, pine seed; *B*, maple fruits; *C*, milkweed seed; *D*, cottonwood seed; *E*, dandelion fruit.

minate, it requires a great deal of oxygen to carry on respiration, which is unusually active at this time. Some seeds, however, such as rice and those of other aquatic plants, will germinate under water, where the percentage of oxygen is low. (3) An optimum **temperature** is also necessary because it influences all the physiological processes, including respiration, digestion, assimilation, and growth. Different seeds, of course, require different temperatures; seeds of early spring crops—such as those of radishes, lettuce, and peas—will germinate when the temperature is just slightly above freezing, but warm-weather crops like cotton, corn, tomato, and pumpkin prefer soil temperatures above 55° F.

These three external conditions are primary requisites to germination, but some seeds are also influenced by *light.* Some of the grasses, the evening primrose, and rhododendron have seeds which will germinate better if light is present. The onion, however, is an example of a plant whose seeds will germinate better in the dark than in light. Most seeds have no preference and will germinate just as well in the light as in the dark.

We also find that there are reasons why the seed itself will not germinate even though the external conditions are optimum. Botanists consider these conditions under the general heading of **dormancy.** The term refers to the fact that for some reason there is a delay in germination, even though all conditions are favorable. Briefly, we might list a few possible reasons: (1) the seed coat is impermeable to water; (2) the seed coat is impermeable to oxygen; (3) the pressure of the expanding embryo is not sufficient to break the very tough seed coat; (4) the seed requires a period of "after-ripening" in order to grow.

Many seed coats have a very high fat content, such as those of honey locust and other legumes; and, until the seeds have had these fatty substances removed by the acids in the soil, the embryo will not receive an adequate supply of moisture for growth. The cocklebur is a good example of a seed which will not germinate because the coat is impervious to oxygen. Two seeds are produced in the capsular fruit of the cocklebur. One is in an upper position and the other in a lower; other than position they are similar in appearance. The lower seed will germinate immediately upon removal from the capsule, but the upper one will not germinate until much later. The coats of the upper seed only are relatively impermeable to oxygen.

In a few seeds, such as those of some members of the mustard family, the embryo can penetrate through the tough seed coat only after it has been in the soil for a few months or even years. During that time freezing and thawing and the action of soil organisms weaken the seed coat so the embryo can penetrate.

Perhaps the most interesting and at the same time the most baffling are those seeds which require a period of after-ripening before germination. Some of these seeds may have immature embryos, but in most cases the failure to germinate is physiological. In some cases the dormancy period can be broken by subjecting them to alternating conditions of freezing and thawing; in others, treatment with dilute acids will hasten germination. In nature it is possible that changes in the climatic conditions help to break the dormancy, and also with

aging of the seeds an acid condition is gradually built up in the protoplasm of the embryo. When the pH reaches a certain point, the after-
ripening period is over, and the seed is capable of germination. The
apple, peach, and hawthorn have seeds requiring an after-ripening
period.

Other reasons frequently are given why seeds will not germinate
immediately: improperly formed embryos, insufficient food, too
young, and too old.

Many stories concerning the longevity of seeds have been told
through the years. Certainly those involving the germination of seeds
that were found buried with the Egyptian mummies have been entirely discredited. It is known, however, that some seeds will last over
fifty years, and there is one creditable report on lotus seeds that had
lain buried in a peat bed probably more than two hundred years and
still retained their viability.

The expression "seed germination" refers to all that happens in connection with the emergence of the young sporophyte from within the
seed and its establishment as an independent plantlet. Primitive agricultural races have always been greatly impressed with this phenomenon and have often dedicated to it some form of religious ceremony.
The coming into existence of "new life" was always impressive, and
to the untrained the germination of seeds in the spring was a large-
scale example of this miracle. We realize today that strictly new life
is not brought into existence but that new organisms are derived only
by a process of reproduction from parent organisms of the same general type. We realize further that seed germination does not even
mark the true beginning of a plant generation, as does the zygote or
the spore. Seed germination is merely the awakening of a young plant
that has been dormant for a time; it now has the opportunity to carry
on from the point at which its development had been arrested.

Development had been arrested when and because the water supply
had been cut off by the completion of the seed coat. Development
recommences when the water that is provided by spring rains and
melting snow soaks through the softening seed coat and reaches the
embryo. Though water might be regarded as the most important
factor, temperature is also involved, for germination will never be a
success if the surrounding temperature is significantly below (or
above) the temperature range to which the species is adjusted. Oxy-

gen, too, is a vital necessity, for respiration goes on at a great rate in the newly awakened embryo.

The fuel for respiration and the materials for growth are derived from the food that has been stored in the seed, either within the embryo itself or surrounding the embryo. Growth does not occur simultaneously at the same rate in all parts of the embryo. While other parts are still growing quite slowly, if at all, that part of the embryo which is to become the first root starts to develop at a great rate. This prospective root is located just within that region of the seed coat which is thinnest and which first becomes well softened by the water. Here the fast-growing rootlet pushes through and for quite a while is the only part of the embryo to have emerged. Positively geotropic and hydrotropic, the young root curves (if necessary) to thrust itself into the soil. Rapidly it establishes itself and commences an intake of water and soil salts, which are moved upward through the simple beginnings of the vascular system to the parts of the embryo which are still within the seed.

Even a very young embryo is organized on a distinct axis, with the young root tip and stem tip at opposite ends. As we have seen, the first chapter in growth is devoted to the extension of the root. After the root has become established, a second chapter commences, in which other portions of the embryo initiate an active growth, while the growth of the root continues. In a manner which differs in detail among seed plants, the growth of these higher embryo regions serves to extricate the young stem tip, either by pushing it straight through the seed coat or by pulling it out backward. As with the root, the young stem, when it first emerges, may not be in the proper orientation. Very soon, however, its negative geotropism and its positive phototropism will direct it upward into the sunlight, Even the embryo within the seed had possessed the tiny beginnings of the first leaf near the upper end of its axis. With the emergence of the stem, these leaves develop rapidly; with the exposure to sunlight, chlorophyll rapidly appears; and in a surprisingly short time the young sporophyte is fully established as an independent plant.

In the angiosperms there are considerable differences in the way seeds germinate, particularly in respect to the cotyledons. The primary organization of the embryo is the same in all of these plants, both dicotyledons and monocotyledons (Fig. 131); that is, they all have a stem tip and a root tip marking the two ends of the main axis. The differences involve the number of cotyledons, where food is stored in the seed, and what happens to the cotyledons once the seed begins to germinate.

In dicotyledonous plants such as beans and peas (see Fig. 123), where the embryo proper fills the entire seed, the two cotyledons are the regions of food storage. When a bean seed germinates, the root tip forces its way through a rupture in the seed coat and works its way

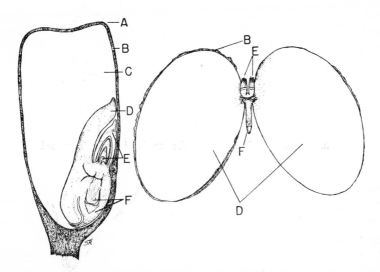

Fig. 131.—Seed types. *Left*, longitudinal section through a corn grain, revealing the monocotyledonous embryo with its endosperm. *Right*, dicotyledonous seed of the bean with its two cotyledons. The orientation and relative size of parts is here distorted for the purpose of display. Homologous parts of the two seeds are: *B*, seed coat; *D*, cotyledon(s); *E*, epicotyl region; and *F*, hypocotyl region. Only the corn has endosperm (*C*). The fruit coat (*A*) of the corn grain is shown, but the fruit coat of the bean, which would have been the pod, is not included.

into the soil (Fig. 132). Shortly this is followed by a rapid elongation in that part of the embryo axis which lies above the root tip but below the attachment of the cotyledons. This region on the main axis is known as the **hypocotyl**, or, in other words, it is that portion of the seedling which is below the cotyledons. The portion of the axis which develops above the cotyledons is the **epicotyl**. Since the root end of the axis is now firmly anchored in the soil, while the epicotyl and cotyledons are still trapped within the seed coat, the elongation of

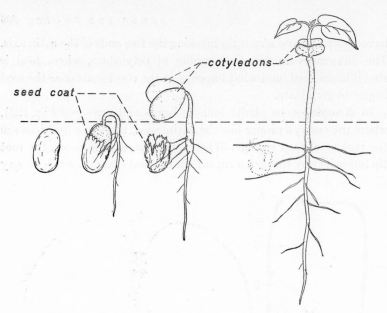

FIG. 132.—Successive stages in the germination of a bean seed

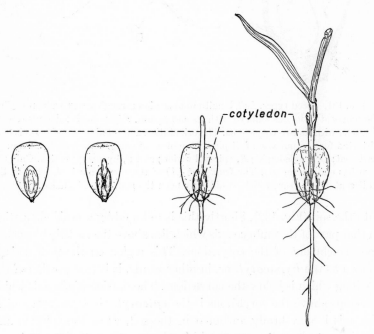

FIG. 133.—Successive stages in the germination of a grain of corn

the hypocotyl inevitably results in its buckling into a characteristic arch. This arch is like a tensed spring, and as development continues the tension increases, until at last the two cotyledons with the stem tip between them are forcibly pulled backward out of the old seed coat. Though the cotyledons may become green and conduct a little photosynthesis, their real usefulness is past, and they soon wither away. Meantime, the first true leaves, which have been lying in embryonic form around the stem tip, enlarge and assume their proper function.

In monocotyledonous plants, such as corn (Fig. 133), the cotyledon remains below the surface of the soil and remains within the seed coat. The hypocotyl gradually enlarges and forms the first root of the developing seedling. The stem and leaves develop from the epicotyl as it emerges from the soil. In corn the endosperm is comparatively large and nourishes the developing seedling until the new leaves have become green and taken over the job of manufacturing food through photosynthesis.

XX. *Heredity and Variation*

The fact that all organisms reproduce their own kind is a universally accepted concept. It would be a sad world indeed if one could never predict what type of offspring a certain pair of parents would have. We always expect cats to produce cats, humans to produce humans, snapdragons to produce snapdragons, pine trees to produce pine trees, etc. This tendency on the part of the parents to produce their own kind and also to produce the particular characteristics of each is known as *heredity*.

The study of heredity is far from an exact science, for the very nature of reproduction allows for variation. We would, of course, expect apple trees to produce apple trees, but that is as far as we can go. If we took the seed of a winesap apple and planted it, would we get a winesap apple tree? Possibly not. The flowers of apple trees are usually cross-pollinated. This means that pollen from some other apple tree might blow into the flowers on a winesap tree, and the zygote resulting would be a cross between the two trees. The pollen may have come from some scrub crabapple tree, and the genetical characteristics carried by it may have prevailed over the more desirable fruit characteristic of the winesap. Consequently, the fruit developing from this new seed would carry the undesirable fruit characteristics of the crabapple tree. Thus we have a variation from the original parents. In this case we may have lost the inherited characteristics for desirable fruit size, flavor, and shape, but we may have gained a more vigorous and sturdy tree. These are all characteristics that are inherited.

Although man has been trying to improve the qualities of animals and plants for many centuries, it was not until 1865, when an Austrian monk, Gregor Mendel, published his work on garden peas, that we knew much about the mode of inheritance. Even then the work was largely ignored until three biologists working independently, in three different countries, discovered his work almost simultaneously. Each of these men had been working on plant-breeding experiments and had obtained some very noteworthy results. Typical of good scientists, they looked through the literature to see if they could find any supporting data by an earlier investigator and there discovered Mendel's work. Its true value was recognized for the first time, and since then (1900) Mendel's experiments have become the cornerstone of all modern work in plant and animal genetics.

Mendel worked with a number of different plant species, and even mice, but he is particularly known for his investigations on garden peas. He made thousands of crosses and kept records on hundreds of thousands of individual pea plants. By his observations of pea plants Mendel observed seven characteristics which he followed through many generations. Taking each characteristic independently, he recorded the number of times this characteristic appeared in the offspring as opposed to its contrasting character. He noticed that in pea seeds smooth seed coat appeared in the progeny three times as often as wrinkled seed coat. When a character appeared more frequently than another it was considered *dominant;* thus smooth seed coat in peas is dominant and wrinkled seed coat is *recessive* to it. Mendel found that if he crossed a plant having smooth seed coat with a wrinkle-coated one, he got plants which all had smooth seed coat. If he self-pollinated these smooth-coated plants, they would have approximately three smooth-coated offspring to every one that was wrinkled. Diagrammatically it is represented in Figure 134.

Further explanation of Figure 134 is necessary because of the use of letters and symbols. P_1 refers to the original parental types. In this case each parent is *homozygous* for its particular characteristics. In other words, the one parent has two factors for smooth, SS, and the other parent is homozygous for wrinkled, ss. The two letters represent pairs of *homologous* chromosomes, which simply means that they both stand for type of seed coat. However, homologous chromosomes need not carry the same quality factor. For example, SS represents a pair of homologous chromosomes, or *genes* on those chromosomes, for smoothness of seed coat; *ss* represents a pair of chromosomes or genes for wrinkled seed coat; *Ss* also represents a pair of homologous chromosomes or genes, but in this case one factor is smooth and the other is wrinkled. Of course, a cross between two garden peas with wrinkled seed coat, *ss* and *ss*, could only result in offspring with wrinkled seed coat. Similarly, a cross involving *SS*

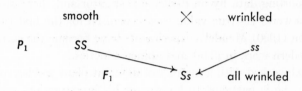

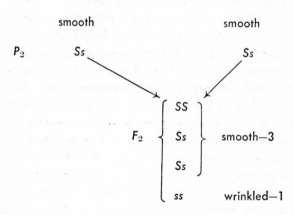

Fig. 134.—Inheritance of seed-coat characteristics in peas, as observed by Mendel.

and *SS* could result only in smooth-coated progeny. However, in our diagram we show a smooth-coated parent and a wrinkle-coated parent producing all smooth-coated progeny since smooth seed coat is the dominant characteristic. But the letters in the progeny reveal the mixture of genes which each has inherited. When the organism has a genetic constitution of contrasting characters, it is said to be **heterozygous.** The appearance of the individual is its **phenotype.**

The actual genetic characters on its chromosomes constitute its **geno-type.** We can always *see* what the phenotype is like—such traits as blue eyes, red flowers, or smooth seed coat—but we do not know what the genotype of an organism is until we have made a number of crosses to see what kind of progeny it can produce.

Thus we discover in our diagram that crossing the F_1 (first filial generation) with itself produces two different phenotypes in the F_2 generation: three smooth-coated offspring and one wrinkled. But if we look more closely, we see that there are three genotypes: *SS*, *Ss*, and *ss*. If we crossed a heterozygous smooth-coated parent, *Ss*, with a homozygous wrinkle-coated parent, *ss*, we would get 50 per cent smooth-coated and 50 per cent wrinkled (Fig. 135). This cross is the

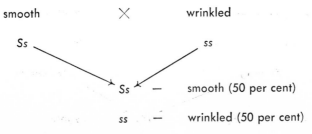

F_IG. 135.—Results of crossing heterozygous individual with homozygous individual who bears the recessive trait.

same, phenotypically, as the one that we started with; yet the ratio in the progeny is altogether different. We, of course, can see that the genotypes are different, and it is the genotype of the individual that determines his phenotype.

When shopping in the supermarket, we may observe that the grocer has peas which vary in color; some will be pale yellow and others greenish (the grocer also has smooth and wrinkled peas). Mendel noticed this difference in color also. In his crosses, similar to the ones we have just illustrated, he found that he would get the same ratios and that yellow color was dominant over green; he also noted that red flower color was dominant over white and that the tall factor in peas was dominant over dwarf.

One very important factor in all of Mendel's work was that he never failed "to see the *tree* in the *forest*." He recognized each character for what it was, a **unit character.** He noticed that a red-flowered garden pea could be tall or short, could have yellow or green seeds, and could have smooth or wrinkled seed coats. Any single character could be found with any other or be ***independent*** of any other. These characters were not inherited together, as in a "closed package." Each unit character was inherited independently of any other.

Let us look at a cross involving two pairs of factors and see how they separate and then are reunited in the new individual. A cross involving two pairs of factors is a ***dihybrid;*** when only one pair is involved, such as we have already illustrated, we call it a ***monohybrid.***

In this dihybrid cross we will represent tallness in garden peas by T and dwarfness by t, yellow seed color by Y and green by y. We might

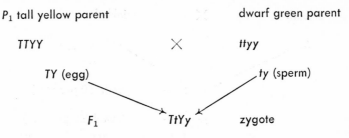

P_1 tall yellow parent dwarf green parent

TTYY × ttyy

TY (egg) ty (sperm)

F_1 TtYy zygote

FIG. 136.—Dihybrid cross involving homozygous parents

make a cross involving two homozygous parents as in Figure 136. Remember that each pair of similar letters represents a pair of homologous chromosomes or a pair of homologous genes on these chromosomes. At reduction division one member of *each* of the *pairs* of homologous chromosomes goes to each daughter cell. Thus when eggs are formed, each egg will receive one genetic factor for stature and one genetic factor for color. Similarly, each sperm will receive one factor for stature and one for color. When the sperm fertilizes the egg to form the zygote, and subsequently the new individual, the paired chromosome situation is again restored, and the new individual has again a pair of factors for stature and a pair for seed color. Although the F_1 will all be tall yellow individuals phenotypically, they are different genotypically from their tall yellow parent. Now if we self-pollinate the F_1, or in other words cross two completely heterozygous individuals, we obtain an entirely different type of ratio in the progeny than we have seen before (Fig. 137).

This is the typical ratio of a dominant-recessive type genetics problem involving two pairs of factors in completely heterozygous individuals. Of course there are many more different genotypes than the 9:3:3:1 ratio shows, but the ratio of the offspring is always for their phenotypes, not genotypes.

Parent	Tall Yellow		Tall Yellow
	(TtYy)	×	(TtYy)

Possible genotypes in sperm

		TY	Ty	tY	ty
Possible genotypes in eggs	TY	TTYY Tall Yellow	TTYy Tall Yellow	TtYY Tall Yellow	TtYy Tall Yellow
	Ty	TTYy Tall Yellow	TTyy Tall green	TtYy Tall Yellow	Ttyy Tall green
	tY	TtYY Tall Yellow	TtYy Tall Yellow	ttYY dwarf Yellow	ttYy dwarf Yellow
	ty	TtYy Tall Yellow	Ttyy Tall green	ttYy dwarf Yellow	ttyy dwarf green

FIG. 137.—Progeny phenotypes resulting from dihybrids cross of heterozygous individuals. The probability of the various types appearing is 9:3:3:1, 9 tall-yellow to 3 tall-green to 3 dwarf-yellow to 1 dwarf-green.

Mendel was undoubtedly very fortunate in his selection of garden peas for his experiments, but he was even more fortunate in the characteristics of the peas he chose to study. In all, he described seven different characters in garden peas, of which we have considered four. The fortunate thing about Mendel's characteristics is that they all had a dominant-recessive relationship to each other, and each pair of characteristics appeared on separate pairs of homologous chromosomes. He used seven characteristics, and there were seven pairs of chromosomes involved.

We know now that all things which are inherited do not have a dominant-recessive relationship. Some factors have incomplete dominance, some are cumulative, others are linked together on certain chromosomes, and others are carried on the chromosomes which determine sex and are therefore said to be sex-linked. It is not our purpose to dwell at length on the various modes of inheritance, but the student would do well to supplement his study of this very important field by reading one or two of the many books dealing with genetics. The mode of inheritance is the same in both plants and animals, so it matters little what type of book is selected except that greater emphasis to the practical aspects of genetics is given in some books than in others.

Our purpose in discussing genetics is to show how variation may occur in organisms. From the earliest days of civilization man has been attempting to improve his domesticated animals and his cultivated plants. Mostly he has done this by *selection.* He easily recognized that some plants were bigger, had better quality of fruit, were sturdier and less susceptible to disease than other plants. From these plants, which he considered better, he selected seed for next year's crop. This method of selection still is widely practiced and often results in an improvement of stock simply by weeding out the less desirable organisms. However, it is not enough.

Centuries ago man learned to cross-pollinate plants. He soon discovered that a cross between two parent stocks might result in progeny with some characteristics different from those of either parent. In some cases the new progeny far exceeded their parents in size, quality of fruit, etc. We call this mixing together of different genetic constitutions in such crosses *hybridization.* Through this process one can bring together the best genes of two or more individuals, and in some cases we find that the new individual can be self-pollinated repeatedly for many generations and will continue to "breed true." Often, however, the cross resulting in the *hybrid* must be repeated each year to produce this fine stock because the new offspring will not breed true or may in fact be sterile. Hybrid corn is an example of a plant which is much superior to its ancestors, but it does not breed true; consequently, the series of crosses necessary to produce it must be carried out constantly in order to provide seed for farmers to grow the desired hybrid. There are also many hybrids among animals, of which the mule is one of the most famous. The mule is the hybrid offspring of the jackass and mare, but it is nearly always sterile; consequently this cross must be made whenever mules are desired.

Variations occasionally occur quite unexpectedly in organisms as a result of unusual changes in the chromosome complement. This type of change is called a *mutation,* and it results in an individual quite different from the other members of the group; usually there is nothing in the immediate ancestry to explain its origin. The changes involved may affect the chromosomes, so that the new characteristics are transmitted to progeny, thus providing us with new varieties quite unlike their ancestors. Most mutations are simply changes in one or more genes on the chromosomes. The change may be dominant or recessive; it may be cumulative, and often it is lethal. In some cases identical genes will mutate independently, just as different genes do. Ordinarily the effects of a mutation are slight, often with no visible aftereffects, but occasionally it results in changes that are visible, desirable, and persistent.

Similar changes may be produced by a multiplication of entire sets of chromosomes, a condition known as *polyploidy.* The usual number of chromosomes in each somatic cell of an organism is said to be *2n* or *diploid.* At reduction division, in the origin of the egg and sperm, each sex cell receives half this number, *n* or *haploid.* Sometimes reduction division does not occur, and an egg may receive the full double set of chromosomes and therefore be diploid. When such an egg is fertilized by a haploid sperm, the resulting organism is *triploid.* Similarly, if two diploid gametes were united, the new organism would be *tetraploid.* Other variations are caused by the addition or deletion of single chromosomes or groups of chromosomes which cause many modifications in the plant in which they are found.

Polyploidy has been of considerable importance in the development of our cultivated plants and in the evolution of organisms. Hybrids are often sterile because the two sets of chromosomes involved are usually not of the same number and are not in homologous pairs. In polyploidy, however, the chromosome number is usually doubled and each chromosome has an identical mate, although now there are twice as many as before. Polyploids are usually fertile, and often their desirable traits are magnified.

Many of our seedless fruits are the result of mutations or polyploidy, and most of our garden vegetables are polyploids. Recent cytological studies show that many closely related species in certain genera have chromosome counts that are multiples of a single species which may have been the ancestor of the others.

Much of the work in the field of inheritance today centers in studies of the cell in cytogenetics. Not only are we interested in the fact that chromosome aberrations occur, but we would like to help nature along a little by stimulating changes which would improve our cultivated plants and domesticated animals. Geneticists are using atomic rays, X-rays, ultraviolet and infrared rays, cosmic rays, chemicals, and heat and cold to force changes in the chromosome complement and genic mutations, in the hope that they will produce something new. For the most part, geneticists are interested in the higher production of fruit and vegetables, in plants with better quality fruit and vegetation and greater resistance to disease, and in seeds and fruit with better keeping qualities. Many geneticists, however, perform cytological experiments simply to learn more about the fundamental mechanisms of inheritance. Thus far it is not possible to predict when and where a chromosomal change will occur or what type of plant will result from any such change; but the fact that chromosomal aberrations can occur in nature and can be induced by man shows us how evolution can occur and why we can expect to improve the natural world about us.

XXI. *The Process of Organic Evolution*

Any survey of the plant kingdom must leave in the mind of the reviewer two very strong impressions. (1) He must be impressed by the almost innumerable examples of adaptation that are manifest in plant structures and plant functions. In case after case he finds the plant well equipped to maintain itself and to perpetuate the species in the environment in which it is growing. In very few cases does he find any conspicuous maladjustment. (2) He must also be impressed by the tremendous diversity of form that he finds among the thousands of species that make up the plant kingdom.

Before the nineteenth century most biologists accounted for these two phenomena by means of the "hypothesis of special creation." According to this hypothesis, each species of plant and animal originated through an independent act. Thus, at some time and place in the past, where there was no pre-existing organism of species *A*, the first representative of this species was suddenly brought into existence, and—the hypothesis goes on to assert—all subsequent members of species *A* were derived by descent without modification from that first representative. It follows that all existing members of species *A* were not only like each other but like that original ancestor of long ago. As an independent event which had no significant connection with this first act of special creation, there was suddenly brought into existence the first representative of species *B*, and all subsequent members of that species were thought to have been derived without modification from this original ancestor. Similar assumptions were made as to the origin of all species. For the million-odd species of existing plants and animals, therefore, there must have been just as many independent acts of special creation in the first place.

In terms of this hypothesis, the two phenomena referred to at the opening of the chapter receive the following interpretation. The adaptive features of organisms are attributed to the intelligence of the creator or creative agency. The diversity of plant and animal kingdoms is attributed to the large number of acts of special creation that occurred.

This "hypothesis of special creation" leaves many questions to be answered—questions as to the identity of the creative agency, the raw materials used, the methods by which they were originally synthesized and organized into the bodies of living plants and animals. The whole account has a distinctly miraculous flavor.

Even so, most of the scientists of the eighteenth century accepted special creation as the true account of the origin of the many known species of plants and animals. Early in the nineteenth century the French biologist Lamarck attempted to convince biologists of the alternative "theory of organic evolution." His attempts met with very little success, however, and it remained for the Englishman Charles Darwin to persuade the biological public to discard special creation and to accept organic evolution in its stead. It was in 1859 that Darwin published his famous *Origin of Species*, a book that has been said to have had a greater influence upon the thought of the Western world than has any other except the Christian Bible. The influence of this book caused biologists to swing over to an acceptance of organic evolution rather rapidly. The rest of the world has been following suit more slowly ever since.

The "theory of organic evolution" is based upon an unbiased, dispassionate observation of the facts of nature, followed by logical inferences drawn from those facts and by a subsequent testing of the inferences by means of other facts. In other words, the "theory of organic evolution" is a product of the "scientific method."

According to the evolutionist, all existing species have been derived by the process of organic evolution, or gradual modification through descent, from one or a few primitive ancestral types. As we shall see, the adaptive features present in plants and animals and the diversification in type that appears in plant and animal kingdoms are both to be accounted for not by the actions of an original creative agency but by the inevitable play of certain forces of nature upon plant and animal populations throughout the hundreds of millions of years during which evolution has been going on.

It is very doubtful that there is any biologist today who does not believe in organic evolution. How could it be otherwise, when the study of nature yields many independent lines of evidence in support of organic evolution and not a single line of evidence that contradicts it? The impressive history that nature has recorded for us in the *fossil record* not only tells us that evolution has occurred but points out many of the exact lines that evolution has followed. The sedimentary rocks of ancient times have buried within them the actual remains of some plants now silicified but still with all cells and tissues intact, so that identification is easy. In other rocks perfect *impressions* of leaves, roots, stems, and other parts can readily be identified. The rocks which were laid down at a certain time by wind and water erosion contain the plants of that time, thus giving us a date for the life of that plant on earth. Usually plants found in the earlier rocks are more primitive and of more ancient origin than those found in upper strata of more recent origin.

We also have the evidence based upon *morphology*. The structural and functional characteristics of plant and animal types, their anatomy, their chemistry, their behavior, when compared to those of other types, yield overwhelming evidence of relationship through common ancestry. The combination of perfections and imperfections in detail that characterizes any of the more complex organisms can receive a sensible interpretation only on the assumption that that organism has been derived from a remote ancestor with somewhat different characteristics. Throughout this book, as each group has been described, those characteristics which were introduced with each new form have been mentioned; possible origins and ancestors for each have been delineated and the progenitors for each group at least suggested. Certainly the history of changes that have been wrought in domesticated animals and cultivated plants during the last few centuries tells us that evolution can occur.

Additional support is gained by the very impressive evidence based on the *geographical distribution* of organisms. Plants, as well as animals, are not widely dispersed over the earth's surface, even though conditions are well suited for the growth of that species in many places. It would seem that such localized distribution points very strongly to the fact that these organisms were evolved in the regions they now inhabit, and, because of physical barriers (oceans, rivers, mountain ranges, canyons, etc.), they have been unable to migrate. Darwin was greatly impressed with the tremendous differences he observed in plants and animals in the different countries he visited during his world cruise. His observations in this connection were largely responsible for his theory of natural selection.

Finally we have the *experimental* evidence. More detailed discussion of this important evidence will be made later in the chapter, but suffice it to say here that investigations concerning the variations in plants and animals show that man can now induce these changes experimentally. Through the use of drugs and radiation, changes in the chromosomes can be wrought, as is proved by later cytological examination. Many species have been under laboratory observation for a long time and hundreds of chromosome aberrations noted. Today the experimental evidence is so important because it shows us organic evolution *in action* rather than merely another observation in support of a theory.

Of course one cannot hope to observe directly the things that occurred during the millions of years of the past, but biologists have been in agreement for some time on the point that evolution *has* occurred. Just *how* it has occurred—what interaction of forces, what machinery of nature, brought about this gradual modification—has resulted in considerable disagreement since the theory of organic evolution was suggested in the first place. Before again considering the experimental evidence for the proof we are seeking, let us look back upon two of the many explanations of evolution which have exercised major influence upon biological thought.

In 1809 Lamarck not only asserted emphatically that organic evolution was true but went further to provide an explanation of how the process had occurred. Since the overhwleming majority of biologists were still staunch "special creationists," Lamarck's ideas were met by a storm of ridicule, and it was not until after his death that they received fair consideration.

Lamarck based his explanation upon the "principle of the blacksmith's arm." He pointed out that during the lifetime of the individual organism any part of its body which is used a great deal will develop in size and functional capacity, while those parts that are not used will gradually deteriorate. Even today biologists agree that, in general, this is a perfectly valid principle. In other words, it appears to be quite true that living organisms may "acquire characters" as the result of special experiences in the lifetime of the individual. This is not in itself evolution. According to Lamarck, however, by being inherited such traits provide a potential start from which evolutionary consequences may follow.

Plausible as this "Lamarckian doctrine" may appear, there are but few modern biologists that believe in it. On the basis of *general observations alone*, biologists were formerly inclined to agree that "inheritance of acquired characters" probably occurred. However, when they put the question to critical *experimental test*, most of them felt obliged to change their views. The controlled experiments that were directed at this question during the last of the nineteenth century and the first of the twentieth provided substantial evidence to the effect that inheritance of acquired characters does not occur. It is always difficult, of course, to prove that a thing is impossible, and perhaps one should not say that any such demonstration has been made in connection with the question under discussion. Indeed, there are still a few biologists that subscribe to the "Lamarckian doctrine." The majority, however, have definitely discarded it, for the overwhelming bulk of experimental work indicates quite clearly that offspring simply do not inherit the special acquirements of their parents.

With the inheritance of acquired characters ruled out, it would seem difficult to comprehend how the course of evolution could have been directed along those channels necessary to lead to the highly adaptive results that we see today. In 1859, however, Charles Darwin provided an answer to that question that seems even today to be essentially valid. Darwin's *Origin of Species* not only succeeded in doing what Lamarck had failed to do—i.e., in convincing the general biological public that organic evolution was true—but it went further and showed how organic evolution could occur without the assistance of the inheritance of acquired characters.

One of the several principles upon which Darwin built his theory is that of the "geometric ratio of increase." All living species have a potential reproductive ratio of more than one to one; i.e., if all reproductive units function and all offspring survive, the second generation will outnumber the first. Earlier we noted how even those organisms with a reproductive ratio of only two (bacteria and blue-green algae) tend to increase their populations tremendously under those conditions which favor survival, growth, and reproduction. At the other extreme, we noted how some of the fungi produced billions of spores. It has been estimated that if all the spores in a giant puffball produced a new puffball, by the third generation we would have a mass the volume of the earth. In all plants and animals there is this potentiality for a geometric ratio of increase, a tendency to increase populations prodigiously in the course of a few generations.

As a result, any small population entering a new locality will rapidly increase in size until it has reached the "saturation point," beyond which limitations in the food supply (and other natural checks) will make any further increase impossible. Though the tendency to increase is still exerting itself, there is no actual increase beyond this point. In other words, the potential geometric ratio of increase and the natural checks have arrived at an equilibrium, which is thereafter maintained until such time as some outside agency may upset it. At any given time most species in most localities have already attained this equilibrium, so that the surviving population of the second generation is essentially equal to that of the first. The maintenance of this equilibrium necessitates that, of the thousands of individuals that start life each generation, only a few hundred (or usually less) actually survive to maturity. The majority are eliminated during the early stages of life. In other words, in most natural situations "death is the rule and life is the exception." For the puffball it is not even one spore in a million that produces another puffball.

Another of the principles upon which Darwin builds his theory is that of the "struggle for existence." He points out that, with rare and at best only temporary exceptions, life is essentially a struggle. Not only man, with his elaborate conscious plans, but also the simplest of animals and plants—which, so far as we know, are entirely unconscious—are engaged, at most times and at most places, in some sort of struggle to keep alive.

In part this struggle is the "competition" between organisms that inevitably results from the geometric ratio of increase. Since space and food supply are limited, animals compete with others of the same species to win food. Less obvious but just as vital is the competition that frequently occurs among plants of the same species. The available light, water, and soil salts are usually present in limited quantities. The more vigorous or more "fortunate" plants secure these essentials, while the others are "crowded out" and die. Competition is interspecific as well as intraspecific. Animals of several different species may be competing for the same food; and this sort of thing is even more likely to be true with the green plants, where all species are dependent upon material and energy in the same forms.

Different in form but no less rigorous is the competition that occurs between the dependent organisms and those other organisms that provide their natural food supply. As we have seen, green plants are the victims of bacteria, fungi, and animals. It follows that life or death of a given green plant will depend very largely upon the activities of these other organisms. Similarly, carnivorous animals are secondarily dependent upon herbivorous animals. Often there exists a "food chain" of many links, starting with the green plant and ending with the dominant carnivore of the region. And wherever one link of this chain joins its neighbor, there is (with few exceptions) a life-and-death competition. In most natural situations these intricate interdependencies have been established, and an "equilibrium of species" has been approximated with about the same number of individuals of each species reaching the adult condition in each generation. But this state of equilibrium does not stand for a state of tranquillity. The equilibrium is not static but dynamic, involving a fairly continuous interplay of natural forces that are roughly balanced in their effects. Throughout this interplay of life there is much death. Where life abounds, there also death abounds.

Competition with other organisms is not, however, the only thing that enters into the struggle for existence. In part, the struggle is imposed by non-living factors of the environment. Often animals struggle to get water, and plants to get water and soil salts, where no other organisms are at hand to compete with them and where life depends upon the purely physical or chemical limitations of the environment and the ability of the organism to meet these limitations. Temperature often enters in to decide the fate of organisms, light also, and the physical or chemical nature of the medium or the substratum. With man, as with other organisms, the struggle for existence is usually quite apparent, and it is likewise quite apparent that it involves

(1) competition with others of the same species, (2) competition with different species, and (3) problems of adjustment to the non-living forces of nature.

Another principle on which Darwin based his theory is that of the "universality of variation." We recognize without difficulty that no two human beings are exactly alike. Were we as familiar with cats or with dogs or with any other species that exists, we would also acknowledge without hesitation that one could never find two individuals that would exactly match each other. With microscopic examination we could establish the fact that no two blades of grass are ever quite alike, and, if our microscopes were a little better, we could doubtless establish the same thing for bacteria and other tiny organisms. So far as their general characteristics are concerned, all individuals of the same species are alike, but when it comes to the more detailed characteristics, a certain amount of variation is always present.

The biologist of today realizes that these variations are of two great types. Some of them are due to the fact that two individuals may have had different experiences. As a result of experience, therefore, or as a "response to environmental influence," the one individual may have one "acquired character" while the other individual has a different acquired character (or set of acquired characters). But even when two individuals of the same species have had the same experiences, they may, and usually do, possess somewhat different characteristics. These latter expressed differences are due to differences in the hereditary endowments of the two individuals. In considering variation, therefore, we can distinguish acquired differences and hereditary differences, and we must make this distinction if we are to see clearly how Darwin's theory accounts for evolutionary results.

Out of these several principles Darwin built an explanation of evolution that is usually referred to as **natural selection.** Owing in part to the "ratio of increase," life is commonly characterized by a struggle for existence. If all members of a species were identical, it would be purely a matter of chance which individuals won out in the struggle and succeeded in surviving. As it actually is, however, the struggling, competing population varies, and some of the elements of this variation may play a critical part in effecting the outcome of the struggle. Some, by virtue of their possession of a character which others lack (or by virtue of a higher grade of expression of that character than appears among the others), may thereby be somewhat better equipped for the struggle. The character in question may be a matter of size, strength, speed, rapidity of growth, efficiency of various protective devices, economy in the performance of certain functions, or any one of a great number of things. Darwin summed up all the possibilities by saying that certain organisms were more "fit" than were others, and by "fit" he meant that they were better adapted to their environment. Darwin then simply pointed out the self-evident fact that the fit stand a better chance of surviving in the struggle for existence than do the unfit. Obviously, it is the survivors that are able to reproduce, while the non-survivors—that is, provided they perish before the reproductive period—will leave no offspring. Thus the inevitable operation of natural forces leads to a certain amount of natural selection, a selection of the more fit in the population to perpetuate the species.

What, then, must be the character of the second generation if it has been derived, in the main, from the more fit members of the first generation? In answering this question, we must keep in mind the distinction between the two fundamental types of variation.

If an individual of the first generation possesses an "average" hereditary endowment, it may still, as the result of "fortunate" experiences, acquire characters which serve to make it fit. It may therefore be preserved by natural selection and leave offspring. Since acquired characters are not inherited, however, these offspring will be no better than were the average members of the first generation.

If a superior individual of the first generation has average experiences, it may still be more fit than most because of its superior hereditary endowment. Being more fit, it may be preserved and leave offspring. These offspring will indeed be better than the offspring of the average members of the first generation, for they will possess the superior hereditary endowments that were passed on to them by their parents.

Nature, of course, in effecting the selection, bases her decision upon expressed characters alone. Hence those chosen as most fit are usually a mixed lot; in some the fitness is due to acquired characters, while in others it is due to hereditary endowments. When nature bases her selection upon acquired characters alone, she fails to improve the average quality of the population. When she bases her selection upon the truly hereditary characters, she effects a real, substantial improvement in the average quality of the population. In a single generation of selection the improvement may be only a slight one, but in the course of thousands of generations the average fitness of the surviving population may be markedly changed. This is evolution, for the final descendants may be so different from the original ancestors as to be regarded as a new species. And it is progressive evolution, for the descendants are better adapted to the environment than were the ancestors.

It should be clear, then, that evolution depends upon hereditary variation. It should be equally clear that natural selection does not produce this variation but merely guides it in the direction of better adaptation. Natural selection could accomplish nothing unless there were agencies at play to produce the hereditary variations with which it works.

Hereditary variants are the result of (1) mutations involving genic changes, (2) polyploids involving complete sets of chromosomes, and (3) hybridization, which involves change in either the quality or quantity of the chromosome makeup, or both. Briefly we may consider the manner in which genes or chromosomes may be altered and the manner in which they bring about variation in a population.

Apparently the genes are well insulated against the influence of most environmental stimuli, for they are perpetuated without change for many generations. On rare occasions, however, some one gene, out of the thousands that are present in a nucleus, changes very suddenly to be a gene of a different sort. This genic change is, of course, a mutation. The new gene will be perpetuated as faithfully as the old, so that mutation may lead to the presence in a population of several individuals that possess the new gene. The effect of the new gene will be to produce in those individuals either a brand new character (or characters) or a different grade or quality of development of some old character.

A given gene mutates only very rarely. There are apparently thousands of different genes within each nucleus, however; there are certainly millions of nuclei within the body of one of our higher organisms; and there may well be thousands or millions of individuals of the same species in the local population. It follows that the mutation of some gene somewhere in the population will be a fairly frequent event.

Apparently, mutations are quite random in their occurrence. It appears to be a matter of chance which gene will mutate next or in what way the resulting new gene will affect the organism. Since mutations are random, we are not surprised to find that most of them have a bad effect upon the organism. For the organism is a complicated, intricate, finely balanced mechanism, and one would expect random changes to impair the efficiency of such a mechanism more often than to improve it.

If, now, most mutations have a bad effect, will not the phenomenon of mutation bring a steady deterioration of the race? Undoubtedly this would result were it not for natural selection. Actually, natural selection acts as a safety valve, eliminating the mutations with no survival value, preserving those capable of expressing themselves under existing conditions, and thus guiding the results of this purely random phenomenon in the direction of continuing evolution. If the new gene so modifies the organism as to make it more fit, the organism itself will probably survive, so that the gene in question will be not only perpetuated but multiplied. If the new gene makes the organism less fit, both organism and gene will probably be exterminated through the action of natural selection, and the race will be no worse off than it was before.

In the course of many generations the new gene that improves the organism will be so effectively multiplied that all surviving members of the population will contain that gene. The resulting improved adaptation, slight though it may be, will be substantial gain and will provide a foundation upon which further adaptive improvements may be added in a similar way upon the introduction of additional new genes by mutation. Progress may be extremely slow, and there may even be long stretches of time through which little or no progress is made. In the long run, however, the accumulation of larger and smaller mutations will be sufficient to account for the origin of a new species.

Thus it is that modern biology explains evolution through random mutation plus natural selection. Adaptation in living organisms is the inevitable result of the operation of these forces of nature upon countless generations of ancestors.

Diversity in plant and animal kingdoms is due to the fact that different lines of descent from the same ancestor have often become separated from each other. Isolated in this way, the two lines may gradually diverge, not only because they may be living under slightly different environmental conditions (which may favor the survival of different genes) but also because the random mutations that occur in one line will probably differ from those that occur in another. Life problems can often be solved in several different ways. Hence chance mutation might well be expected to launch one line of descent in the direction of one form of adaptation, and another (isolated) line in the direction of a different form of adaptation.

Earlier it was stated that there were two great natural agencies that accounted for the gene differences between organisms, i.e., for hereditary variations. It was further stated that mutation was the primary agency. The secondary agency is sex.

Other things being equal, the rate of evolutionary progress will depend upon the frequency with which new hereditary variations are introduced into a population. Evolutionary progress at a slow rate will result from mutation alone. Sex, however, has a way of increasing still further the hereditary variation that is introduced by mutation. By thus increasing the frequency with which new hereditary variations appear in the population, sex expedites evolution. The student can develop a clear understanding of the action of sex only through a knowledge of the machinery of heredity.

Accumulation of mutations may bring into existence two varieties of the same species which differ from each other by two genes. One variety may possess genes a and B, while the other variety possesses genes A and b. With asexual reproduction these two varieties will perpetuate themselves faithfully, so that the species will continue to include only these two varieties until such time as a new mutation might occur. With sexual reproduction, however, the two varieties merge genetically. Under these conditions the machinery of heredity will operate to effect new combinations of the ancestral genes. Among the descendants there will emerge not merely the old combinations, Ab and aB, but two new combinations, ab and AB. Four varieties now exist where there were but two before. Sex has not produced variation in a homogeneous population, but it has multiplied a preexisting variation that had been the result of mutation.

This simple example falls far short of showing how prodigiously sex may multiply variation. If the two original varieties had differed not by merely two genes but by ten, sex could produce from these two original varieties no less than 1,024 varieties. Would not that combination of characters of the highest adaptive value be much more likely to be found among the 1,024 varieties than among the original two?

Nature has answered this question in the affirmative, for she has preserved sex as the prevailing method of reproduction among our highest plants and animals. As we have seen before, sex is not the only method of reproduction; and of the several methods it is certainly not the most economical in perpetuating and multiplying the species. It is the only method, however, which makes possible a mixing of the hereditary characters from two parents, and it is, therefore, the only method of reproduction that can lead to a multiplication of variation. So the student should not think of sex as *the* method of reproduction, or merely as *a* method of reproduction; he should think of sex instead as that method of reproduction which has the peculiar power to multiply variation. This is the real function of sex, and it is a function which is of value only in making possible a more rapid evolution than might otherwise occur.

Hybridization is today a very important method in improving the quality of animals and plants for man. It is also a process which has been taking place for millions of years in nature and which undoubtedly will continue for many more millions. Hybridization is a cross between two parental types which differ in certain respects. They may be of the same species or not. The resulting offspring is a hybrid, and it may be very similar to either one or both of the parents or quite different. One example we might use concerns two species of grasses.

Spartina stricta is a species that grows in England, while *Spartina alterniflora* is a species native to the New England states. As a result of commerce, some of the seeds from the New England species were transported to England. Soon *S. alterniflora* was growing near *S. stricta* in England. Hybrids resulted from natural crosses between the two species, and one of them proved to be an outstanding type with characteristics more desirable than either of its parents. It was found to breed true, unlike many hybrids, and it was given the name *Spartina townsendii* and recognized as a distinct species.

Upon cytological examination it was found that the hybrid *S. townsendii* has 126 chromosomes, *S. alterniflora* has 70, and *S.*

stricta has 56. Thus in some manner *S. townsendii* received complete sets of chromosomes from each parent rather than the usual half and thus became a polyploid.

In nature this type of hybridization is not common, but that it can occur shows us the importance of this process in producing a new species.

In our brief discussion of the process of organic evolution two points should be apparent. (1) Variation within organisms does occur by changes in the chromosome complement. These changes are brought about by hybridization, polyploidy, and mutation. All these processes may occur in nature or in the laboratory. (2) The second point is, What causes changes? Through the action of drugs and radiation, chromosome and genic changes can be induced in the laboratory. What causes them to occur in nature may be conjectural. Perhaps it is the sheer weight of numbers. It is estimated that certain genes mutate about 1 among 100,000 individuals. Considering the millions of species, it is quite probable that some genes, somewhere, are mutating every day. Considering the age of the earth, the number of mutants could be almost astronomical. It is also possible that natural radiation, perhaps cosmic rays, may be the necessary stimulus.

We no longer have to theorize, like Lamarck, Darwin, and others, as to how evolution occurs. We have the proof. If we could now synthesize life out of some inorganic materials, we would have a fairly complete picture of the origin and development of the biological world.

Supplementary Readings

BOOKS OF GENERAL INTEREST

DARWIN, C. R. *The Voyage of the Beagle.* London: Dent, 1950.

DOBZHANSKY, T. *Evolution, Genetics, and Man.* New York: John Wiley & Sons, 1955.

DODSON, E. O. *A Textbook of Evolution.* Philadelphia: W. B. Saunders Co., 1952.

EAMES, A. J. *Morphology of Vascular Plants—Lower Groups.* New York: McGraw-Hill Book Co., 1936.

FULLER, H. J., and TIPPO, O. *College Botany.* New York: Henry Holt & Co., 1954.

HAUPT, A. W. *Plant Morphology.* New York: McGraw-Hill Book Co., 1953.

HUXLEY, J. S. *Evolution: The Modern Synthesis.* New York: Harper & Bros., 1943.

LEOPOLD, A. C. *Auxins and Plant Growth.* Berkeley: University of California Press, 1955.

MANGHAM, SIDNEY. *Earth's Green Mantle.* New York: Macmillan Co., 1939.

MEYER, B. S., and ANDERSON, D. B. *Plant Physiology* (2d ed.). New York: D. Van Nostrand Co., 1952.

OOSTING, HENRY J. *Plant Communities.* San Francisco: Freeman & Co., 1956.

ROBBINS, W. W., WEIER, T. E., and STOCKING, C. R. *Botany: An Introduction to Plant Science* (2d ed.). New York, 1957.

SIMPSON, G. G., PITTENDRIGH, C. S., and TIFFANY, L. H. *Life: An Introduction to Biology.* New York: Harcourt, Brace & Co., 1957.

SINNOTT, E. W., and WILSON, K. S. *Botany Principles and Problems.* New York: McGraw-Hill Book Co., 1955.

WATTS, MAY THEILGAARD. *Reading the Landscape.* New York: Macmillan Co., 1957.

WILSON, C. L., and LOOMIS, W. E. *Botany.* New York: Dryden Press, 1957.

BOOKS ON THE LOWER PLANTS

ALEXOPOULOS, C. J. *Introductory Mycology*. New York: John Wiley & Sons, 1952.

BESSEY, E. A. *Morphology and Taxonomy of the Fungi*. Philadelphia: Blakiston Co., 1950.

CHAPMAN, V. H. *Seaweeds and Their Uses*. London: Lange, Maxwell, & Springer, 1950.

CHRISTENSEN, C. M. *Common Edible Mushrooms*. Minneapolis: University of Minnesota Press, 1943.

CHRISTENSEN, C. M. *The Molds and Man*. Minneapolis: University of Minnesota Press, 1951.

CONARD, H. S. *How To Know the Mosses*. Dubuque, Iowa: Wm. C. Brown Co., 1956.

FINK, B. *The Lichen Flora of the United States*. Ann Arbor: University of Michigan Press, 1935.

FITZPATRICK, H. M. *The Lower Fungi—Phycomycetes*. New York: McGraw-Hill Book Co., 1930.

FLEMING, A. *Penicillin: Its Practical Applications*. Philadelphia: Blakiston Co., 1946.

FRITSCH, F. E. *The Structure and Reproduction of the Algae*. London: Cambridge University Press, 1945.

GRANT, M. P. *Microbiology and Human Progress*. New York: Rinehart & Co., 1953.

GUBERLET, MURIEL LEWIN. *Seaweeds at Ebb Tide*. Seattle: University of Washington Press, 1956.

GÜSSOW, H. T., and ODELL, W. S. *Mushrooms and Toadstools*. Ottawa, Ontario: Canada Department of Agriculture, 1927.

HARDY, ALISTER C. *The Open Sea. Its Natural History: The World of Plankton*. Boston: Houghton Mifflin Co., 1957.

MACBRIDE, T. H., and MARTIN, G. W. *The Myxomycetes*. New York: Macmillan Co., 1934.

MARTIN, G. W. "The Myxomycetes," *Botanical Review*, VI (1940), 356–88.

PRESCOTT, G. W. *How To Know the Fresh-Water Algae*. Dubuque, Iowa: Wm. C. Brown Co., 1954.

PRESCOTT, G. W. *Algae of the Western Great Lakes Area*. Bloomfield Hills, Mich.: Cranbrook Institute, 1957.

SCHWIMMER, M., and SCHWIMMER, D. *The Role of Algae and Plankton in Medicine*. New York: Grune and Stratton, 1955.

SMITH, G. M. *The Fresh-Water Algae of the United States*. New York: McGraw-Hill Book Co., 1950.

SMITH, G. M. *Cryptogamic Botany*, Vols. I–II (2d ed.). New York: McGraw-Hill Book Co., 1955.

TIFFANY, L. H. *Algae: The Grass of Many Waters*. Springfield, Ill.: Charles C Thomas, 1958.

TILDEN, JOSEPHINE E. *The Algae and Their Life Relations.* Minneapolis: University of Minnesota Press, 1935.

WOLF, F. A., and WOLF, F. T. *The Fungi,* Vol. I. New York: John Wiley & Sons, 1947.

WOLSTENHOLME, G. E. W., and MILLAR, E. C. P. *The Nature of Viruses.* Boston: Little, Brown & Co., 1957.

BOOKS ON THE HIGHER PLANTS

ALLPORT, N. L. *The Chemistry and Pharmacy of Vegetable Drugs.* Brooklyn: Chemical Publishing Co., 1944.

ANDREWS, H. N. *Ancient Plants and the World They Lived In.* Ithaca, N.Y.: Comstock, 1947.

BAILEY, L. H. *Manual of Cultivated Plants* (rev. ed.). New York: Macmillan Co., 1949.

BROWN, N. C. *Forest Products* (4th ed.). New York: John Wiley & Sons, 1950.

CHAMBERLAIN, C. J. *Gymnosperms: Structure and Evolution.* Chicago: University of Chicago Press, 1935.

CORE, E. L. *Plant Taxonomy.* Englewood Cliffs, N.J.: Prentice-Hall, 1955.

EAMES, A. J., and MACDANIELS, L. H. *Introduction to Plant Anatomy.* New York: McGraw-Hill Book Co., 1947.

ESAU, KATHERINE. *Plant Anatomy.* New York: John Wiley & Sons, 1953.

GLEASON, H. A. *The New Britton and Brown Illustrated Flora,* Vol. I. New York: New York Botanical Garden, 1952.

GLESINGER, E. *The Coming Age of Wood.* New York: Simon & Schuster, 1949.

GUENTHER, E. *The Essential Oils.* 4 vols. New York: D. Van Nostrand, 1948–50.

HILL, A. F. *Economic Botany.* New York: McGraw-Hill Book Co., 1952.

LAWRENCE, G. H. M. *The Taxonomy of Vascular Plants.* New York: Macmillan Co., 1951.

MAHESHWARI, P. *An Introduction to the Embryology of Angiosperms.* New York: McGraw-Hill Book Co., 1950.

MEDSGER, O. P. *Edible Wild Plants.* New York: Macmillan Co., 1939.

MUENSCHER, W. C. *Poisonous Plants of the United States.* New York: Macmillan Co., 1939.

NAVEZ, Y. R., and MAZUYER, G. *Natural Perfume Materials.* New York: Reinhold Publishing Corp., 1947.

ROBERT, J. C. *The Story of Tobacco in America.* New York: Alfred A. Knopf, 1949.

SCHERY, R. *Plants for Man.* Englewood Cliffs, N.J.: Prentice-Hall, 1952.

STOVER, E. L. *An Introduction to the Anatomy of Seed Plants.* Boston: D. C. Heath & Co., 1951.

WARDLAW, C. W. *Embryogenesis in Plants.* New York: John Wiley & Sons, 1955.

Index

Classification of the Plant Kingdom

● **Subkingdom THALLOPHYTA**

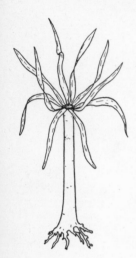

The Algae

Phylum **CYANOPHYTA**—*blue-green algae*
Phylum **EUGLENOPHYTA**—*euglenoids*
Phylum **CHRYSOPHYTA**—*yellow-greens,*
golden-browns, and diatoms
Phylum **PYRROPHYTA**—*dinoflagellates*
Phylum **CHLOROPHYTA**—*green algae*
Phylum **PHAEOPHYTA**—*brown algae*
Phylum **RHODOPHYTA**—*red algae*

Fungi and Bacteria

Phylum **SCHIZOMYCOPHYTA** —*bacteria*
Phylum **MYXOMYCOPHYTA**—*slime molds*
Phylum **EUMYCOPHYTA**—*true fungi*

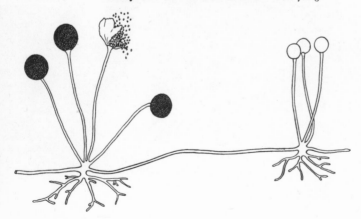